CRUSADER HYMNS

for

church, school, and home

Compiled and Edited by

Cliff Barrows and Donald Hustad

HOPE PUBLISHING COMPANY

Established 1892

5707 West Lake Street

Chicago, Illinois 60644

1967

Printed in U.S.A.

Foreword

In modern speech, a "crusader" is one who has enlisted in a struggle for good, and against evil. Thus, a "Crusade of Mercy" is a humanitarian effort to eliminate poverty and to promote health among the world's millions. In the Church, an "evangelistic crusade" is a call to become a disciple of Jesus Christ, and to join His war against sin, in our own personalities and in the society of which we are a part.

The Apostle Paul, in Ephesians chapter six, has described the life of a Christian as a battle "against principalities, against powers, against the rulers of the darkness of this world, against spiritual wickedness in high places." The same passage of scripture compares the spiritual weapons of the believer-soldier to breastplate, helmet, sword and shield – pieces of armor which were in common use in Paul's day and also during the Middle Ages. The beautiful line drawings in this book represent life during the historic crusades of the 11th, 12th and 13th centuries, and are the work of the renowned artist Stanley Fleming.

In **Crusader Hymns** we have sought to provide Christian songs that are appropriate for every vicissitude of life, and to make the message of each hymn clear, so that its use may be meaningful. This is accomplished in part by grouping the hymns according to topic, and also by artwork and the comment which introduces each section of the book. The Table of Contents (opposite page) indicates the divisions of the hymnal, and the Topical Index (pages 274-277) provides lists of hymns under almost one hundred different headings relating to subject and use.

The Alphabetical Index (pages 278-288) includes a brief statement about each hymn in the book. In some instances, facts are given about the author and composer, or about the circumstances which led to the hymn's writing. Often the message of the text is restated or outlined in a few words. Choir directors or songleaders may want to use this information in introducing the hymn to a choir or a congregation. Of the many volumes on hymnody which were used in preparing this material, we especially recommend Wm. J. Reynold's **Hymns of Our Faith** (Broadman Press, 1964) for further study.

We also believe that hymn singing must be pleasurable, if it is to be meaningful. From their wide activity in church music, editors Cliff Barrows and Donald Hustad have brought together many of the familiar hymns and gospel songs which are known and enjoyed the world around. They have also included some of the newer hymns and folk hymns which are rapidly becoming favorites. In a few instances, they have coupled a familiar text to a new tune which may add freshness and vitality to the singing. At the same time, for those who prefer it, the traditional melody is included on an adjacent page.

Finally, we would like to dedicate this book to the memory of Gordon D. Shorney, for many years President of Hope Publishing Company. Mr. Shorney was deeply interested in hymns and hymn singing throughout his lifetime, and gave invaluable help in the preparation of **Crusader Hymns.**

A hymnal of this size and scope will be widely used, in family devotions, in the church school, the prayer service, in youth groups and clubs, in the Bible conference and the evangelistic crusade, as well as in the regular services of the church. Whether the group be large or small, it is our hope and expectation that the singing of these hymns will refresh the human spirit and bring delight to the heart of our Lord.

"Praise ye the Lord; for it is good to sing praises unto our God."

(Psalm 147:1)

The Publishers

contents

		hymn numbers
hymns of worship		1-52
hymns of salvation		53-133
the call of christ	53-69	
the work of christ	70-88	
the believer's experience	89-133	
hymns of the christian life		134-209
aspiration and consecration	134-177	
trust and assurance	178-187	
peace and comfort	188-201	
the holy scriptures	202-206	
the church	207-209	
hymns of service and challenge		210-238
the christian pilgrim	210-215	
the christian soldier	216-225	
the christian witness	226-238	
hymns of the christian hope		239-253
hymns of all seasons		254-284
thanksgiving	254-257	
christmas	258-268	
palm sunday	269-270	
easter	271-277	
the changing year	278-279	
national days	280-284	
scripture readings		numbers 285-311
index of authors, composers, and sources		pages 269-271
index of tunes		pages 272-273
topical index		pages 274-277
alphabetical index of scripture readings		page 277
general index of hymns		pages 278-288

hymns of worship

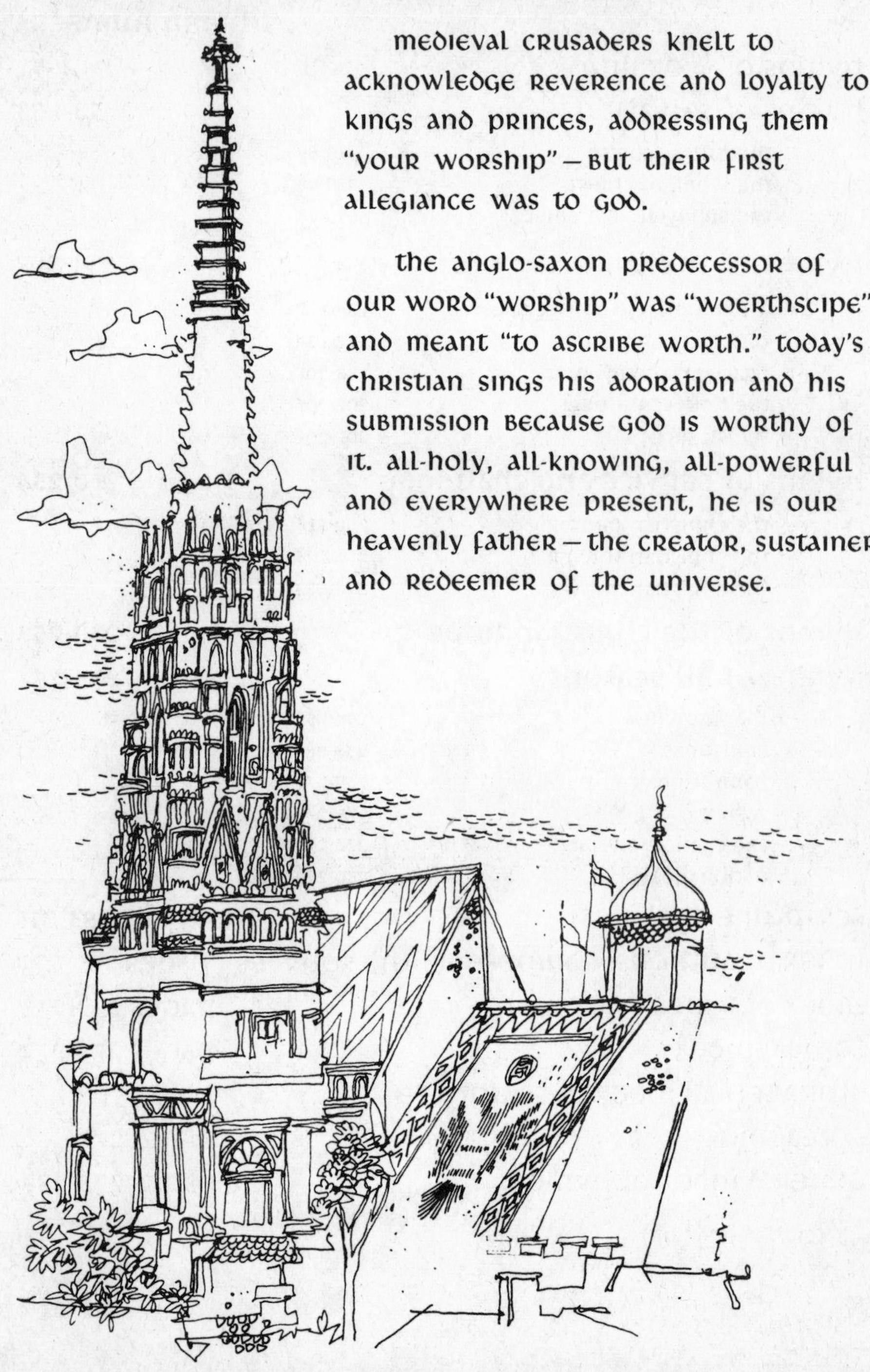

medieval crusaders knelt to acknowledge reverence and loyalty to kings and princes, addressing them "your worship" – but their first allegiance was to God.

the anglo-saxon predecessor of our word "worship" was "woerthscipe" and meant "to ascribe worth." today's christian sings his adoration and his submission because God is worthy of it. all-holy, all-knowing, all-powerful and everywhere present, he is our heavenly father – the creator, sustainer and redeemer of the universe.

Praise, my soul, the King of heaven 10

LAUDA ANIMA. 8 7 8 7 8 7

Henry F. Lyte

John Goss

1. Praise, my soul, the King of heav - en, To His feet thy
2. Praise Him for His grace and fa - vor To our fa - thers
3. Fa - ther - like, He tends and spares us; Well our fee - ble
4. An - gels, help us to a - dore Him, Ye be - hold Him
trib - ute bring; Ran - somed, healed, re - stored, for - giv - en,
in dis - tress; Praise Him, still the same for - ev - er,
frame He knows, In His hands He gen - tly bears us,
face to face; Sun and moon, bow down be - fore Him;
Who, like me, His praise should sing? Al - le - lu - ia!
Slow to chide, and swift to bless. Al - le - lu - ia!
Res - cues us from all our foes. Al - le - lu - ia!
Dwell - ers all in time and space, Al - le - lu - ia!
Al - le - lu - ia! Praise the Ev - er - last - ing King!
Al - le - lu - ia! Glo - rious in His faith - ful - ness!
Al - le - lu - ia! Wide - ly as His mer - cy flows!
Al - le - lu - ia! Praise with us the God of grace! A - MEN.

11 Holy God, We Praise Thy Name

TE DEUM. 7 8 7 8 7 7
German, 18th Century
Trans. by Clarence Walworth
Katholisches Gesangbuch, 1774
1. Ho - ly God, we praise Thy name; Lord of all, we bow be - fore Thee;
2. Hark, the loud ce - les - tial hymn An - gel choirs a - bove are rais - ing;
3. Lo! the ap - os - tol - ic train Joins Thy sa - cred name to hal - low;
4. Ho - ly Fa - ther, Ho - ly Son, Ho - ly Spir - it, Three we name Thee;
All on earth Thy scep - ter claim, All in heav'n a - bove a - dore Thee.
Cher - u - bim and Ser - a - phim, In un - ceas - ing cho - rus prais - ing,
Proph - ets swell the glad re - frain, And the white - robed mar - tyrs fol - low;
While in es - sence on - ly One, Un - di - vid - ed God we claim Thee,
In - fi - nite Thy vast do - main, Ev - er - last - ing is Thy reign.
Fill the heav'ns with sweet ac - cord: Ho - ly, ho - ly, ho - ly Lord.
And, from morn to set of sun, Through the Church the song goes on.
And a - dor - ing bend the knee, While we sing our praise to Thee. A - MEN.
12 O God, Our Help in Ages Past
ST. ANNE. C.M.
Isaac Watts
From Psalm 90
Ascribed to William Croft
1. O God, our help in a - ges past, Our hope for years to come,
2. Un - der the shad - ow of Thy throne Still may we dwell se - cure;
3. Be - fore the hills in or - der stood, Or earth re - ceived her frame,
4. A thou - sand a - ges, in Thy sight, Are like an eve - ning gone;
5. O God, our help in a - ges past, Our hope for years to come,

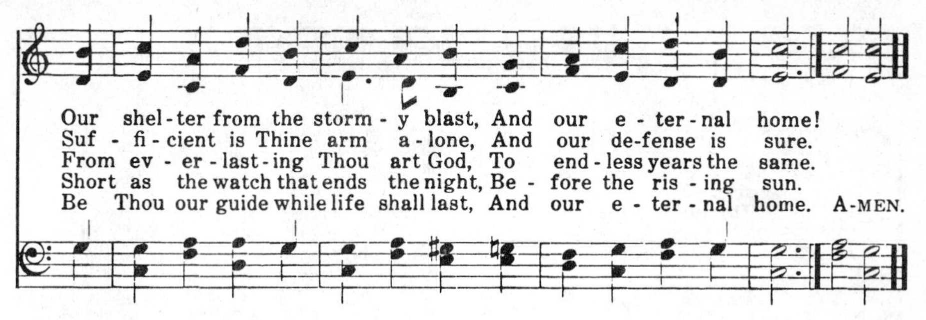
Our shel-ter from the storm-y blast, And our e-ter-nal home!
Suf-fi-cient is Thine arm a-lone, And our de-fense is sure.
From ev-er-last-ing Thou art God, To end-less years the same.
Short as the watch that ends the night, Be-fore the ris-ing sun.
Be Thou our guide while life shall last, And our e-ter-nal home. A-MEN.

GIVE TO OUR GOD IMMORTAL PRAISE 13

WARRINGTON. L.M.

Isaac Watts
From Psalm 136

Ralph Harrison

1. Give to our God im-mor-tal praise; Mer-cy and
2. Give to the Lord of lords re-nown; The King of
3. He built the earth, He spread the sky, And fixed the
4. He fills the sun with morn-ing light; He bids the
5. He sent His Son with pow'r to save From guilt, and
6. Through this vain world He guides our feet, And leads us

truth are all His ways: Won-ders of grace to God be-
kings with glo-ry crown: His mer-cies ev-er shall en-
star-ry lights on high: Won-ders of grace to God be-
moon di-rect the night: His mer-cies ev-er shall en-
dark-ness, and the grave: Won-ders of grace to God be-
to His heav'n-ly seat: His mer-cies ev-er shall en-

long; Re-peat His mer-cies in your song.
dure, When lords and kings are known no more.
long; Re-peat His mer-cies in your song.
dure, When suns and moons shall shine no more.
long; Re-peat His mer-cies in your song.
dure, When this vain world shall be no more. A-MEN.

14 We Lift Our Voice Rejoicing

FOURSQUARE. 7 6 7 6 D. Ref.

Jack W. Hayford — Jack W. Hayford

1. We lift our voice re - joic - ing, Be - cause the Lord a - bove
2. We lift our eyes in faith to The cross where - on He died,
3. We lift our hearts to wor - ship The con-quering Sav-iour's name,
Hath sent His Son to save us, And man - i - fest His love.
Re - deemed at match-less price, now In Christ we're just - i - fied.
Our tongues speak forth the prais - es Of Him who is the same.
Let ev - ery hill re - ech - o With this the song we raise,
His blood hath washed our gar-ments, His peace hath filled our souls,
Christ Je - sus reigns in pow - er Through-out e - ter - ni - ty.
"To Him whose blood hath bought us Be glo - ry, pow'r and praise."
The cross is now our glo - ry Since grace hath made us whole.
As yes - ter - day, so now, and For - ev - er He shall be.
Refrain
We praise Thee, O Fa - ther, Un - speak - a - ble our joy,

In Christ our hearts find glo - ry sin's pow'r can not de - stroy.

Who Is He in Yonder Stall? 15

HANBY. 7 7 7 7 Ref.

Benjamin R. Hanby | Benjamin R. Hanby

1. Who is He in yon - der stall, At whose feet the shep-herds fall?
2. Who is He the peo - ple bless For His words of gen - tle - ness?
3. Who is He that stands and weeps At the grave where Laz - arus sleeps?
4. Lo! at mid - night, who is He Prays in dark Geth - se - ma - ne?
5. Who is He who from the grave Comes to suc - cour, help, and save?

Who is He in deep dis - tress, Fast - ing in the wil - der - ness?
Who is He to whom they bring, All the sick and sor - row - ing?
Who is He the gathering throng Greet with loud tri - um - phant song?
Who is He on yon - der tree Dies in grief and ag - o - ny?
Who is He who from His throne Rules through all the worlds a - lone?

REFRAIN

'Tis the Lord! oh won-drous sto - ry! 'Tis the Lord! the King of glo - ry! At His feet we hum-bly fall, Crown Him! crown Him, Lord of all!

16 **ALL CREATURES OF OUR GOD AND KING**

LASST UNS ERFREUEN. 8 8 4 4 8 8 Alleluias.

St. Francis of Assisi
Trans. by William H. Draper

Geistliche Kirchengesänge, 1623

1. All crea-tures of our God and King, Lift up your voice and with us
2. Thou rush-ing wind that art so strong, Ye clouds that sail in heav'n a-
3. Dear moth-er earth, who day by day Un - fold - est bless-ings on our
4. And all ye men of ten-der heart, For - giv - ing oth - ers, take your
5. Let all things their Cre - a - tor bless, And wor - ship Him in hum - ble-
Praise God from whom all bless - ings flow, Praise Him all crea - tures here be-
Harmony
Unison
sing, Al-le - lu - ia! Al - le - lu - ia! Thou burn-ing sun with gold - en
long, O praise Him! Al - le - lu - ia! Thou ris - ing morn, in praise re-
way, O praise Him! Al - le - lu - ia! The flow'rs and fruits that in thee
part, O sing ye! Al - le - lu - ia! Ye who long pain and sor - row
ness. O praise Him! Al - le - lu - ia! Praise, praise the Fa-ther, praise the
low, Al - le - lu - ia! Al - le - lu - ia! Praise Him a - bove, ye heav'n-ly
Harmony
beam, Thou sil - ver moon with soft - er gleam! O praise Him, O
joice, Ye lights of eve-ning, find a voice! O praise Him, O
grow, Let them His glo - ry al - so show! O praise Him, O
bear, Praise God and on Him cast your care! O praise Him, O
Son, And praise the Spir - it, Three in One! O praise Him, O
host, Praise Fa - ther, Son and Ho - ly Ghost, Al-le - lu - ia, Al-le-
Unison
praise Him, Al - le - lu - ia! Al - le - lu - ia! Al - le - lu - ia! A-MEN.
lu - ia!

JOIN ALL THE GLORIOUS NAMES 17

DARWALL. 6 6 6 6 8 8

Isaac Watts

John Darwall

1. Join all the glo - rious names Of wis - dom, love, and power,
2. Great Pro - phet of my God, My tongue would bless Thy name:
3. Je - sus, my great High Priest, Of - fered His blood, and died;
4. Thou art my Coun - sel - lor, My Pat - tern, and my Guide,
5. My Sav - iour and my Lord, My Con - quer'r and my King,
That ev - er mor - tals knew, That an - gels
By Thee the joy - ful news Of our sal-
My guilt - y con - science seeks No sac - ri-
And Thou my Shep - herd art; Oh, keep me
Thy scep - tre and Thy sword, Thy reign - ing
ev - er bore: All are too poor to speak His worth,
va - tion came, The joy - ful news of sins for - giv'n,
fice be - side: His pow'r - ful blood did once a - tone
near Thy side; Nor let my feet e'er turn a - stray,
grace I sing: Thine is the pow'r; be - hold I sit
Too poor to set my Sav - iour forth.
Of hell sub - dued and peace with heav'n.
And now it pleads be - fore the throne.
To wan - der in the crook - ed way.
In will - ing bonds be - neath Thy feet.
A - MEN.

18 For the Beauty of the Earth

DIX. 7 7 7 7 7 7

Folliott S. Pierpoint

Conrad Kocher, adapted

1. For the beau - ty of the earth, For the glo - ry
2. For the beau - ty of each hour Of the day and
3. For the joy of hu - man love, Broth - er, sis - ter,
4. For Thy Church that ev - er - more Lift - eth ho - ly
of the skies, For the love which from our birth
of the night, Hill and vale, and tree, and flower,
par - ent, child, Friends on earth, and friends a - bove,
hands a - bove, Of - fering up on ev - ery shore
O - ver and a - round us lies, Lord of all, to
Sun and moon, and stars of light, Lord of all, to
For all gen - tle thoughts and mild, Lord of all, to
Her pure sac - ri - fice of love, Lord of all, to
Thee we raise This our hymn of grate - ful praise.
Thee we raise This our hymn of grate - ful praise.
Thee we raise This our hymn of grate - ful praise.
Thee we raise This our hymn of grate - ful praise. A-MEN.

Praise Ye the Lord, the Almighty

LOBE DEN HERREN. 14 14 4 7 8

Joachim Neander
Trans. by Catherine Winkworth

Stralsund Gesangbuch, 1665

1. Praise ye the Lord, the Al - might - y, the King of cre - a- tion! O my soul, praise Him, for He is thy health and sal- va - - tion! All ye who hear, Now to His tem - ple draw near; Join me in glad ad - o - ra - - - - tion!
2. Praise ye the Lord, who o'er all things so won-drous - ly reign- eth, Shel - ters thee un - der His wings, yea, so gen - tly sus- tain - - eth! Hast thou not seen How thy de - sires e'er have been Grant - ed in what He or - dain - - - - eth?
3. Praise ye the Lord, who with mar - vel - ous wis - dom hath made thee! Decked thee with health, and with lov - ing hand guid - ed and stayed thee; How oft in grief Hath not He brought thee re- lief, Spread-ing His wings for to shade . . . thee!
4. Praise ye the Lord! O let all that is in me a - dore Him! All that hath life and breath, come now with prais - es be- fore Him! Let the A - men Sound from His peo - ple a- gain: Glad - ly for aye we a - dore . . . Him. A - MEN.

REJOICE, MY SOUL!

HARVEY. L.M. Ref.

Avis B. Christiansen

Donald P. Hustad

1. Re - joice, my soul! re - joice and sing E - ter - nal praise to Christ thy King;
2. Re - joice, my soul! re - joice in Him Whose pow'r hath conquered death and sin;
3. Re - joice, my soul! re - joice and sing! Glad hom-age yield to Christ, thy King!

All glo - rious is His ho - ly name, Through ev-er-last-ing years the same.
Who rose in vic - t'ry from the grave, And lives, al-might-y now to save.
Whose name all men shall one day own Be - fore His ev - er - last - ing throne.

REFRAIN

Re - joice, my soul! re - joice and sing Glad songs of praise to Christ, thy King.

Let notes of ad - o - ra - tion rise And ech - o through the vault-ed skies.

Let heav'n and earth His pow'r pro-claim, And mag - ni - fy His ho - ly name!

Re - joice, my soul! re - joice and sing! For Christ the Lord is King!
There is no name so sweet on earth
21
THE SWEETEST NAME. 8 7 8 7 D.
Source Unknown
William B. Bradbury
1. There is no name so sweet on earth, No name so sweet in heav - en,
2. And when He hung up - on the tree, They wrote His name a - bove Him;
3. So now, up - on His Fa-ther's throne, Al-might - y to re - lease us
4. O Je - sus, by that match-less name, Thy grace shall fail us nev - er;
The name be - fore His won-drous birth, To Christ the Sav - iour giv - en.
That all might see the rea - son we For ev - er-more must love Him.
From sin and pains, He glad - ly reigns, The Prince and Sav - iour, Je - sus.
To - day as yes - ter - day the same, Thou art the same for - ev - er.
Refrain
We love to sing of Christ our King, And hail him bless - ed Je - sus;
For there's no word ear ev - er heard So dear, so sweet as "Je - sus."

22

FOREVER

PLAGAL. 8 7 8 7

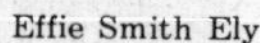
Effie Smith Ely

Donald P. Hustad

1. We sigh for hu - man love, from which A whim or chance may sev - er,
2. We seek earth's peace in things that pass Like foam up - on the riv - er,
3. Man's help, for which we long, gives way, As trees in storm-winds quiv - er,
4. Turn un - to Thee our wav-'ring hearts, O Thou who fail - est nev - er;

And leave un-sought the love of God, Tho' God's love lasts for - ev - er.
While steadfast as the stars on high, God's peace a - bides for - ev - er.
But might - ier than all hu - man need God's help re - mains for - ev - er.
Give us Thy love and Thy great peace, And be our Help for - ev - er! A-MEN.

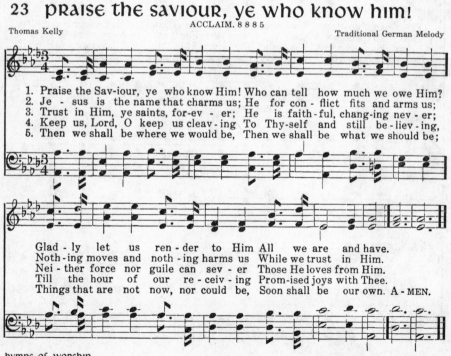

23

PRAISE THE SAVIOUR, YE WHO KNOW HIM!

ACCLAIM. 8 8 8 5

Thomas Kelly

Traditional German Melody

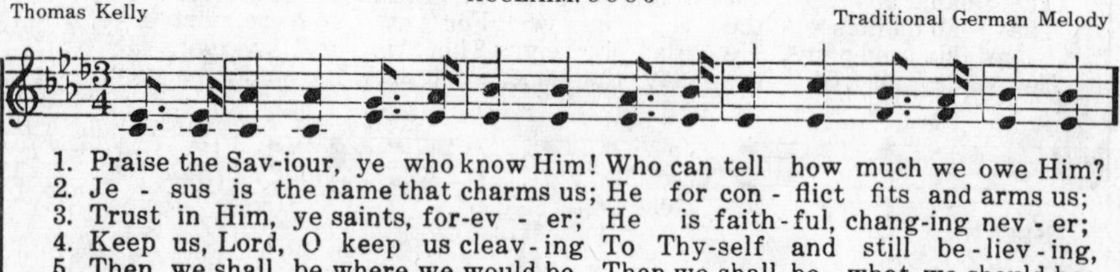

1. Praise the Sav-iour, ye who know Him! Who can tell how much we owe Him?
2. Je - sus is the name that charms us; He for con - flict fits and arms us;
3. Trust in Him, ye saints, for-ev - er; He is faith-ful, chang-ing nev - er;
4. Keep us, Lord, O keep us cleav - ing To Thy-self and still be-liev - ing,
5. Then we shall be where we would be, Then we shall be what we should be;

Glad - ly let us ren - der to Him All we are and have.
Noth - ing moves and noth - ing harms us While we trust in Him.
Nei - ther force nor guile can sev - er Those He loves from Him.
Till the hour of our re - ceiv - ing Prom-ised joys with Thee.
Things that are not now, nor could be, Soon shall be our own. A - MEN.

O for a thousand tongues to sing 24

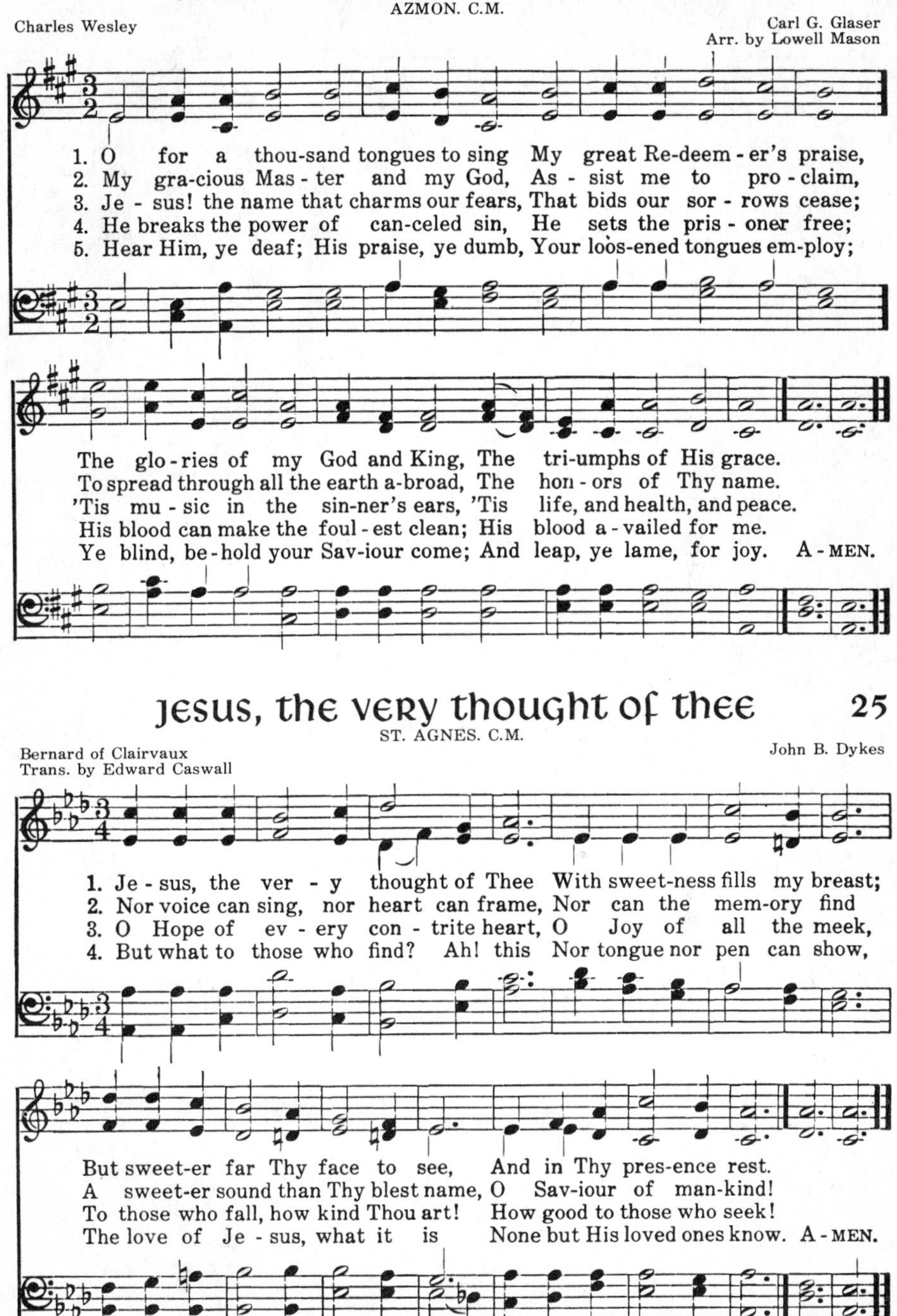
AZMON. C.M.
Charles Wesley
Carl G. Glaser
Arr. by Lowell Mason
1. O for a thou-sand tongues to sing My great Re-deem-er's praise, The glo-ries of my God and King, The tri-umphs of His grace.
2. My gra-cious Mas-ter and my God, As-sist me to pro-claim, To spread through all the earth a-broad, The hon-ors of Thy name.
3. Je-sus! the name that charms our fears, That bids our sor-rows cease; 'Tis mu-sic in the sin-ner's ears, 'Tis life, and health, and peace.
4. He breaks the power of can-celed sin, He sets the pris-oner free; His blood can make the foul-est clean; His blood a-vailed for me.
5. Hear Him, ye deaf; His praise, ye dumb, Your loos-ened tongues em-ploy; Ye blind, be-hold your Sav-iour come; And leap, ye lame, for joy. A-MEN.
Jesus, the very thought of Thee 25
ST. AGNES. C.M.
Bernard of Clairvaux
Trans. by Edward Caswall
John B. Dykes
1. Je-sus, the ver-y thought of Thee With sweet-ness fills my breast; But sweet-er far Thy face to see, And in Thy pres-ence rest.
2. Nor voice can sing, nor heart can frame, Nor can the mem-ory find A sweet-er sound than Thy blest name, O Sav-iour of man-kind!
3. O Hope of ev-ery con-trite heart, O Joy of all the meek, To those who fall, how kind Thou art! How good to those who seek!
4. But what to those who find? Ah! this Nor tongue nor pen can show, The love of Je-sus, what it is None but His loved ones know. A-MEN.

26 REJOICE, YE PURE IN HEART

MARION. S.M. Ref.

Edward H. Plumptre — Arthur H. Messiter

1. Rejoice, ye pure in heart, Rejoice, give thanks, and sing;
2. With all the angel choirs, With all the saints on earth,
3. Still lift your standard high, Still march in firm array;
4. Yes, on through life's long path, Still chanting as ye go;
5. Then on, ye pure in heart, Rejoice, give thanks, and sing;

Your festal banner wave on high, The cross of Christ your King.
Pour out the strains of joy and bliss, True rapture, noblest mirth!
As warriors through the darkness toil Till dawns the golden day.
From youth to age, by night and day, In gladness and in woe.
Your festal banner wave on high, The cross of Christ your King.

REFRAIN

Rejoice, (Rejoice,) rejoice, (rejoice,) Rejoice, give thanks, and sing! A-MEN.

27 COME, WE THAT LOVE THE LORD

ST. THOMAS. S.M.

Isaac Watts — Aaron Williams

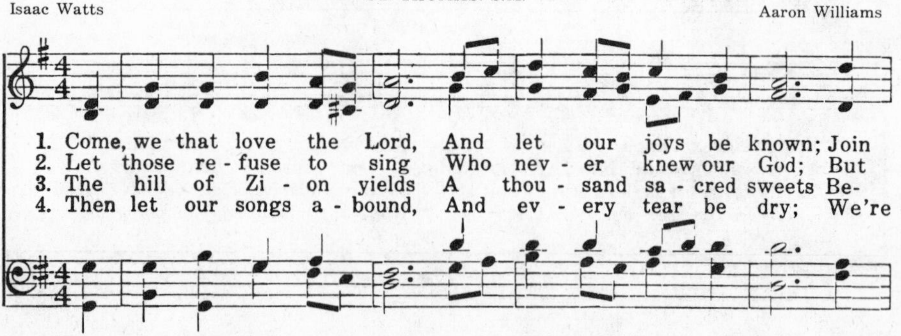
1. Come, we that love the Lord, And let our joys be known; Join
2. Let those refuse to sing Who never knew our God; But
3. The hill of Zion yields A thousand sacred sweets Be-
4. Then let our songs abound, And every tear be dry; We're

in a song with sweet ac - cord, And thus sur - round the throne.
chil - dren of the heaven - ly King May speak their joys a - broad.
fore we reach the heaven - ly fields, Or walk the gold - en streets.
march-ing thro' Em - man-uel's ground To fair - er worlds on high. A-MEN.

come, thou almighty king

28

MOSCOW (ITALIAN HYMN). 6 6 4 6 6 6 4

Source Unknown

Felice de Giardini

1. Come, Thou Al - might - y King, Help us Thy name to sing,
2. Come, Thou In - car - nate Word, Gird on Thy might - y sword,
3. Come, Ho - ly Com - fort - er, Thy sa - cred wit - ness bear
4. To the great One in Three E - ter - nal prais - es be
Help us to praise: Fa - ther, all - glo - ri - ous, O'er all vic-
Our prayer at - tend: Come, and Thy peo - ple bless, And give Thy
In this glad hour: Thou who al - might - y art, Now rule in
Hence, ev - er - more! His sov-ereign maj - es - ty May we in
to - ri - ous, Come, and reign o - ver us, An - cient of Days.
word suc-cess: Spir - it of ho - li - ness, On us de - scend.
ev - ery heart, And ne'er from us de - part, Spir - it of power.
glo - ry see, And to e - ter - ni - ty Love and a - dore! A - MEN.

PRAISE HIM! PRAISE HIM!

JOYFUL SONG. 12 10 12 10 D.

Fanny J. Crosby

Chester G. Allen

1. Praise Him! praise Him! Je-sus, our bless-ed Re-deem-er! Sing, O Earth, His
2. Praise Him! praise Him! Je-sus, our bless-ed Re-deem-er! For our sins He
3. Praise Him! praise Him! Je-sus, our bless-ed Re-deem-er! Heavenly por-tals
won-der-ful love pro-claim! Hail Him! hail Him! highest archangels in glo-ry;
suffered, and bled and died; He our Rock, our hope of e-ter-nal sal-va-tion,
loud with ho-san-nas ring! Je-sus, Sav-iour, reigneth for-ev-er and ev-er;
Strength and hon-or give to His ho-ly name! Like a shep-herd Je-sus will
Hail Him! hail Him! Je-sus the Cru-ci-fied. Sound His prais-es! Je-sus who
Crown Him! crown Him! Prophet and Priest and King! Christ is com-ing! o-ver the
REFRAIN
guard His children, In His arms He carries them all day long:
bore our sor-rows; Love unbounded, wonderful, deep and strong: Praise Him! praise Him!
world vic-to-rious, Power and glo-ry un-to the Lord be-long:
tell of His ex-cel-lent greatness; Praise Him! praise Him! ever in joy-ful song!

COME, CHRISTIANS, JOIN TO SING

MADRID. 6 6 6 6 D.

Christian Henry Bateman

Traditional Melody
Harm. by David Evans

1. Come, Chris - tians, join to sing Al - le - lu - ia! A - men!
2. Come, lift your hearts on high, Al - le - lu - ia! A - men!
3. Praise yet our Christ a - gain, Al - le - lu - ia! A - men!
Loud praise to Christ our King; Al - le - lu - ia! A - men!
Let prais - es fill the sky; Al - le - lu - ia! A - men!
Life shall not end the strain; Al - le - lu - ia! A - men!
Let all, with heart and voice, Be - fore His throne re - joice;
He is our Guide and Friend; To us He'll con - de - scend;
On heav - en's bliss - ful shore His good - ness we'll a - dore,
Praise is His gra - cious choice: Al - le - lu - ia! A - men!
His love shall nev - er end: Al - le - lu - ia! A - men!
Sing - ing for - ev - er - more, "Al - le - lu - ia! A - men!" A-MEN.

31 CROWN HIM WITH MANY CROWNS

DIADEMATA. S.M.D.

Matthew Bridges and
Godfrey Thring

George J. Elvey

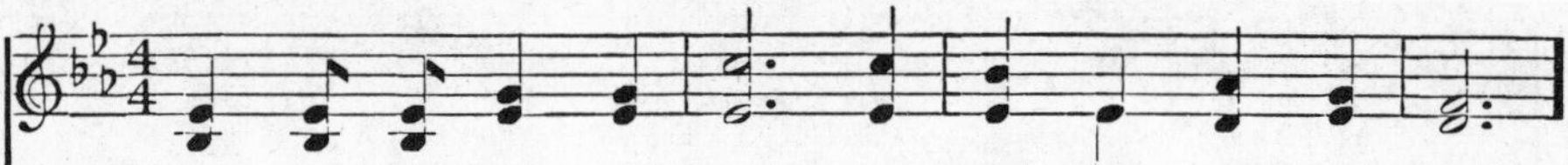

1. Crown Him with man - y crowns, The Lamb up - on His throne;
2. Crown Him the Son of God Be - fore the worlds be - gan,
3. Crown Him the Lord of life, Who tri-umphed o'er the grave,
4. Crown Him the Lord of love! Be - hold His hands and side,

Hark! how the heaven-ly an - them drowns All mu - sic but its own!
And ye, who tread where He hath trod, Crown Him the Son of man;
And rose vic - to - rious in the strife For those He came to save;
Rich wounds, yet vis - i - ble a - bove, In beau - ty glo - ri - fied:

A - wake, my soul, and sing Of Him who died for thee,
Who ev - ery grief hath known That wrings the hu - man breast,
His glo - ries now we sing Who died, and rose on high,
All hail, Re - deem - er, hail! For Thou hast died for me:

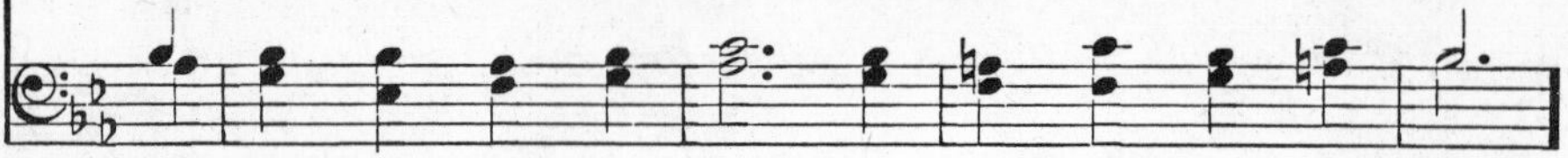

And hail Him as thy matchless King Through all e - ter - ni - ty.
And takes and bears them for His own, That all in Him may rest.
Who died, e - ter - nal life to bring, And lives that death may die.
Thy praise shall nev-er, nev - er fail Throughout e - ter - ni - ty. A-MEN.

MY GOD AND KING! 36

ALL THE WORLD. 14 12 12 14

George Herbert — Robert G. McCutchan

1. Let all the world in ev - ery cor - ner sing, "My God and King!" The heavens are not too high, His praise may thith - er fly; The earth is not too low, His prais - es there may grow. Let all the world in ev - ery cor - ner sing, "My God and King!" God and King!"
2. Let all the world in ev - ery cor - ner sing, "My God and King!" The Church with psalms must shout, No door can keep them out: But more than all, the heart Must bear the lar - gest part. Let all the world in
1
2

37 I Love Thee

I LOVE THEE. 11 11 11 11

Source Unknown — Ingall's *Christian Harmony*, 1805

1. I love Thee, I love Thee, I love Thee, my Lord;
2. I'm hap - py, I'm hap - py, oh, won - drous ac - count!
3. O Je - sus, my Sav - iour, with Thee I am blest,
4. Oh, who's like my Sav - iour? He's Sa - lem's bright King;
I love Thee, my Sav - iour, I love Thee, my God;
My joys are im - mor - tal, I stand on the mount;
My life and sal - va - tion, my joy and my rest;
He smiles and He loves me and helps me to sing;
I love Thee, I love Thee, and that Thou dost know;
I gaze on my treas - ure and long to be there,
Thy name be my theme, and Thy love be my song;
I'll praise Him, I'll praise Him with notes loud and clear,
But how much I love Thee my ac - tions will show.
With Je - sus and an - gels and kin - dred so dear.
Thy grace shall in - spire both my heart and my tongue.
While riv - ers of pleas - ure my spir - it shall cheer. A - MEN.

The God of Abraham Praise

LEONI. 6 6 8 4 D.

Thomas Olivers
Based on *The Yigdal*
by Daniel ben Judah

Hebrew Melody
Arr. by Meyer Lyon

1. The God of A-braham praise, Who reigns en-throned a - bove;
An - cient of ev - er - last - ing days, And God of love.
Je - ho - vah, great I AM, By earth and heaven con - fessed;
I bow and bless the sa - cred Name, For - ev - er blest.

2. The God of A-braham praise, At whose su - preme com - mand
From earth I rise, and seek the joys At His right hand.
I all on earth for - sake, Its wis - dom, fame, and power;
And Him my on - ly por - tion make, My shield and tower.

3. He by Him - self hath sworn, I on His oath de - pend;
I shall, on ea - gles' wings up - borne, To heaven as - cend;
I shall be - hold His face, I shall His power a - dore,
And sing the won - ders of His grace For - ev - er - more.

4. The whole tri - um - phant host Give thanks to God on high;
"Hail, Fa - ther, Son and Ho - ly Ghost!" They ev - er cry.
Hail, A-braham's God and mine! I join the heaven - ly lays;
All might and maj - es - ty are Thine, And end - less praise. A-MEN.

39 FAIREST LORD JESUS

CRUSADERS' HYMN. 5 6 8 5 5 8

From the German
4th Verse trans. by Joseph A. Seiss

Schlesische Volkslieder, 1842
Arr. by Richard S. Willis

1. Fair - est Lord Je - sus! Ru - ler of all na - ture,
2. Fair are the mead - ows, Fair - er still the wood - lands,
3. Fair is the sun - shine, Fair - er still the moon - light,
4. Beau - ti - ful Sav - iour! Lord of the na - tions!
O Thou of God and man the Son! Thee will I cher - ish,
Robed in the bloom - ing garb of spring: Je - sus is fair - er,
And all the twink - ling star - ry host: Je - sus shines bright - er,
Son of God and Son of Man! Glo - ry and hon - or,
Thee will I hon - or, Thou, my soul's Glo - ry, Joy, and Crown!
Je - sus is pur - er, Who makes the woe - ful heart to sing.
Je - sus shines pur - er, Than all the an - gels heaven can boast.
Praise, a - do - ra - tion, Now and for - ev - er - more be Thine! A-MEN.
40 THE LORD'S MY SHEPHERD, I'LL NOT WANT
CRIMOND. C.M.
Psalm 23
Scottish Psalter, 1650
Jessie Seymour Irvine
Harm. by David Grant
1. The Lord's my Shep - herd, I'll not want; He makes me down to lie
2. My soul He doth re - store a - gain; And me to walk doth make
3. Yea, though I walk through death's dark vale, Yet will I fear no ill;
4. My ta - ble Thou hast fur - nish - ed In pres - ence of my foes;
5. Good - ness and mer - cy all my life Shall sure - ly fol - low me;

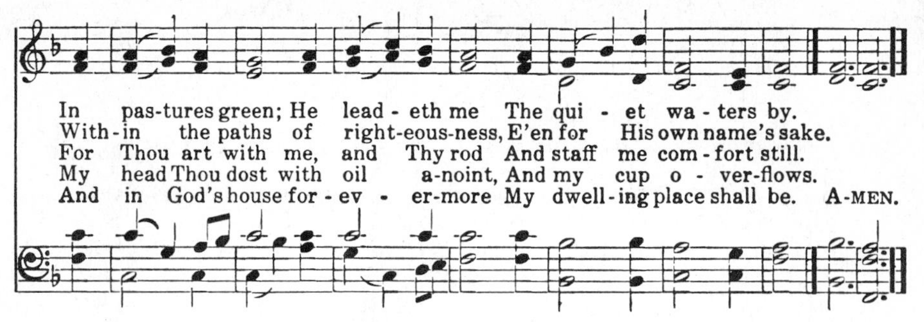
In pas-tures green; He lead-eth me The qui - et wa-ters by.
With-in the paths of right-eous-ness, E'en for His own name's sake.
For Thou art with me, and Thy rod And staff me com-fort still.
My head Thou dost with oil a-noint, And my cup o - ver-flows.
And in God's house for - ev - er-more My dwell-ing place shall be. A-MEN.

When Morning Gilds the Skies 41

LAUDES DOMINI. 6 6 6 6 6 6

From the German, c. 1800
Trans. by Edward Caswall

Joseph Barnby

1. When morn - ing gilds the skies, My heart a - wak - ing cries:
2. Does sad - ness fill my mind, A sol - ace here I find:
3. In heaven's e - ter - nal bliss The love - liest strain is this,
4. Be this, while life is mine, My can - ti - cle di - vine,

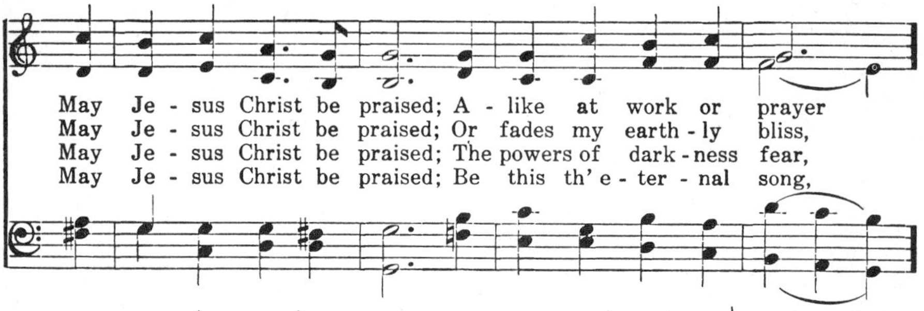

May Je - sus Christ be praised; A - like at work or prayer
May Je - sus Christ be praised; Or fades my earth - ly bliss,
May Je - sus Christ be praised; The powers of dark - ness fear,
May Je - sus Christ be praised; Be this th' e - ter - nal song,

To Je - sus I re - pair: May Je - sus Christ be praised.
My com - fort still is this: May Je - sus Christ be praised.
When this sweet chant they hear: May Je - sus Christ be praised.
Through all the a - ges long: May Je - sus Christ be praised. AMEN

42 What a Wonderful Saviour!

BENTON HARBOR. 8 7 8 7 Ref.

Elisha A. Hoffman | Elisha A. Hoffman

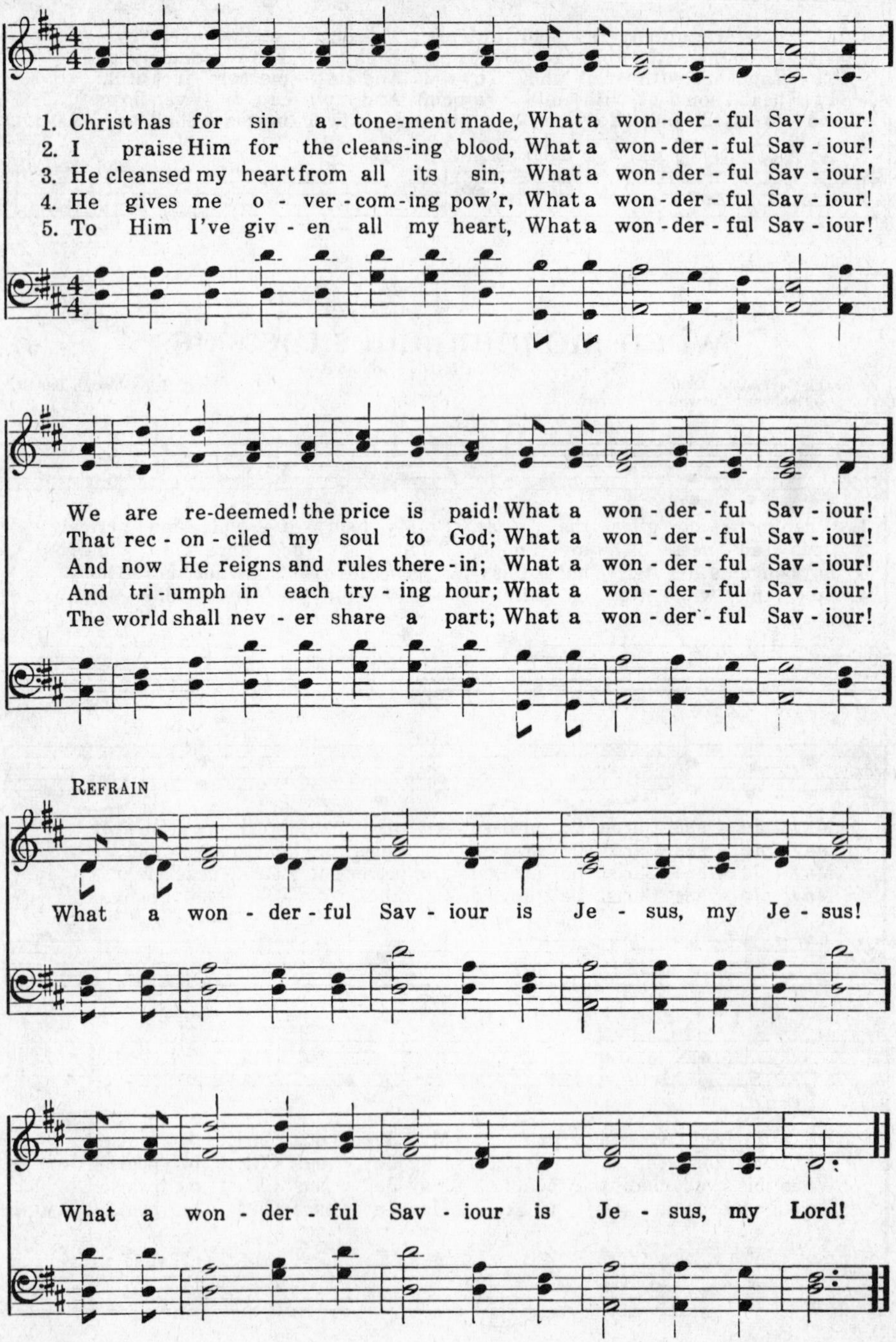

1. Christ has for sin a - tone-ment made, What a won - der - ful Sav - iour!
2. I praise Him for the cleans-ing blood, What a won - der - ful Sav - iour!
3. He cleansed my heart from all its sin, What a won - der - ful Sav - iour!
4. He gives me o - ver - com - ing pow'r, What a won - der - ful Sav - iour!
5. To Him I've giv - en all my heart, What a won - der - ful Sav - iour!

We are re-deemed! the price is paid! What a won - der - ful Sav - iour!
That rec - on - ciled my soul to God; What a won - der - ful Sav - iour!
And now He reigns and rules there - in; What a won - der - ful Sav - iour!
And tri - umph in each try - ing hour; What a won - der - ful Sav - iour!
The world shall nev - er share a part; What a won - der`- ful Sav - iour!

REFRAIN

What a won - der - ful Sav - iour is Je - sus, my Je - sus!
What a won - der - ful Sav - iour is Je - sus, my Lord!

Immortal, Invisible, God Only Wise 43

JOANNA. 11 11 11 11

Walter Chalmers Smith

Welsh Hymn Melody

1. Im - mor - tal, in - vis - i - ble, God on - ly wise,
2. Un - rest - ing, un - hast - ing, and si - lent as light,
3. To all, life Thou giv - est, to both great and small,
4. Great Fa - ther of glo - ry, pure Fa - ther of light,
In light in - ac - ces - si - ble hid from our eyes,
Nor want - ing, nor wast - ing, Thou rul - est in might;
In all life Thou liv - est, the true life of all.
Thine an - gels a - dore Thee, all veil - ing their sight;
Most bless - ed, most glo - rious, the An - cient of Days,
Thy jus - tice like moun - tains high soar - ing a - bove
We blos - som and flour - ish as leaves on the tree,
All praise we would ren - der; O help us to see
Al - might - y, vic - to - rious, Thy great name we praise.
Thy clouds, which are foun - tains of good - ness and love.
And with - er and per - ish— but nought chang-eth Thee.
'Tis on - ly the splen - dor of light hid - eth Thee! A - MEN.

44 This Is My Father's World

TERRA BEATA. S.M.D.

Maltbie D. Babcock — Franklin L. Sheppard

1. This is my Fa-ther's world, And to my lis - tening ears All
2. This is my Fa-ther's world, The birds their car - ols raise, The
3. This is my Fa-ther's world, O let me ne'er for - get That
na - ture sings, and round me rings The mu - sic of the spheres.
morn - ing light, the lil - y white, De - clare their Mak - er's praise.
though the wrong seems oft so strong, God is the Rul - er yet.
This is my Fa-ther's world: I rest me in the thought Of
This is my Fa-ther's world: He shines in all that's fair; In the
This is my Fa-ther's world: The bat - tle is not done; Je-
rocks and trees, of skies and seas—His hand the won - ders wrought.
rus - tling grass I hear Him pass, He speaks to me ev-ery-where.
sus who died shall be sat - is - fied, And earth and heaven be one. A - MEN.

HERE, O MY LORD

LANGRAN. 10 10 10 10

Horatius Bonar

James Langran

1. Here, O my Lord, I see Thee face to face;
2. Here would I feed up - on the bread of God;
3. This is the hour of ban - quet and of song;
4. Too soon we rise; the sym - bols dis - ap - pear;
5. Feast af - ter feast thus comes and pass - es by,
Here would I touch and han - dle things un - seen,
Here drink with Thee the roy - al wine of heav'n;
This is the heav'n - ly ta - ble spread for me;
The feast, though not the love, is past and gone;
Yet, pass - ing, points to the glad feast a - bove,
Here grasp with firm - er hand th'e - ter - nal grace,
Here would I lay a - side each earth - ly load,
Here let me feast, and feast - ing, still pro - long
The bread and wine re - move, but Thou art here,
Giv - ing sweet fore - taste of the fes - tal joy,
And all my wea - ri - ness up - on Thee lean.
Here taste a - fresh the calm of sin for - giv'n.
The brief bright hour of fel - low - ship with Thee.
Near - er than ev - er; still my shield and sun.
The Lamb's great brid - al feast of bliss and love. A - MEN.

46 PRAISE YE THE TRIUNE GOD!

FLEMMING. 11 11 11 5

Source Unknown — Friedrich F. Flemming

1. Praise ye the Fa - ther! for His lov - ing kind - ness, Ten - der - ly
2. Praise ye the Sav - iour! great is His com - pas - sion, Gra - cious - ly
3. Praise ye the Spir - it! Com - fort - er of Is - rael, Sent of the
cares He for His err - ing chil - dren; Praise Him, ye an - gels,
cares He for His cho - sen peo - ple; Young men and maid - ens,
Fa - ther and the Son to bless us; Praise ye the Fa - ther,
praise Him in the heav - ens, Praise ye Je - ho - vah!
ye old men and chil - dren, Praise ye the Sav - iour!
Son and Ho - ly Spir - it, Praise ye the Tri - une God! A - MEN.
47 JESUS, GENTLEST SAVIOUR
EUDOXIA. 6 5 6 5
Frederick W. Faber
Sabine Baring-Gould
1. Je - sus, gen - tlest Sav - iour, God of might and power,
2. Na - ture can - not hold thee, Heav'n is all too strait
3. Out be - yond the shin - ing Of the far - thest star,
4. Yet the hearts of child - ren Hold what worlds can - not,
5. Je - sus, gent - lest Sav - iour, Thou art with us now;
6. Mul - ti - ply our gra - ces, Give us love and fear,

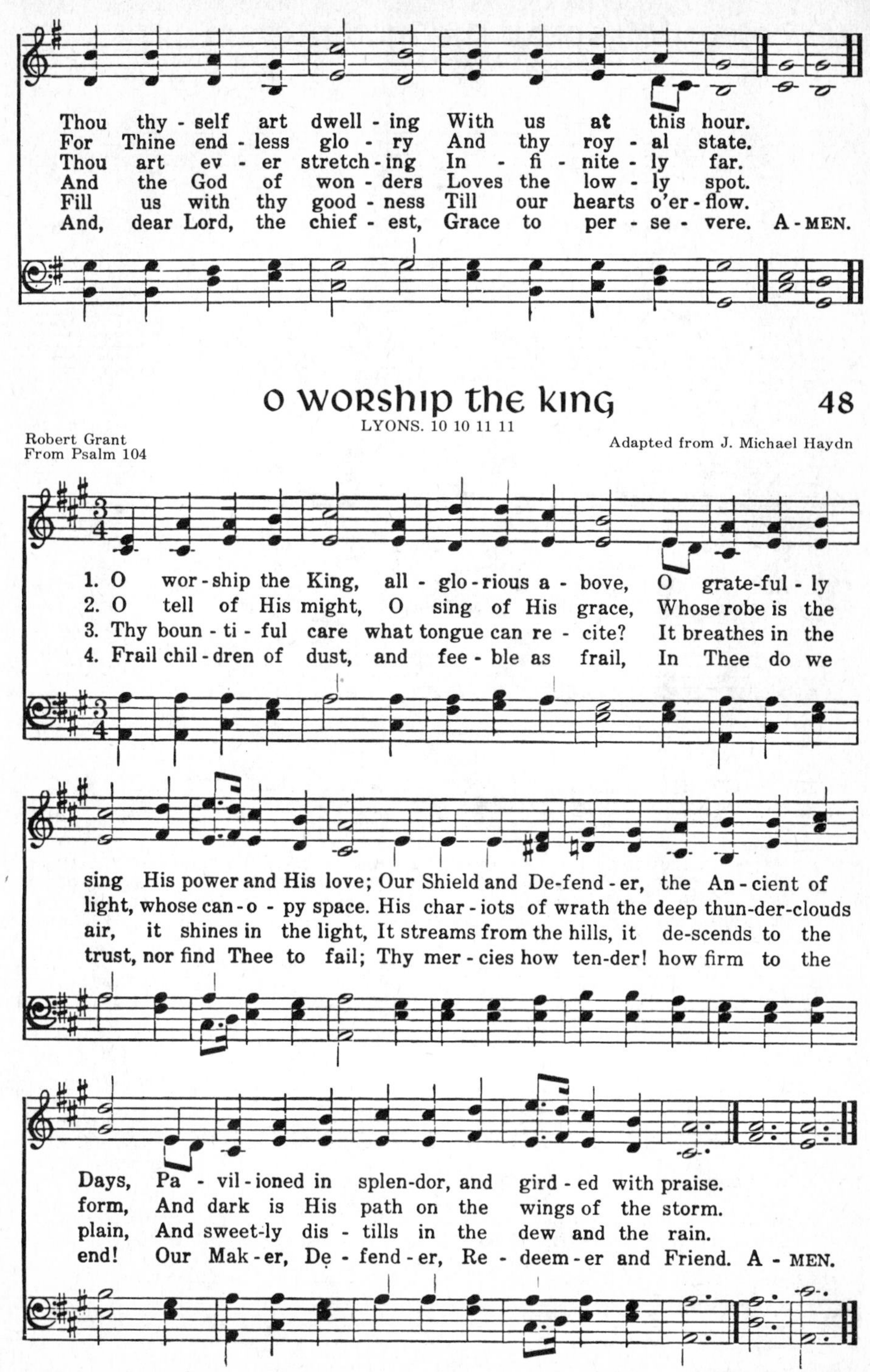
Thou thy - self art dwell - ing With us at this hour.
For Thine end - less glo - ry And thy roy - al state.
Thou art ev - er stretch - ing In - fi - nite - ly far.
And the God of won - ders Loves the low - ly spot.
Fill us with thy good - ness Till our hearts o'er - flow.
And, dear Lord, the chief - est, Grace to per - se - vere. A - MEN.
O WORSHIP THE KING
48
LYONS. 10 10 11 11
Robert Grant
From Psalm 104
Adapted from J. Michael Haydn
1. O wor - ship the King, all - glo - rious a - bove, O grate - ful - ly
2. O tell of His might, O sing of His grace, Whose robe is the
3. Thy boun - ti - ful care what tongue can re - cite? It breathes in the
4. Frail chil - dren of dust, and fee - ble as frail, In Thee do we
sing His power and His love; Our Shield and De - fend - er, the An - cient of
light, whose can - o - py space. His char - iots of wrath the deep thun - der - clouds
air, it shines in the light, It streams from the hills, it de - scends to the
trust, nor find Thee to fail; Thy mer - cies how ten - der! how firm to the
Days, Pa - vil - ioned in splen - dor, and gird - ed with praise.
form, And dark is His path on the wings of the storm.
plain, And sweet - ly dis - tills in the dew and the rain.
end! Our Mak - er, De - fend - er, Re - deem - er and Friend. A - MEN.

49 O Could I Speak the Matchless Worth

ARIEL. 8 8 6 D.

Samuel Medley

Wolfgang A. Mozart
Arr. by Lowell Mason

1. O could I speak the match - less worth,
2. I'd sing the pre - cious blood He spilt,
3. I'd sing the char - ac - ters He bears,
4. Soon the de - light - ful day will come
O could I sound the glo - ries forth Which in my Sav - iour shine,
My ran - som from the dread-ful guilt Of sin and wrath di - vine!
And all the forms of love He wears, Ex - alt - ed on His throne:
When my dear Lord will bring me home, And I shall see His face;
I'd soar and touch the heav'nly strings, And vie with Ga-briel while he sings
I'd sing His glo - rious right-eous-ness, In which all-per - fect heavenly dress
In loft - iest songs of sweet-est praise, I would to ev - er - last - ing days
Then with my Sav - iour, Brother, Friend, A blest e - ter - ni - ty I'll spend,
In notes al - most di - vine, In notes al - most di - vine.
My soul shall ev - er shine, My soul shall ev - er shine.
Make all His glo - ries known, Make all His glo - ries known.
Tri - um - phant in His grace, Tri - um-phant in His grace. A-MEN.

awake, my soul, and with the sun 50

MORNING HYMN. L.M.

Thomas Ken — Francois H. Barthélémon

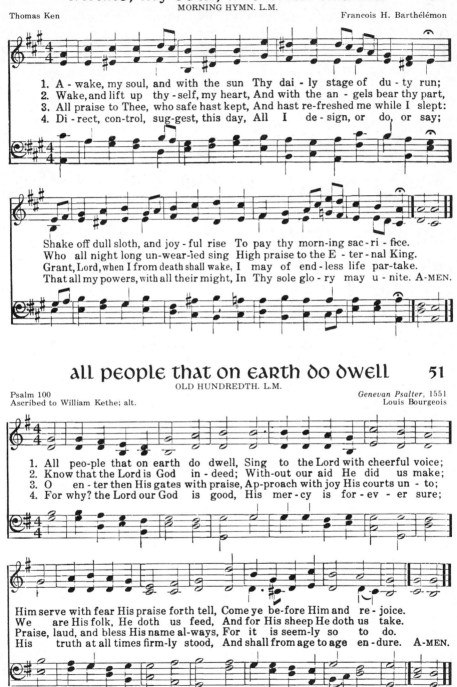

1. A - wake, my soul, and with the sun Thy dai - ly stage of du - ty run;
2. Wake, and lift up thy - self, my heart, And with the an - gels bear thy part,
3. All praise to Thee, who safe hast kept, And hast re-freshed me while I slept:
4. Di - rect, con-trol, sug-gest, this day, All I de - sign, or do, or say;

Shake off dull sloth, and joy - ful rise To pay thy morn-ing sac - ri - fice.
Who all night long un-wear-ied sing High praise to the E - ter - nal King.
Grant, Lord, when I from death shall wake, I may of end - less life par-take.
That all my powers, with all their might, In Thy sole glo - ry may u - nite. A-MEN.

all people that on earth do dwell 51

OLD HUNDREDTH. L.M.

Psalm 100
Ascribed to William Kethe; alt. — *Genevan Psalter*, 1551
Louis Bourgeois

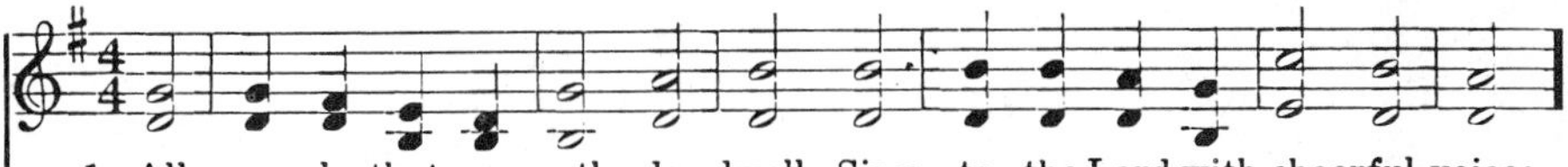

1. All peo-ple that on earth do dwell, Sing to the Lord with cheerful voice;
2. Know that the Lord is God in - deed; With-out our aid He did us make;
3. O en - ter then His gates with praise, Ap-proach with joy His courts un - to;
4. For why? the Lord our God is good, His mer - cy is for - ev - er sure;

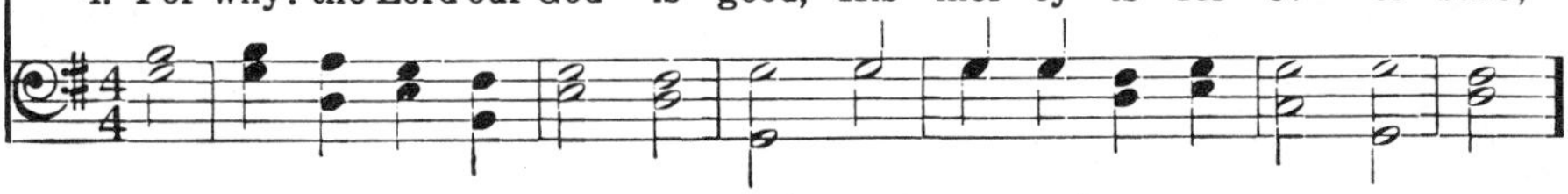

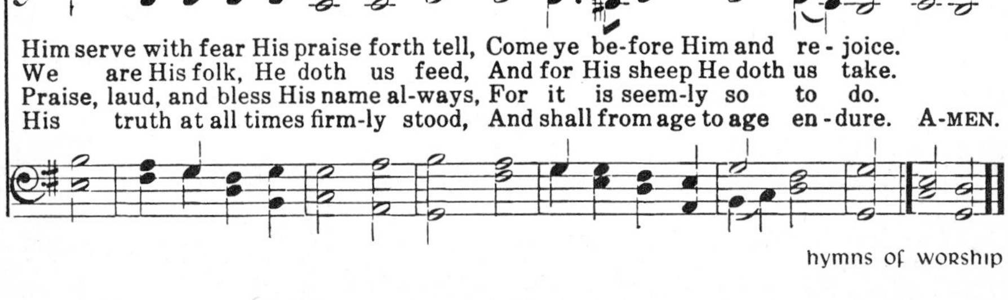
Him serve with fear His praise forth tell, Come ye be-fore Him and re - joice.
We are His folk, He doth us feed, And for His sheep He doth us take.
Praise, laud, and bless His name al-ways, For it is seem-ly so to do.
His truth at all times firm-ly stood, And shall from age to age en - dure. A-MEN.

52 How Great Thy Loving Kindness Is

INFINITY. 8 6 8 6 8 8 8 6

E. Margaret Clarkson — E. Margaret Clarkson

1. How great Thy lov - ing kind - ness is, O God of grace, to me!
2. How great Thy lov - ing kind - ness is! Be - fore I sought Thy face,
3. How great Thy lov - ing kind - ness is! So in - fi - nite Thou art,
4. How great Thy lov - ing kind - ness is, To car - ry all my care,
5. How great Thy lov - ing kind - ness is! When pil - grim days are past,
How stead-fast is Thy faith - ful - ness, Thy mer - cies, O how free!
Lo, I was sought of Thee, and found By pure, re - sist - less grace,
So far tran - scend - ing high - est thought Of mor - tal mind or heart,
To walk be - side me day by day My joys and griefs to share!
In Je - sus' like - ness per - fect - ed I'll see Thy face at last,
I wor-ship Thee, my God and King, With burn-ing heart Thy prais - es sing:
Was lift - ed in its might - y flow And taught re-deem-ing love to know:
Yet Thou didst give Thy - self for me In ut - ter-most hu - mil - i - ty:
Thy way is per - fect: Thou wilt lead, Make plain my path, sup - ply my need:
Thru - out e - ter - nal years to sing Thy ho - ly praise, my God and King:
Refrain
How great Thy lov - ing kind - ness is, How vast, how rich, how free!
How great Thy lov - ing kind - ness is, O God of grace, to me!

Hymns of Salvation

The word "crusader" is derived from the Latin "crux" – meaning "cross." In the age of chivalry knights decorated their shields and banners with the cross, to proclaim their faith in Jesus Christ.

In any age preaching and singing about the cross is central, for it is through the death and resurrection of Christ that we have forgiveness of sins and the assurance of eternal life.

Songs of salvation express both the sorrow we feel over Christ's suffering on our behalf, and the joy we experience through our new and redeemed life in him.

53 Come, Ye Sinners, Poor and Wretched

BRYN CALFARIA. 8 7 8 7 4 7

Joseph Hart

William Owen

1. Come, ye sin - ners, poor and wretch-ed, Weak and wound-ed, sick and sore;
2. Come, ye need - y, come, and wel-come; God's free boun-ty glo - ri - fy;
3. Come, ye wea - ry, heav - y la - den, Bruised and brok-en by the fall;
4. Lo! th'in-car-nate God, as-cend-ed, Pleads the mer-it of His blood;
Je - sus read - y stands to save you, Full of pit - y, joined with power:
True be-lief and true re-pent-ance, Ev - ery grace that brings us nigh,
If you tar - ry till you're bet-ter, You will nev - er come at all:
Ven-ture on Him, ven-ture whol-ly; Let no oth - er trust in-trude:
He is a - ble, He is a - ble, He is a - ble,
With-out mon - ey, with-out mon - ey, with-out mon - ey,
Not the right - eous, not the right - eous, not the right - eous,
None but Je - sus, none but Je - sus, none but Je - sus,
1. He is a - ble, He is a - ble, He is a - ble,
He is will-ing, doubt no more; He is will - ing, doubt no more.
Come to Je - sus Christ and buy; Come to Je - sus Christ and buy.
Sin - ners Je - sus came to call; Sin - ners Je - sus came to call.
Can do help-less sin - ners good; Can do help - less sin - ners good. A - MEN.

YE MUST BE BORN AGAIN

BORN AGAIN. Irregular. Ref.

William T. Sleeper

George C. Stebbins

1. A rul - er once came to Je - sus by night To ask Him the way of sal - va-tion and light; The Mas-ter made an-swer in words true and plain,
2. Ye chil-dren of men, at - tend to the word So sol - emn - ly ut - tered by Je - sus the Lord; And let not this mes-sage to you be in vain,
3. O ye who would en - ter that glo - ri - ous rest, And sing with the ran-somed the song of the blest; The life ev - er - last - ing if ye would ob - tain,
4. A dear one in heav-en thy heart yearns to see, At the beau - ti - ful gate may be watching for thee; Then list to the note of this sol - emn re - frain,

"Ye must be born a - gain." a - gain.

REFRAIN

"Ye must be born a- gain, a - gain, Ye must be born a - gain; a - gain; I ver - i - ly, ver - i - ly say un - to thee, Ye must be born a - gain." a - gain.

55 Christ Receiveth Sinful Men

NEUMEISTER. 7 7 7 7 Ref.

Erdmann Neumeister
Trans. by Emma F. Bevan

James McGranahan

1. Sin - ners Je - sus will re - ceive; Sound this word of grace to all
2. Come, and He will give you rest; Trust Him, for His word is plain;
3. Now my heart con - demns me not, Pure be - fore the law I stand;
4. Christ re - ceiv - eth sin - ful men, E - ven me with all my sin;
Who the heaven - ly path - way leave, All who lin - ger, all who fall.
He will take the sin - ful - est; Christ re - ceiv - eth sin - ful men.
He who cleansed me from all spot, Sat - is - fied its last de - mand.
Purged from ev - ery spot and stain, Heaven with Him I en - ter in.
Refrain
Sing it o'er and o'er a - gain; Christ re -
Sing it o'er a - gain, sing it o'er a - gain; Christ re -
ceiv - - eth sin - ful men; Make the mes - - sage
ceiv - eth sin - ful men, Christ re - ceiv - eth sin - ful men; Make the message plain,
clear and plain: Christ re - ceiv - eth sin - ful men.
make the message plain:

I Heard the Voice of Jesus Say

VOX DILECTI. C.M.D.

Horatius Bonar — John B. Dykes

1. I heard the voice of Je - sus say, "Come un - to Me and rest;
2. I heard the voice of Je - sus say, "Be - hold, I free - ly give
3. I heard the voice of Je - sus say, "I am this dark world's Light;
Lay down, thou wea - ry one, lay down Thy head up - on My breast."
The liv - ing wa - ter; thirst - y one, Stoop down, and drink, and live."
Look un - to Me, thy morn shall rise, And all thy day be bright."
I came to Je - sus as I was, Wea - ry, and worn, and sad;
I came to Je - sus, and I drank Of that life - giv - ing stream;
I looked to Je - sus, and I found In Him my Star, my Sun;
I found in Him a rest - ing-place, And He has made me glad.
My thirst was quenched, my soul revived, And now I live in Him.
And in that Light of life I'll walk, Till travel-ing days are done. A-MEN.

57 Just as I am, without one plea

WOODWORTH. L.M.

Charlotte Elliott — William B. Bradbury

1. Just as I am, with-out one plea, But that Thy blood was shed for me, And
2. Just as I am, and wait-ing not To rid my soul of one dark blot, To
3. Just as I am, though tossed about With many a con-flict, many a doubt, Fight-
4. Just as I am, poor, wretched, blind; Sight, rich-es, heal-ing of the mind, Yea,
5. Just as I am, Thou wilt re-ceive, Wilt welcome, pardon, cleanse, relieve; Be-

that Thou bidd'st me come to Thee, O Lamb of God, I come! I come!
Thee whose blood can cleanse each spot, O Lamb of God, I come! I come!
ings and fears with-in, with-out, O Lamb of God, I come! I come!
all I need, in Thee I find, O Lamb of God, I come! I come!
cause Thy prom-ise I be-lieve, O Lamb of God, I come! I come! A-MEN.

58 Only Trust Him

MINERVA. C.M. Ref.

John H. Stockton — John H. Stockton

1. Come, ev-ery soul by sin op-pressed, There's mer-cy with the Lord,
2. For Je-sus shed His pre-cious blood, Rich bless-ings to be-stow;
3. Yes, Je-sus is the Truth, the Way, That leads you in-to rest:
4. Come, then, and join this ho-ly band, And on to glo-ry go,

And He will sure-ly give you rest By trust-ing in His word.
Plunge now in-to the crim-son flood That wash-es white as snow.
Be-lieve in Him with-out de-lay, And you are ful-ly blest.
To dwell in that ce-les-tial land, Where joys im-mor-tal flow.

Refrain
1
2
On - ly trust Him, on - ly trust Him, On - ly trust Him now.
He will save you, He will save you, He will (Omit..........) save you now.
come to the saviour now
59
INVITATION. 6 6 6 6 D.
John M. Wigner
Frederick C. Maker
1. Come to the Sav - iour now, He gen - tly call - eth thee;
2. Come to the Sav - iour now, Ye who have wan - dered far;
3. Come to the Sav - iour, all, What - e'er your bur - dens be;
In true re - pent - ance bow, Be - fore Him bend the knee;
Re - new your sol - emn vow, For His by right you are;
Hear now His lov - ing call, "Cast all your care on me."
He wait - eth to be - stow Sal - va - tion, peace, and love,
Come, like poor wan - d'ring sheep Re - turn - ing to His fold;
Come, and for ev - ery grief, In Je - sus you will find
True joy on earth be - low, A home in heav'n a - bove.
His arm will safe - ly keep, His love will ne'er grow cold.
A sure and safe re - lief, A lov - ing Friend and kind.
the call of christ

BELIEVE ON THE LORD JESUS CHRIST

BELIEVE. 10 7 10 7 Ref.

Avis B. Christiansen — Harry D. Clarke

1. "What must I do?" the trem-bling jail - or cried, When dazed by fear and won-der; "Be - lieve on Christ!" was all that Paul re-plied, "And thou shalt be saved from sin."
2. What must I do! O wea - ry, trem-bling soul, Just turn to-day to Je - sus; He will re - ceive, for - give and make thee whole — Christ a - lone can set thee free.
3. His blood is all thy plea for sav - ing grace, The pre-cious fount of cleans-ing! O come, ac - cept His love, be - hold His face, And be saved for - ev - er - more.
REFRAIN
Be - lieve on the Lord Je - sus Christ, Be - lieve on the Lord Je - sus Christ, Be - lieve on the Lord Je - sus Christ, And thou shalt be saved!
Be - lieve
Be - lieve
Be - lieve

Give Me Thy Heart

ZERUIAH. 10 10 10 10 Ref.

Eliza E. Hewitt | William J. Kirkpatrick

1. "Give Me thy heart," says the Fa - ther a - bove, No gift so pre-cious to
2. "Give Me thy heart," says the Sav-iour of men, Call - ing in mer - cy a-
3. "Give Me thy heart," says the Spir - it di - vine, "All that thou hast, to My
Him as our love; Soft - ly He whis - pers, wher-ev - er thou art,
gain and a - gain; "Turn now from sin, and from e - vil de - part,
keep - ing re - sign; Grace more a - bound - ing is Mine to im - part,
"Grate - ful - ly trust Me, and give Me thy heart."
Have I not died for thee? give Me thy heart."
Make full sur - ren - der and give Me thy heart."
Refrain
"Give Me thy heart,
give Me thy heart," Hear the soft whis-per, wher-ev - er thou art: From this dark
world He would draw thee a - part; Speak-ing so ten - der-ly, "Give Me thy heart."

62 Look to the Lamb of God

PINE STREET. 10 6 10 6 Ref.
H. G. Jackson
James M. Black
1. If you from sin are long-ing to be free, Look to the Lamb of God;
2. When Satan tempts, and doubts and fears assail, Look to the Lamb of God;
3. Are you a-wea-ry, does the way seem long? Look to the Lamb of God;
4. Fear not when shad-ows on your path-way fall, Look to the Lamb of God;
He, to re-deem you, died on Cal-va-ry, Look to the Lamb of God.
You in His strength shall o-ver all pre-vail, Look to the Lamb of God.
His love will cheer and fill your heart with song, Look to the Lamb of God.
In joy or sor-row Christ is all in all, Look to the Lamb of God.
REFRAIN
Look to the Lamb of God, Look to the Lamb of God,
the Lamb of God, the Lamb of God,
For He a-lone is a-ble to save you, Look to the Lamb of God.
63 Art Thou Weary, Heavy Laden?
STEPHANOS. 8 5 8 3
John Mason Neale
Based on an ancient Greek Hymn
Henry W. Baker
1. Art thou wea-ry, heav-y lad-en, Art thou sore dis-trest?
2. Hath He marks to lead me to Him, If He be my Guide?
3. Is there di-a-dem, as Mon-arch, That His brow a-dorns?
4. If I still hold close-ly to Him, What hath He at last?
5. If I ask Him to re-ceive me, Will He say me nay?
6. Find-ing, follow-ing, keep-ing, strug-gling, Is He sure to bless?

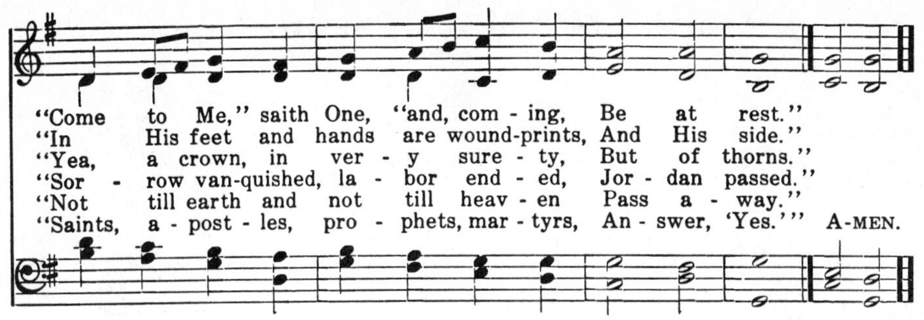
"Come to Me," saith One, "and, com - ing, Be at rest."
"In His feet and hands are wound-prints, And His side."
"Yea, a crown, in ver - y sure - ty, But of thorns."
"Sor - row van-quished, la - bor end - ed, Jor - dan passed."
"Not till earth and not till heav - en Pass a - way."
"Saints, a - post - les, pro - phets, mar - tyrs, An - swer, 'Yes.'" A-MEN.

HAVE YOU ANY ROOM FOR JESUS? 64

ANY ROOM. 8 7 8 7 Ref.

Source Unknown
Arr. by Daniel W. Whittle

C. C. Williams

1. Have you an - y room for Je - sus, He who bore your load of sin?
2. Room for pleas-ure, room for busi - ness, But for Christ the Cru - ci - fied,
3. Have you an - y room for Je - sus, As in grace He calls a - gain?
4. Room and time now give to Je - sus, Soon will pass God's day of grace;

As He knocks and asks ad - mis - sion, Sin - ner, will you let Him in?
Not a place that He can en - ter, In the heart for which He died?
O, to - day is time ac - cept - ed, To-mor - row you may call in vain.
Soon thy heart left cold and si - lent, And thy Sav-iour's pleading cease.

REFRAIN

Room for Je - sus, King of glo - ry! Has - ten now, His word o - bey;
Swing the heart's door wide-ly o - pen, Bid Him en - ter while you may.

65 O Jesus, Thou Art Standing

ST. HILDA. 7 6 7 6 D.

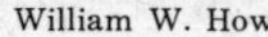

William W. How — Justin H. Knecht and Edward Husband

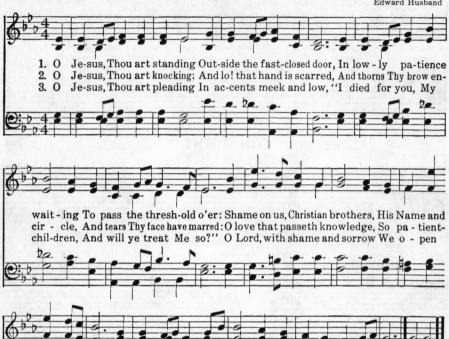

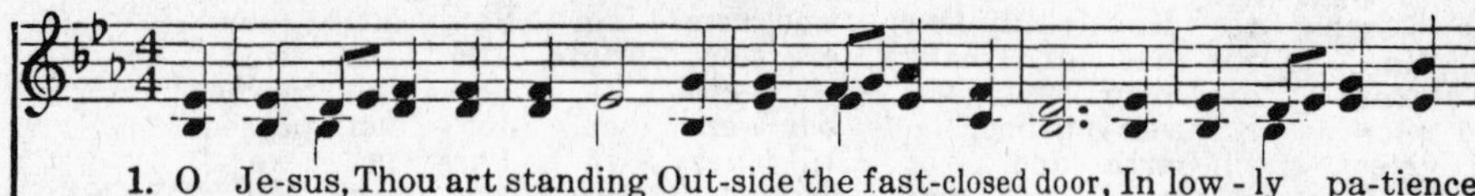

1. O Je-sus, Thou art standing Out-side the fast-closed door, In low - ly pa-tience
2. O Je-sus, Thou art knocking; And lo! that hand is scarred, And thorns Thy brow en-
3. O Je-sus, Thou art pleading In ac-cents meek and low, "I died for you, My

wait - ing To pass the thresh-old o'er: Shame on us, Christian brothers, His Name and
cir - cle, And tears Thy face have marred: O love that passeth knowledge, So pa - tient-
chil-dren, And will ye treat Me so?" O Lord, with shame and sorrow We o - pen

sign who bear, O shame, thrice shame up-on us, To keep Him standing there!
ly to wait! O sin that hath no e - qual, So fast to bar the gate!
now the door; Dear Saviour, en-ter, en - ter, And leave us nev-er-more! A-MEN.

66 Just As I Am, Thine Own to Be

JUST AS I AM. 8 8 8 6

Marianne Hearn — Joseph Barnby

1. Just as I am, Thine own to be, Friend of the young, who lov - est me,
2. In the glad morn-ing of my day, My life to give, my vows to pay,
3. I would live ev. - er in the light, I would work ev - er for the right,
4. Just as I am, young, strong, and free, To be the best that I can be

To con-se-crate my-self to Thee, O Je-sus Christ, I come.
With no re-serve and no de-lay, With all my heart I come.
I would serve Thee with all my might; Therefore to Thee I come.
For truth, and righteousness and Thee, Lord of my life, I come. A-MEN.

Lead Me to Calvary 67

DUNCANNON. C.M. Ref.

Jennie Evelyn Hussey

William J. Kirkpatrick

1. King of my life, I crown Thee now, Thine shall the glo - ry be;
2. Show me the tomb where Thou wast laid, Ten - der - ly mourned and wept;
3. Let me like Ma-ry, through the gloom, Come with a gift to Thee;
4. May I be will-ing, Lord, to bear Dai - ly my cross for Thee;
Lest I for-get Thy thorn-crowned brow, Lead me to Cal - va - ry.
An - gels in robes of light ar - rayed Guard-ed Thee whilst Thou slept.
Show to me now the emp - ty tomb, Lead me to Cal - va - ry.
E - ven Thy cup of grief to share, Thou hast borne all for me.
Refrain
Lest I for-get Geth-sem - a - ne; Lest I for-get Thine ag - o - ny;
Lest I for-get Thy love for me, Lead me to Cal - va - ry.

JESUS, I COME

JESUS, I COME. Irregular.

William T. Sleeper | George C. Stebbins

1. Out of my bond - age, sor-row, and night, Je-sus, I come, Je-sus, I come;
2. Out of my shame-ful fail - ure and loss, Je-sus, I come, Je-sus, I come;
3. Out of un - rest and ar - ro-gant pride, Je-sus, I come, Je-sus, I come;
4. Out of the fear and dread of the tomb, Je-sus, I come, Je-sus, I come;
In - to Thy free-dom, gladness, and light, Je-sus, I come to Thee; Out of my
In - to the glo-rious gain of Thy cross, Je-sus, I come to Thee; Out of earth's
In - to Thy bless-ed will to a - bide, Je-sus, I come to Thee; Out of my-
In - to the joy and light of Thy home, Je-sus, I come to Thee; Out of the
sick - ness in - to Thy health, Out of my want and in - to Thy wealth,
sor - rows in - to Thy balm, Out of life's storms and in - to Thy calm,
self to dwell in Thy love, Out of de-spair in - to rap-tures a - bove,
depths of ru - in un - told, In - to the peace of Thy shel-ter - ing fold,
Out of my sin and in - to Thy-self, Je-sus, I come to Thee.
Out of dis-tress to ju - bi-lant psalm, Je-sus, I come to Thee.
Up-ward for aye on wings like a dove, Je-sus, I come to Thee.
Ev - er Thy glo-rious face to be-hold, Je-sus, I come to Thee.
A-MEN.

Is My Name Written There?

KIDDER. 7 6 7 6 D. Ref.

Mary A. Kidder — Frank M. Davis

1. Lord, I care not for rich - es, Nei - ther sil - ver nor gold; I would make sure of heav - en, I would en - ter the fold. In the book of Thy king - dom, With its pa - ges so fair, Tell me, Je - sus, my Sav - iour, Is my name writ - ten there?

2. Lord, my sins they are man - y, Like the sands of the sea, But Thy blood, O my Sav - iour, Is suf - fi - cient for me; For Thy prom-ise is writ - ten, In bright let - ters that glow, "Tho' your sins be as scar - let, I will make them like snow."

3. Oh! that beau - ti - ful cit - y, With its man - sions of light, With its glo - ri - fied be - ings, In pure gar - ments of white; Where no e - vil thing com - eth To de - spoil what is fair; Where the an - gels are watch-ing, Yes, my name's writ - ten there. (3) Yes, my name's, etc.

REFRAIN

Is my name writ-ten there, On the page white and fair? In the book of Thy king - dom, Is my name writ - ten there?
(3) Yes, my name's writ - ten there.

70 When I Survey the Wondrous Cross

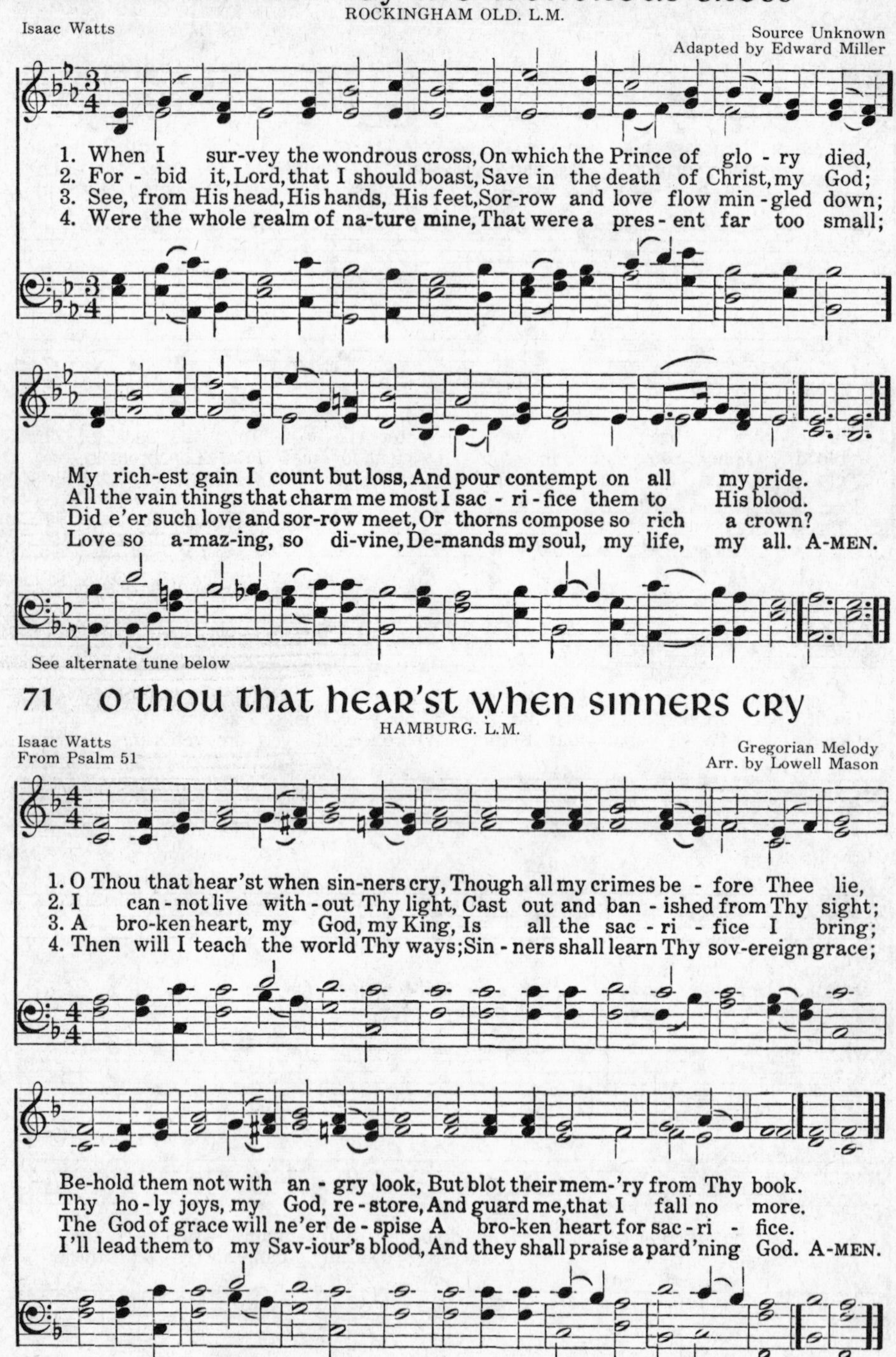
ROCKINGHAM OLD. L.M.
Isaac Watts
Source Unknown
Adapted by Edward Miller
1. When I survey the wondrous cross, On which the Prince of glo - ry died,
2. For - bid it, Lord, that I should boast, Save in the death of Christ, my God;
3. See, from His head, His hands, His feet, Sor-row and love flow min-gled down;
4. Were the whole realm of na-ture mine, That were a pres - ent far too small;
My rich-est gain I count but loss, And pour contempt on all my pride.
All the vain things that charm me most I sac - ri - fice them to His blood.
Did e'er such love and sor-row meet, Or thorns compose so rich a crown?
Love so a-maz-ing, so di-vine, De-mands my soul, my life, my all. A-MEN.
See alternate tune below
71 O Thou That Hear'st When Sinners Cry
HAMBURG. L.M.
Isaac Watts
From Psalm 51
Gregorian Melody
Arr. by Lowell Mason
1. O Thou that hear'st when sin-ners cry, Though all my crimes be - fore Thee lie,
2. I can - not live with - out Thy light, Cast out and ban - ished from Thy sight;
3. A bro-ken heart, my God, my King, Is all the sac - ri - fice I bring;
4. Then will I teach the world Thy ways; Sin - ners shall learn Thy sov-ereign grace;
Be-hold them not with an - gry look, But blot their mem-'ry from Thy book.
Thy ho-ly joys, my God, re - store, And guard me, that I fall no more.
The God of grace will ne'er de - spise A bro-ken heart for sac - ri - fice.
I'll lead them to my Sav-iour's blood, And they shall praise a pard'ning God. A-MEN.

In the Cross of Christ I Glory

72

RATHBUN. 8 7 8 7

John Bowring — Ithamar Conkey

1. In the cross of Christ I glo - ry, Tower-ing o'er the wrecks of time;
2. When the woes of life o'er-take me, Hopes de-ceive, and fears an - noy,
3. When the sun of bliss is beam-ing Light and love up - on my way,
4. Bane and bless - ing, pain and pleas-ure, By the cross are sanc - ti - fied;
All the light of sa - cred sto - ry Gath-ers round its head sub-lime.
Nev - er shall the cross for-sake me: Lo! it glows with peace and joy.
From the cross the ra-diance stream-ing Adds more lus - ter to the day.
Peace is there that knows no meas-ure, Joys that through all time a - bide. A-MEN.
HALLELUJAH, WHAT A SAVIOUR!
73
MAN OF SORROWS. 7 7 7 8
Philip P. Bliss
Philip P. Bliss
1. "Man of Sor-rows," what a name For the Son of God who came
2. Bear - ing shame and scoff - ing rude, In my place con-demned He stood;
3. Guilt - y, vile and help - less, we; Spot-less Lamb of God was He;
4. Lift - ed up was He to die, "It is fin - ished," was His cry;
5. When He comes, our glo - rious King, All His ran-somed home to bring,
Ru - ined sin - ners to re-claim! Hal - le - lu - jah! what a Sav - iour!
Sealed my par - don with His blood; Hal - le - lu - jah! what a Sav - iour!
"Full a - tone-ment" can it be? Hal - le - lu - jah! what a Sav - iour!
Now in heaven ex - alt - ed high; Hal - le - lu - jah! what a Sav - iour!
Then a - new this song we'll sing: Hal - le - lu - jah! what a Sav - iour! A-MEN.

74 And Can It Be That I Should Gain?

SAGINA. 8 8 8 8 8 8 Ref.

Charles Wesley — Thomas Campbell

1. And can it be that I should gain An in - terest in the
2. 'Tis mys-tery all! Th' Im-mor - tal dies! Who can ex - plore His
3. He left His Fa - ther's throne a - bove, So free, so in - fi-
4. Long my im-pris - oned spir - it lay Fast bound in sin and
5. No con-dem - na - tion now I dread; Je - sus, and all in
Sav - iour's blood? Died He for me, who caused His pain? For me, who
strange de - sign? In vain the first-born ser - aph tries To sound the
nite His grace; Emp-tied Him - self of all but love, And bled for
na - ture's night; Thine eye dif - fused a quick'ning ray, I woke, the
Him, is mine! A - live in Him, my liv - ing Head, And clothed in
Him to death pur-sued? A - maz - ing love! how can it be That
depths of love Di - vine! 'Tis mer - cy all! let earth a - dore, Let
A - dam's help-less race; 'Tis mer - cy all, im - mense and free; For,
dun-geon flamed with light; My chains fell off, my heart was free; I
right - eous-ness Di - vine, Bold I ap-proach th'e - ter - nal throne, And
Thou, my God, shouldst die for me?
an - gel minds in - quire no more.
O my God, it found out me.
rose, went forth, and fol - lowed Thee.
claim the crown, thro' Christ my own.
Refrain
A - maz - ing love! how
A - maz-ing love!

can it be That Thou, my God, shouldst die for me. A-MEN.
How can it be That Thou, my God, shouldst die for me.

GRACE! 'TIS A CHARMING SOUND 75

GRACE. S.M. Ref.

Philip Doddridge; 1, 3
Augustus M. Toplady; 2, 4, 5

Ira D. Sankey

1. Grace! 'tis a charm-ing sound, Har - mo - nious to the ear; Heav'n with the ech - o shall re - sound, And all the earth shall hear.
2. 'Twas grace that wrote my name In life's e - ter - nal book; 'Twas grace that gave me to the Lamb, Who all my sor - rows took.
3. Grace taught my wand'ring feet To tread the heav'n-ly road; And new sup - plies each hour I meet, While press - ing on to God.
4. Grace taught my soul to pray, And made mine eyes o'er - flow; 'Twas grace which kept me to this day, And will not let me go.
5. O let Thy grace in - spire My soul with strength di - vine: May all my pow'rs to Thee as - pire, And all my days be Thine.

REFRAIN

Saved by grace a - lone! This is all my plea:
Je - sus died for all man - kind, And Je - sus died for me.

GRACE GREATER THAN OUR SIN

MOODY. 9 9 9 9 Ref.

Julia H. Johnston — Daniel B. Towner

1. Mar - vel - ous grace of our lov - ing Lord, Grace that ex - ceeds our
2. Sin and de - spair like the sea waves cold, Threat-en the soul with
3. Dark is the stain that we can - not hide, What can a - vail to
4. Mar - vel - ous, in - fi - nite, match-less grace, Free - ly be-stowed on
sin and our guilt, Yon - der on Cal - va - ry's mount out-poured,
in - fi - nite loss; Grace that is great - er, yes, grace un - told,
wash it a - way? Look! there is flow - ing a crim - son tide;
all who be - lieve; You that are long - ing to see His face,
There where the blood of the Lamb was spilt.
Points to the Ref - uge, the might - y Cross.
Whit - er than snow you may be to - day.
Will you this mo - ment His grace re - ceive?
REFRAIN
Grace, grace,
Marvel - vel - ous grace,
God's grace, Grace that will par - don and cleanse with-in; Grace,
in - fi - nite grace,
Mar - vel - ous
grace, God's grace, Grace that is great - er than all our sin.
grace, in - fi - nite grace,

THE OLD RUGGED CROSS

OLD RUGGED CROSS. Irregular. Ref.

George Bennard | George Bennard

1. On a hill far a-way stood an old rug-ged cross, The em-blem of
2. Oh, that old rug-ged cross, so de-spised by the world, Has a won-drous at-
3. In the old rug-ged cross, stained with blood so di-vine, A won-drous
4. To the old rug-ged cross I will ev-er be true, Its shame and re-
suf-fering and shame; And I love that old cross where the dear-est and best
trac-tion for me; For the dear Lamb of God left His glo-ry a-bove
beau-ty I see; For 'twas on that old cross Je-sus suf-fered and died
proach glad-ly bear; Then He'll call me some day to my home far a-way,
For a world of lost sin-ners was slain.
To bear it to dark Cal-va-ry.
To par-don and sanc-ti-fy me.
Where His glo-ry for-ev-er I'll share.
Refrain
So I'll cher-ish the old rug-ged cross, the
cross, ... Till my tro-phies at last I lay down; I will cling to the
old rug-ged cross,
old rug-ged cross, ... And ex-change it some day for a crown.
cross, the old rug-ged cross,

78

NAILED UPON GOLGOTHA'S TREE

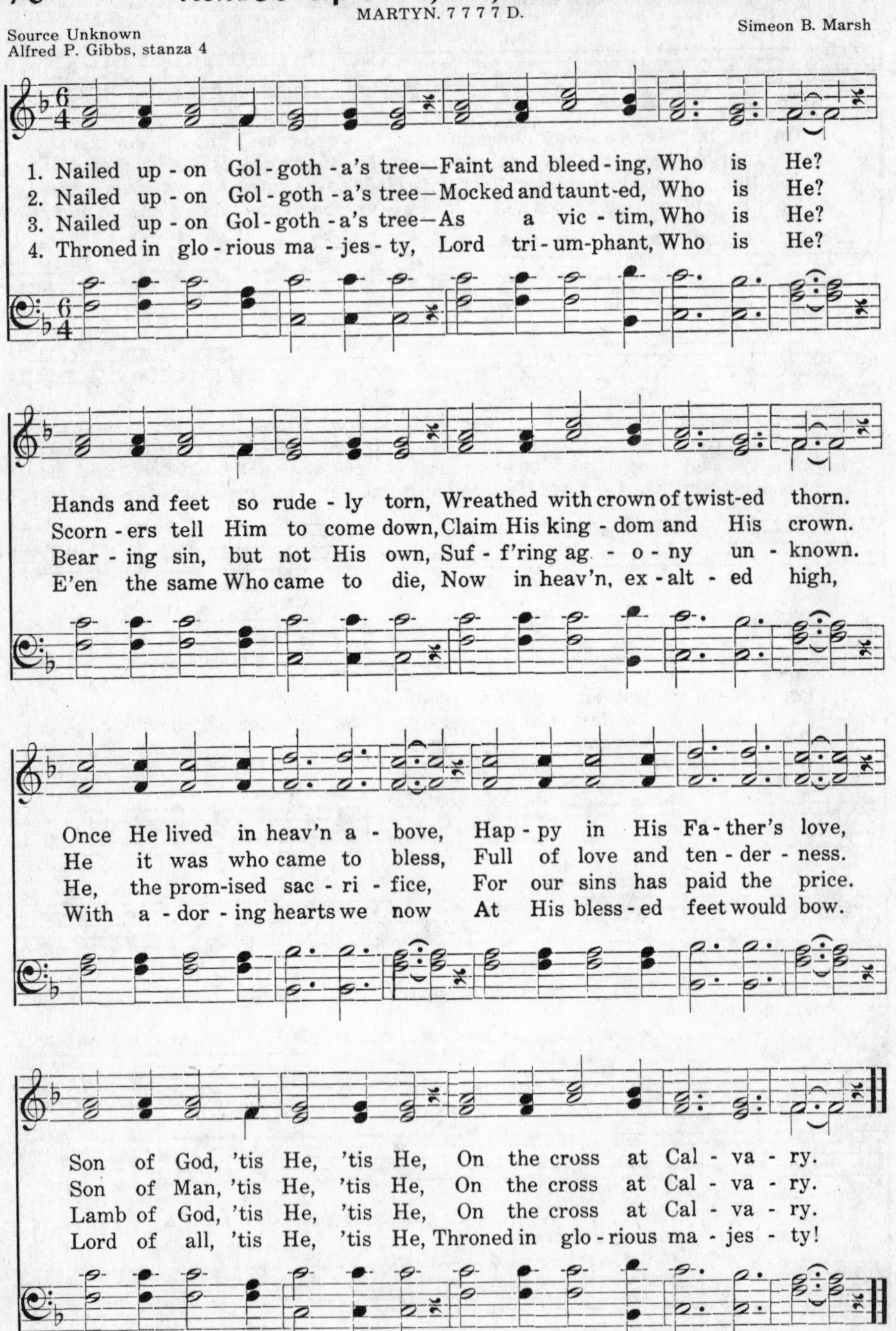
MARTYN. 7 7 7 7 D.
Source Unknown
Alfred P. Gibbs, stanza 4
Simeon B. Marsh
1. Nailed up - on Gol - goth - a's tree—Faint and bleed - ing, Who is He?
2. Nailed up - on Gol - goth - a's tree—Mocked and taunt - ed, Who is He?
3. Nailed up - on Gol - goth - a's tree—As a vic - tim, Who is He?
4. Throned in glo - rious ma - jes - ty, Lord tri - um - phant, Who is He?
Hands and feet so rude - ly torn, Wreathed with crown of twist - ed thorn.
Scorn - ers tell Him to come down, Claim His king - dom and His crown.
Bear - ing sin, but not His own, Suf - f'ring ag - o - ny un - known.
E'en the same Who came to die, Now in heav'n, ex - alt - ed high,
Once He lived in heav'n a - bove, Hap - py in His Fa - ther's love,
He it was who came to bless, Full of love and ten - der - ness.
He, the prom - ised sac - ri - fice, For our sins has paid the price.
With a - dor - ing hearts we now At His bless - ed feet would bow.
Son of God, 'tis He, 'tis He, On the cross at Cal - va - ry.
Son of Man, 'tis He, 'tis He, On the cross at Cal - va - ry.
Lamb of God, 'tis He, 'tis He, On the cross at Cal - va - ry.
Lord of all, 'tis He, 'tis He, Throned in glo - rious ma - jes - ty!

JESUS, LOVER OF MY SOUL

ABERYSTWYTH. 7 7 7 7 D.

Charles Wesley

Joseph Parry

1. Je - sus, Lov - er of my soul, Let me to Thy bos - om fly,
2. Oth - er ref - uge have I none; Hangs my help - less soul on Thee;
3. Thou, O Christ, art all I want; More than all in Thee I find;
4. Plen - teous grace with Thee is found, Grace to cov - er all my sin;
While the near - er wa - ters roll, While the tem - pest still is high:
Leave, ah! leave me not a - lone, Still sup - port and com - fort me.
Raise the fall - en, cheer the faint, Heal the sick, and lead the blind.
Let the heal - ing streams a - bound; Make and keep me pure with - in.
Hide me, O my Sav - iour, hide, Till the storm of life is past;
All my trust on Thee is stayed, All my help from Thee I bring;
Just and ho - ly is Thy name, I am all un - right - eous - ness;
Thou of life the Foun - tain art, Free - ly let me take of Thee;
Safe in - to the ha - ven guide; O re - ceive my soul at last!
Cov - er my de - fense - less head With the shad - ow of Thy wing.
False and full of sin I am, Thou art full of truth and grace.
Spring Thou up with - in my heart, Rise to all e - ter - ni - ty.
A - MEN.

See alternate tune on opposite page

By Faith in Christ We Live

BAUHOFER. Irregular. Ref.

Audrey B. Schultz

Audrey B. Schultz

1. By faith in Christ we live, Not trust - ing in our deeds:
2. By faith in Christ we live, We claim His right - eous - ness;
3. Of this we are a - ssured—Je - sus, our great High Priest,
4. By faith in Christ we live, Our plea is grace a - lone;
Our con - fi - dence and hope is in the Christ of Cal - va - ry.
Un - wor - thy in our-selves, but trust - ing Him who died for us.
Doth in - ter - cede in heav'n for all who come to God by Him.
O match-less gift of God's great love — we claim it for our own!
Refrain
O won - drous grace of God! (of God!) By faith we have re - ceived
The gift of our sal - va - tion Through the cross of Cal - va - ry.

There Is a Fountain

CLEANSING FOUNTAIN. 8 6 8 6 6 6 8 6

William Cowper

Early American Melody
Arr. by Lowell Mason

1. There is a foun-tain filled with blood Drawn from Im-man-uel's veins;
2. The dy-ing thief re-joiced to see That foun-tain in his day;
3. Dear dy-ing Lamb, Thy pre-cious blood Shall nev-er lose its power,
4. E'er since by faith I saw the stream Thy flow-ing wounds sup-ply,
5. When this poor lisp-ing, stammering tongue Lies si-lent in the grave,
And sin-ners, plunged be-neath that flood, Lose all their guilt-y stains:
And there may I, though vile as he, Wash all my sins a-way:
Till all the ran-somed Church of God Be saved, to sin no more:
Re-deem-ing love has been my theme, And shall be till I die:
Then in a no-bler, sweet-er song, I'll sing Thy power to save:
Lose all their guilt-y stains, Lose all their guilt-y stains; And
Wash all my sins a-way, Wash all my sins a-way; And
Be saved, to sin no more, Be saved, to sin no more; Till
And shall be till I die, And shall be till I die; Re-
I'll sing Thy power to save, I'll sing Thy power to save; Then
sin-ners, plunged be-neath that flood, Lose all their guilt-y stains.
there may I, though vile as he, Wash all my sins a-way.
all the ran-somed Church of God Be saved, to sin no more.
deem-ing love has been my theme, And shall be till I die.
in a no-bler, sweet-er song I'll sing Thy power to save. A-MEN.

82 Jesus, Thy Blood and Righteousness

GERMANY. L.M.

Nicolaus L. von Zinzendorf
Trans. by John Wesley; alt.

William Gardiner's *Sacred Melodies*, 1815

1. Je - sus, Thy blood and right-eousness My beau-ty are, my glo - rious dress;
2. Bold shall I stand in Thy great day, For who aught to my charge shall lay?
3. Lord, I be-lieve Thy precious blood, Which, at the mer-cy seat of God,
4. Lord, I be-lieve were sin-ners more Than sands up-on the o - cean shore,

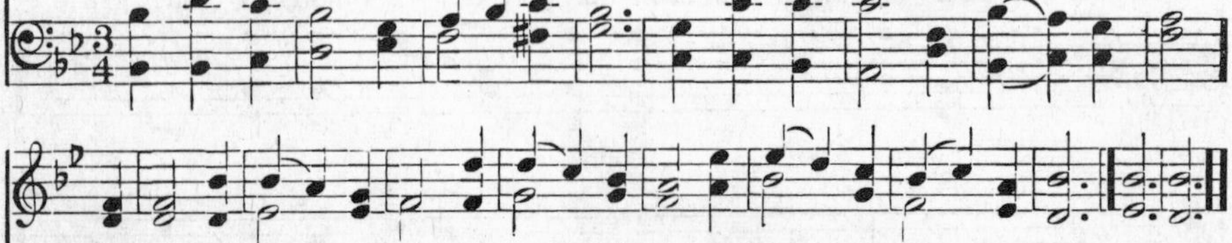

'Midst flaming worlds, in these arrayed, With joy shall I lift up my head.
Ful - ly ab-solved through these I am, From sin and fear, from guilt and shame.
For - ev - er doth for sin-ners plead, For me, e'en for my soul, was shed.
Thou hast for all a ran - som paid, For all a full a-tone-ment made. A-MEN.

83 I Am Not Skilled to Understand

GREENWELL. 8 8 8 7

Dora Greenwell

William J. Kirkpatrick

1. I am not skilled to un-der-stand What God hath willed, what God hath planned;
2. I take Him at His word indeed: "Christ died for sin - ners," this I read;
3. That He should leave His place on high And come for sin - ful man to die,
4. And oh, that He ful-filled may see The tra-vail of His soul in me,
5. Yes, liv - ing, dy - ing, let me bring My strength, my sol - ace from this Spring;

I on - ly know at His right hand Is One who is my Sav - iour!
For in my heart I find a need Of Him to be my Sav - iour!
You count it strange? so once did I, Be - fore I knew my Sav - iour!
And with His work con - tent-ed be, As I with my dear Sav - iour!
That He who lives to be my King Once died to be my Sav - iour! A-MEN.

I Saw the Cross of Jesus

84

WHITFIELD. 7 6 7 6 D.

Frederick Whitfield

Source Unknown

1. I saw the cross of Je - sus, When bur - dened with my sin;
2. I love the cross of Je - sus, It tells me what I am—
3. I trust the cross of Je - sus In ev - ery try - ing hour,
4. Safe in the cross of Je - sus! There let my wea - ry heart

I sought the cross of Je - sus, To give me peace with - in;
A vile and guilt - y crea - ture, Saved on - ly through the Lamb;
My sure and cer - tain ref - uge, My nev - er - fail - ing tower;
Still rest in peace un - shak - en, Till with Him, ne'er to part;

I brought my soul to Je - sus, He cleansed it in His blood;
No right-eous - ness nor mer - it, No beau - ty can I plead;
In ev - ery fear and con - flict, I more than con - queror am;
And then in strains of glo - ry I'll sing His won - drous power,

And in the cross of Je - sus I found my peace with God.
Yet in the cross I glo - ry, My ti - tle there I read.
Liv - ing, I'm safe, or dy - ing, Thro' Christ, the ris - en Lamb.
Where sin can nev - er en - ter, And death is known no more.

85 O the Deep, Deep Love of Jesus

TON-Y-BOTEL. 8 7 8 7 D.

S. Trevor Francis — Thomas J. Williams

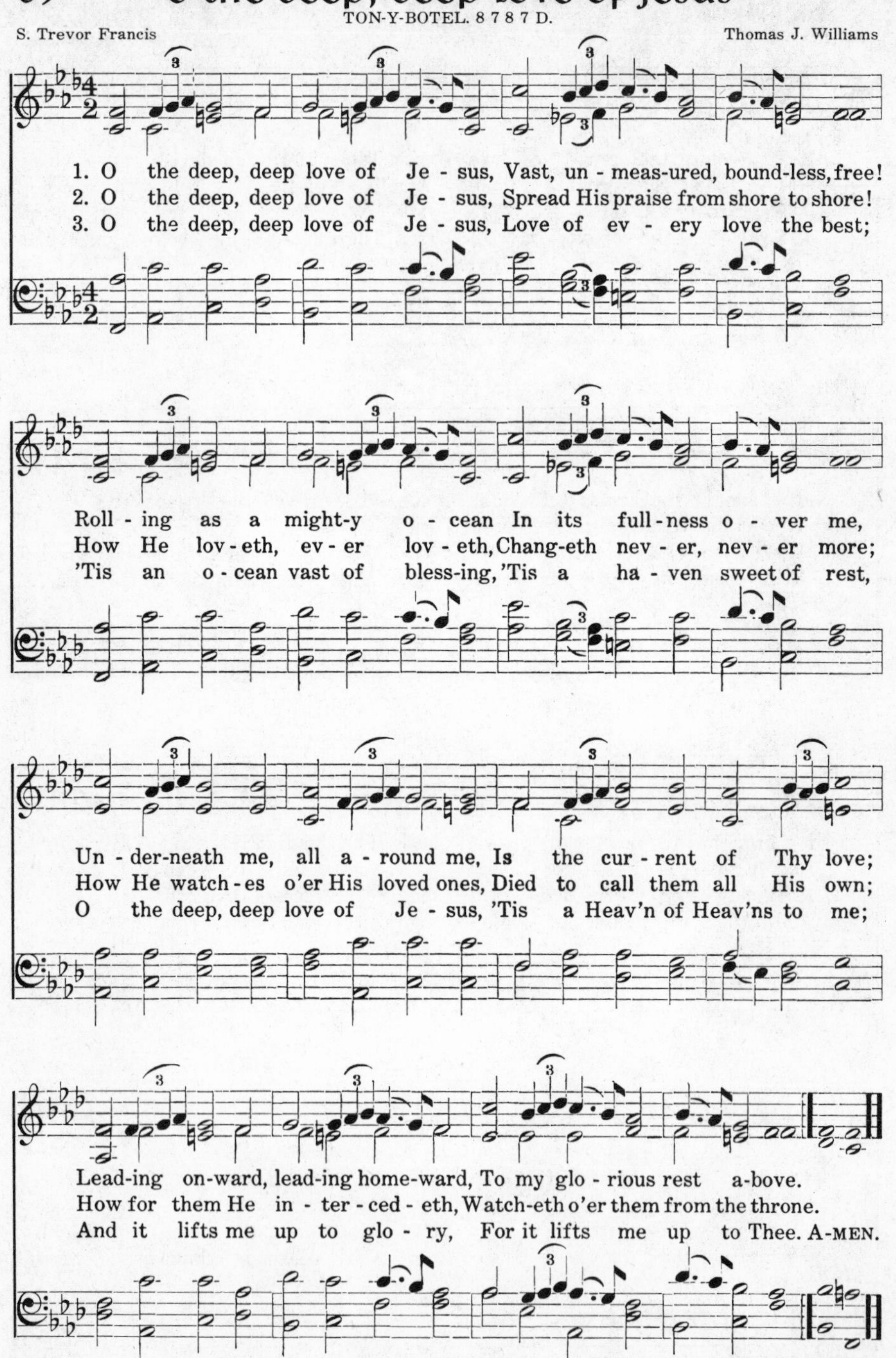
1. O the deep, deep love of Je - sus, Vast, un - meas-ured, bound-less, free!
2. O the deep, deep love of Je - sus, Spread His praise from shore to shore!
3. O the deep, deep love of Je - sus, Love of ev - ery love the best;
Roll - ing as a might-y o - cean In its full-ness o - ver me,
How He lov - eth, ev - er lov - eth, Chang-eth nev - er, nev - er more;
'Tis an o - cean vast of bless-ing, 'Tis a ha - ven sweet of rest,
Un - der-neath me, all a - round me, Is the cur - rent of Thy love;
How He watch - es o'er His loved ones, Died to call them all His own;
O the deep, deep love of Je - sus, 'Tis a Heav'n of Heav'ns to me;
Lead-ing on-ward, lead-ing home-ward, To my glo - rious rest a-bove.
How for them He in - ter - ced - eth, Watch-eth o'er them from the throne.
And it lifts me up to glo - ry, For it lifts me up to Thee. A-MEN.

IVORY PALACES 86

MONTREAT. 9 6 9 6 Ref.

Henry Barraclough

Henry Barraclough
Arr. by Donald P. Hustad

1. My Lord has gar-ments so won-drous fine, And myrrh their tex-ture fills;
2. His life had al - so its sor - rows sore, For al - oes had a part;
3. His gar-ments too were in cas - sia dipped, With heal - ing in a touch;
4. In gar-ments glo - ri - ous He will come, To o - pen wide the door;

Its fra-grance reached to this heart of mine, With joy my be - ing thrills.
And when I think of the cross He bore, My eyes with tear-drops start.
Each time my feet in some sin have slipped, He took me from its clutch.
And I shall en - ter my heaven-ly home, To dwell for - ev - er - more.

mf REFRAIN

Out of the i - vo - ry pal - a - ces, In - to a world of woe,

p

On - ly His great, e - ter - nal love Made my Sav-iour go.

mf

87

JESUS SAVES

JESUS SAVES. 7 6 7 6 7 7 7 6

Priscilla J. Owens — William J. Kirkpatrick

1. We have heard the joy - ful sound: Je - sus saves! Je - sus saves!
2. Waft it on the roll - ing tide; Je - sus saves! Je - sus saves!
3. Sing a - bove the bat - tle strife, Je - sus saves! Je - sus saves!
4. Give the winds a might - y voice, Je - sus saves! Je - sus saves!

Spread the ti - dings all a - round: Je - sus saves! Je - sus saves!
Tell to sin - ners far and wide: Je - sus saves! Je - sus saves!
By His death and end - less life, Je - sus saves! Je - sus saves!
Let the na - tions now re - joice— Je - sus saves! Je - sus saves!

Bear the news to ev - ery land, Climb the steeps and cross the waves;
Sing, ye is - lands of the sea; Ech - o back, ye o - cean caves;
Sing it soft - ly through the gloom, When the heart for mer - cy craves;
Shout sal - va - tion full and free, High - est hills and deep - est caves;

On - ward!—'tis our Lord's com - mand; Je - sus saves! Je - sus saves!
Earth shall keep her ju - bi - lee: Je - sus saves! Je - sus saves!
Sing in tri - umph o'er the tomb— Je - sus saves! Je - sus saves!
This our song of vic - to - ry— Je - sus saves! Je - sus saves!

At the Cross

HUDSON. C.M. Ref.

Isaac Watts
Ralph E. Hudson, refrain

Ralph E. Hudson

1. A - las, and did my Sav - iour bleed? And did my Sov-'reign die?
2. Was it for crimes that I have done, He groaned up - on the tree?
3. Well might the sun in dark-ness hide, And shut his glo - ries in,
4. But drops of grief can ne'er re - pay The debt of love I owe:

Would He de-vote that sa - cred head For such a worm as I?
A - maz - ing pit - y! grace un-known! And love be - yond de - gree!
When Christ, the might - y Mak - er, died For man the crea-ture's sin.
Here, Lord, I give my - self a - way, 'Tis all that I can do!

Refrain

At the cross, at the cross where I first saw the light, And the burden of my heart rolled a - way, (rolled a-way,) It was there by faith I re - ceived my sight, And now I am hap-py all the day!

He Lives

ACKLEY. Irregular. Ref.

Alfred H. Ackley | Alfred H. Ackley

1. I serve a ris - en Sav-iour, He's in the world to -day; I know that He is liv - ing, what-ev - er men may say; I see His hand of mer - cy, I hear His voice of cheer, And just the time I need Him He's al - ways near.
2. In all the world a-round me I see His lov - ing care, And tho' my heart grows wea-ry, I nev - er will de - spair; I know that He is lead - ing thro' all the storm-y blast, The day of His ap - pear-ing will come at last.
3. Rejoice, rejoice, O Christian, lift up your voice and sing E - ter - nal hal - le - lu - jahs to Je - sus Christ the King! The Hope of all who seek Him, the Help of all who find, None oth-er is so lov - ing, so good and kind.
Refrain
He lives, He lives, Christ Je - sus lives to - day! He walks with me and
He lives, He lives,
talks with me a - long life's nar - row way. He lives, He lives, sal-
He lives, He lives,

THE SOLID ROCK

SOLID ROCK. L.M. Ref.

Edward Mote

William B. Bradbury

1. My hope is built on noth-ing less Than Je-sus' blood and right-eous-ness;
2. When dark-ness veils His love - ly face, I rest on His un - chang-ing grace;
3. His oath, His cov - e-nant, His blood, Sup-port me in the whelm-ing flood;
4. When He shall come with trumpet sound, Oh, may I then in Him be found;

I dare not trust the sweet-est frame, But whol-ly lean on Je - sus' name.
In ev - ery high and storm-y gale, My an-chor holds with - in the veil.
When all a - round my soul gives way, He then is all my hope and stay.
Dressed in His right-eous-ness a - lone, Fault-less to stand be - fore the throne.

REFRAIN

On Christ, the sol - id Rock, I stand; All oth - er ground

is sink - ing sand, All oth - er ground is sink - ing sand.

93 I WILL SING OF MY REDEEMER

HYFRYDOL. 8 7 8 7 D.

Philip P. Bliss — Rowland H. Prichard

1. I will sing of my Re - deem - er And His won-drous love to me;
2. I will tell the won-drous sto - ry, How my lost es - tate to save,
3. I will praise my dear Re - deem - er, His tri-umph - ant power I'li tell,
4. I will sing of my Re - deem - er And His heaven-ly love for me;

On the cru - el cross He suf - fered, From the curse to set me free.
In His bound-less love and mer - cy, He the ran - som free - ly gave.
How the vic - to - ry He giv - eth O - ver sin, and death, and hell.
He from death to life hath brought me, Son of God, with Him to be.

Refrain

Sing, oh, sing of my Re - deem - er, With His blood He pur-chased me,

On the cross He sealed my par - don, Paid the debt, and made me free.

I Will Sing the Wondrous Story

WONDROUS STORY. 8 7 8 7 Ref.

Francis H. Rowley — Peter P. Bilhorn

1. I will sing the won-drous sto-ry Of the Christ who died for me,
How He left His home in glo-ry For the cross of Cal-va-ry.

2. I was lost, but Je-sus found me, Found the sheep that went a-stray,
Threw His lov-ing arms a-round me, Drew me back in-to His way.

3. I was bruised, but Je-sus healed me; Faint was I from man-y a fall;
Sight was gone, and fears pos-sessed me, But He freed me from them all.

4. Days of dark-ness still come o'er me, Sor-row's paths I oft-en tread,
But the Sav-iour still is with me; By His hand I'm safe-ly led.

5. He will keep me till the riv-er Rolls its wa-ters at my feet;
Then He'll bear me safe-ly o-ver, Where the loved ones I shall meet.

Refrain

Yes, I'll sing the won-drous sto-ry Of the Christ who died for me
(Yes, I'll sing the won-drous sto-ry Of the Christ who died for me,)
Sing it with the saints in glo-ry, Gath-ered by the crys-tal sea.
(Sing it with the saints in glo-ry, Gath-ered by the crys-tal sea.)

95 I Love to Tell the Story

HANKEY. 7 6 7 6 D. Ref.

A. Catherine Hankey — William G. Fischer

1. I love to tell the sto - ry Of un - seen things a - bove, Of
2. I love to tell the sto - ry, More won-der - ful it seems Than
3. I love to tell the sto - ry, 'Tis pleas - ant to re - peat What
4. I love to tell the sto - ry, For those who know it best Seem

Je - sus and His glo - ry, Of Je - sus and His love. I love to
all the gold - en fan - cies Of all our gold - en dreams. I love to
seems, each time I tell it, More won - der - ful - ly sweet. I love to
hun - ger - ing and thirst - ing To hear it like the rest. And when, in

tell the sto - ry, Be - cause I know 'tis true; It sat - is - fies my
tell the sto - ry, It did so much for me; And that is just the
tell the sto - ry, For some have nev - er heard The mes - sage of sal-
scenes of glo - ry, I sing the new, new song, 'Twill be the old, old

long-ings As noth-ing else can do.
rea - son I tell it now to thee.
va - tion From God's own Ho-ly Word.
sto - ry That I have loved so long.

REFRAIN

I love to tell the sto - ry, 'Twill be my theme in glo - ry To tell the old, old sto - ry Of Je-sus and His love.

Tell Me the Old, Old Story

OLD, OLD STORY. 7 6 7 6 D. Ref.

A. Catherine Hankey — William H. Doane

1. Tell me the old, old sto - ry Of un-seen things a - bove, Of Je - sus
2. Tell me the sto - ry slow - ly, That I may take it in— That won-der-
3. Tell me the sto - ry soft - ly, With ear-nest tones and grave; Re-mem-ber,
4. Tell me the same old sto - ry When you have cause to fear That this world's
and His glo - ry, Of Je - sus and His love. Tell me the sto - ry
ful re - demp-tion, God's rem - e - dy for sin. Tell me the sto - ry
I'm the sin - ner Whom Je - sus came to save. Tell me the sto - ry
emp - ty glo - ry Is cost - ing me too dear. Yes, and when that world's
sim - ply, As to a lit - tle child, For I am weak and wea - ry,
oft - en, For I for - get so soon; The "ear - ly dew" of morn - ing
al - ways, If you would real - ly be, In an - y time of troub - le,
glo - ry Is dawn-ing on my soul, Tell me the old, old sto - ry:
And help - less and de - filed.
Has passed a - way at noon.
A com - fort - er to me.
"Christ Je - sus makes thee whole."
Refrain
Tell me the old, old sto - ry, Tell me the
old, old sto - ry, Tell me the old, old sto - ry Of Je - sus and His love.

97 Blessed Assurance

ASSURANCE. 9 10 9 9 Ref.

Fanny J. Crosby

Phoebe P. Knapp

1. Bless-ed as - sur - ance, Je - sus is mine! Oh, what a fore - taste of glo - ry di - vine! Heir of sal - va - tion, pur-chase of God, Born of His Spir - it, washed in His blood.

2. Per - fect sub - mis - sion, per - fect de - light, Vi - sions of rap - ture now burst on my sight; An - gels de - scend - ing, bring from a - bove Ech - oes of mer - cy, whis-pers of love.

3. Per - fect sub - mis - sion, all is at rest, I in my Sav - iour am hap - py and blest; Watch-ing and wait - ing, look - ing a - bove, Filled with His goodness, lost in His love.

REFRAIN

This is my sto - ry, this is my song, Prais-ing my Sav-iour all the day long; This is my sto - ry, this is my song, Prais - ing my Sav - iour all the day long.

Oh, It Is Wonderful!

HOMER. 13 13 13 13 Ref.
Charles H. Gabriel
Charles H. Gabriel
Arr. by Donald P. Hustad
1. I stand all amazed at the love Jesus offers me, Confused at the grace that so fully He proffers me; I tremble to know that for me He was crucified—That for me, a sinner, He suffered, He bled, and died.
2. I marvel that He would descend from His throne divine, To rescue a soul so rebellious and proud as mine; That He should extend His great love unto such as I; Sufficient to own, to redeem, and to justify.
3. I think of His hands pierced and bleeding to pay the debt! Such mercy, such love and devotion can I forget? No, no! I will praise and adore at the mercy-seat, Until at the glorified throne I kneel at His feet.
Refrain
Oh, it is wonderful that He should care for me, Enough to die for me! Oh, it is wonderful, wonderful to me!

99 REDEEMED

REDEEMED. 9 8 9 8 Ref.

Fanny J. Crosby | William J. Kirkpatrick

1. Redeemed-how I love to pro-claim it! Re-deemed by the blood of the Lamb;
2. Redeemed and so hap-py in Je-sus, No lan-guage my rapture can tell;
3. I think of my bless-ed Re-deem-er, I think of Him all the day long;
4. I know I shall see in His beau-ty The King in whose law I de-light;
Redeemed through His in-fi-nite mer-cy, His child, and for-ev-er, I am.
I know that the light of His pres-ence With me doth con-tin-ual-ly dwell.
I sing, for I can-not be si-lent; His love is the theme of my song.
Who lov-ing-ly guard-eth my foot-steps, And giv-eth me songs in the night.
Refrain
Re-deemed, re-deemed, Re-deemed by the blood of the Lamb;
re-deemed, re-deemed,
Re-deemed, re-deemed, His child, and for-ev-er, I am.
re-deemed, re-deemed,

Trust - ing Thee for full sal - va - tion, Great and free.
Ev - ery day and hour sup - ply - ing All my need.
Words which Thou Thy - self shalt give me Must pre - vail.
I am trust - ing Thee for - ev - er, And for all. A-MEN.
NOW I BELONG TO JESUS 103
ELLSWORTH. 10 10 9 6 Ref.
Norman J. Clayton
Norman J. Clayton
1. Je - sus my Lord will love me for-ev - er, From Him no pow'r of e - vil can
2. Once I was lost in sin's deg-ra-da-tion, Je - sus came down to bring me sal-
3. Joy floods my soul for Jesus has saved me, Freed me from sin that long had en-
sev - er, He gave His life to ran - som my soul, Now I be-long to Him;
va - tion, Lift - ed me up from sor-row and shame, Now I be-long to Him;
slaved me, His pre-cious blood He gave to re-deem, Now I be-long to Him;
REFRAIN
Now I be - long to Je - sus, Je - sus be - longs to me,
Not for the years of time a - lone, But for e - ter - ni - ty.

104 I am His, and He is Mine

EVERLASTING LOVE. 7 7 7 7 D.

George Wade Robinson — James Mountain

1. Loved with ev - er - last - ing love, Led by grace that love to know;
2. Heav'n a - bove is soft - er blue, Earth a - round is sweet-er green!
3. Things that once were wild a - larms Can - not now dis - turb my rest;
4. His for - ev - er, on - ly His; Who the Lord and me shall part?
Spir - it, breath-ing from a - bove, Thou hast taught me it is so!
Some-thing lives in ev - ery hue Christ-less eyes have nev - er seen:
Closed in ev - er - last - ing arms, Pil - lowed on the lov - ing breast.
Ah, with what a rest of bliss Christ can fill the lov - ing heart!
Oh, this full and per - fect peace! Oh, this trans - port all di - vine!
Birds with glad - der songs o'er - flow, Flow'rs with deep - er beau-ties shine,
Oh, to lie for - ev - er here, Doubt, and care, and self re - sign,
Heav'n and earth may fade and flee, First-born light in gloom de - cline;
In a love which can - not cease, I am His, and He is mine.
Since I know, as now I know, I am His, and He is mine.
While He whis - pers in my ear, I am His, and He is mine.
But while God and I shall be, I am His, and He is mine.

the roll - ing sea; Won - - - der - ful
might - y roll - ing sea; High - er than the moun - tain,
grace, all - suf - fi - - - cient for
spar - kling like a foun - tain, All - suf - fi - cient grace for e - ven
me, for e - ven me, Broad - er than the scope of my trans-
me, trans-
gres - sions, Great - er far than all my sin and shame;
gres- sions, sing it! my sin and shame;
O mag - ni - fy the pre - cious name of Je - sus, Praise His name!

107 all my life long

SATISFIED. 8 7 8 7 Ref.
Clara Tear Williams
Ralph E. Hudson
1. All my life-long I had pant-ed For a drink from some cool spring
2. Feed-ing on the husks a-round me Till my strength was al-most gone,
3. Poor I was, and sought for rich-es, Some-thing that would sat-is-fy;
4. Well of wa-ter, ev-er spring-ing, Bread of life, so rich and free,
That I hoped would quench the burn-ing Of the thirst I felt with-in.
Longed my soul for some-thing bet-ter, On-ly still to hun-ger on.
But the dust I gath-ered round me On-ly mocked my soul's sad cry.
Un-told wealth that nev-er fail-eth, My Re-deem-er is to me.
Refrain
Hal-le-lu-jah! I have found Him—Whom my soul so long has craved!
Je-sus sat-is-fies my long-ings; Thro' His blood I now am saved.
108 amazing grace! how sweet the sound
AMAZING GRACE. C.M.
John Newton, 1-3
John P. Rees, 4 (ascribed)
Early American Melody
Arr. by Edwin O. Excell
1. A-maz-ing grace! how sweet the sound, That saved a wretch like me! I
2. 'Twas grace that taught my heart to fear, And grace my fears re-lieved; How
3. Through man-y dan-gers, toils and snares, I have al-read-y come; 'Tis
4. When we've been there ten thou-sand years, Bright shin-ing as the sun, We've

once was lost, but now am found, Was blind, but now I see.
pre - cious did that grace ap - pear The hour I first be-lieved!
grace hath brought me safe thus far, And grace will lead me home.
no less days to sing God's praise Than when we first be - gun. A - MEN.
'TIS SO SWEET TO TRUST IN JESUS
109
TRUST IN JESUS. 7 7 8 7 Ref.
Louisa M. R. Stead
William J. Kirkpatrick
1. 'Tis so sweet to trust in Je - sus, Just to take Him at His word;
2. O how sweet to trust in Je - sus, Just to trust His cleans-ing blood;
3. Yes, 'tis sweet to trust in Je - sus, Just from sin and self to cease;
4. I'm so glad I learned to trust Thee, Pre-cious Je - sus, Sav-iour, Friend;
Just to rest up - on His prom-ise; Just to know, "Thus saith the Lord."
Just in sim - ple faith to plunge me 'Neath the heal - ing, cleans-ing flood!
Just from Je - sus sim - ply tak - ing Life and rest, and joy and peace.
And I know that Thou art with me, Wilt be with me to the end.
REFRAIN
Je - sus, Je - sus, how I trust Him! How I've proved Him o'er and o'er!
Je - sus, Je - sus, pre - cious Je - sus! O for grace to trust Him more!
THE BELIEVER'S EXPERIENCE

110 SAVED!

PEOPLES CHURCH. 9 9 9 9 Ref.

Oswald J. Smith — Roger M. Hickman

1. Saved! saved! saved! my sins are all for - giv'n; Christ is mine! I'm on my way to heav'n; Once a guilt - y sin - ner, lost, un - done, Now a child of God, saved thro' His Son.
2. Saved! saved! saved! by grace and grace a - lone; Oh, what won - drous love to me was shown, In my stead Christ Je - sus bled and died, Bore my sins, for me was cru - ci - fied.
3. Saved! saved! saved! oh, joy be - yond com - pare! Christ my life, and I His con - stant care; Yield - ing all and trust-ing Him a - lone, Liv - ing now each mo - ment as His own.

Refrain

Saved! I'm saved thro' Christ, my all in all; (my all in all;)
Saved! I'm saved, what-ev - er may be - fall; He died up - on the cross for me, He bore the aw - ful

All Things in Jesus

OKMULGEE. 10 10 10 10 Ref.

Harry Dixon Loes — Harry Dixon Loes

1. Friends all around us are trying to find What the heart yearns for, by sin undermined; I have the secret, I know where 'tis found: Only in Jesus true pleasures abound.
2. Some carry burdens whose weight has for years Crushed them with sorrow and blinded with tears; Yet One stands ready to help them just now, If they with faith and in penitence bow.
3. No other name stirs the joy-chords within, And thro' none else is remission of sin; He knows the pain of the heart sorely tried, All of its needs will in Him be supplied.
4. Jesus is all this sad world needs today; Blindly men strive, for sin darkens the way. O to draw back the grim curtains of night— One glimpse of Jesus, and all will be bright!
Refrain
All that I want is in Jesus; He satisfies, joy He supplies;
Jesus, in Jesus, with the freely;
Life would be worthless without Him, All things in Jesus I find.
without Him, without Him,

114 complete in thee

TALMADGE. L.M. Ref.

Aaron R. Wolfe and
James M. Gray

Talmadge J. Bittikofer

1. Com-plete in Thee! no work of mine May take, dear Lord, the place of Thine;
2. Com-plete in Thee! no more shall sin, Thy grace hath conquered, reign within;
3. Com-plete in Thee—each want supplied, And no good thing to me de-nied;
4. Dear Sav-iour! when be-fore Thy bar All tribes and tongues as-sem-bled are,
Thy blood hath par - don bought for me, And I am now com-plete in Thee.
Thy voice shall bid the tempt-er flee, And I shall stand com-plete in Thee.
Since Thou my por - tion, Lord, wilt be, I ask no more, com-plete in Thee.
A - mong Thy cho - sen will I be, At Thy right hand, com-plete in Thee.
REFRAIN
Yea, jus - ti - fied! O bless-ed thought! And sanc-ti - fied! Sal-va-tion wrought!
Thy blood hath par - don bought for me, And glo - ri - fied, I too, shall be!

I've Heard the King

HIGHLANDS. 9 12 9 12 Ref.

Grant C. Tullar — Donald P. Hustad

1. I've heard the King! The King of heav-en! Nor can I e'er for-get the
2. I've heard the King! The King of glo-ry; For whom my heart's door o-pened
3. I've heard the King! Oh, had I missed Him, My life for-ev-er-more could
4. I've heard the King! and now I'm tell-ing To all the world the gos-pel

mu-sic of His voice. I've heard the King! His call I've answered. I've made the
wide and He came in. I've heard the King! Oh, bless-ed hear-ing, His voice spoke
not re-gain the loss. From heav'n He came, the world to ran-som, And this He
of un-dy-ing love, That oth-ers too may catch the mu-sic His voice can

King of heav'n my ev-er-last-ing choice.
peace and par-don for my guilt and sin.
did one day on Calv'ry's cru-el cross.
bring, and find their way to heav'n a-bove.

REFRAIN

He came to me, and with Him came a bless-ing. He spoke to me, and glo-ry filled my soul; His voice I heard, so charm-ing and so won-drous. I've heard the King, and hear-ing am made whole.

116

One Day!

CHAPMAN. 11 10 11 10 Ref.

J. Wilbur Chapman — Charles H. Marsh

1. One day when heav - en was filled with His prais - es, One day when
2. One day they led Him up Cal - va - ry's moun - tain, One day they
3. One day they left Him a - lone in the gar - den, One day He
4. One day the grave could con - ceal Him no lon - ger, One day the
5. One day the trum - pet will sound for His com - ing, One day the

sin was as black as could be, Je - sus came forth to be
nailed Him to die on the tree; Suf - fer - ing an - guish, de-
rest - ed, from suf - fer - ing free; An - gels came down o'er His
stone rolled a - way from the door; Then He a - rose, o - ver
skies with His glo - ry will shine; Won - der - ful day, my be-

born of a vir - gin, Dwelt a - mong men, my ex - am - ple is He!
spised and re - ject - ed, Bear - ing our sins, my Re - deem - er is He!
tomb to keep vig - il; Hope of the hope - less, my Sav - iour is He!
death He has con - quered; Now is as - cend - ed, my Lord ev - er - more!
lov - ed ones bring - ing; Glo - ri - ous Sav - iour, this Je - sus is mine!

REFRAIN

Liv - ing, He loved me; dy - ing, He saved me; Bur - ied, He

car - ried my sins far a - way; Ris - ing, He jus - ti - fied

ONCE FOR ALL 119

ONCE FOR ALL. 10 10 9 8 Ref.

Philip P. Bliss — Philip P. Bliss

1. Free from the law, O hap - py con - di - tion, Je - sus hath
2. Now are we free—there's no con-dem - na - tion, Je - sus pro-
3. "Chil - dren of God," O glo - ri - ous call - ing, Sure - ly His

bled, and there is re - mis - sion; Cursed by the law and bruised by the
vides a per - fect sal - va - tion; "Come un - to Me," O hear His sweet -
grace will keep us from fall - ing; Pass - ing from death to life at His

fall, Grace hath redeemed us once for all.
call, Come, and He saves us once for all.
call, Bless - ed sal - va - tion once for all.

REFRAIN

Once for all, O sin-ner, re-

ceive it; Once for all, O broth - er, be - lieve it; Cling to the

cross, the bur - den will fall, Christ hath re-deemed us once for all.

120 Since Jesus Came into My Heart

McDANIEL. 12 8 12 8 Ref.

Rufus H. McDaniel

Charles H. Gabriel

1. What a won-der-ful change in my life has been wrought Since Je-sus came in-to my heart! I have light in my soul for which long I have sought, Since Je-sus came in-to my heart!
2. I have ceased from my wandering and go-ing a-stray, Since Je-sus came in-to my heart! And my sins, which were man-y, are all washed a-way, Since Je-sus came in-to my heart!
3. There's a light in the val-ley of death now for me, Since Je-sus came in-to my heart! And the gates of the Cit-y be-yond I can see, Since Je-sus came in-to my heart!
4. I shall go there to dwell in that Cit-y, I know, Since Je-sus came in-to my heart! And I'm hap-py, so hap-py, as on-ward I go, Since Je-sus came in-to my heart!
Refrain
Since Je-sus came in-to my heart, Since Je-sus came in-to my heart,
Since Je-sus came in, came in-to my heart, Since Je-sus came in, came in-to my heart,
Floods of joy o'er my soul like the sea bil-lows roll, Since Je-sus came in-to my heart.

In Tenderness He Sought Me

CLARENDON. 7 6 7 6 8 8 Ref.
W. Spencer Walton
Adoniram J. Gordon
1. In ten - der - ness He sought me, Wea - ry and sick with sin,
2. He washed the bleed - ing sin-wounds, And poured in oil and wine;
3. He point - ed to the nail - prints, For me His blood was shed,
4. I'm sit - ting in His pres - ence, The sun - shine of His face,
5. So while the hours are pass - ing, All now is per - fect rest;
And on His shoul-ders brought me Back to His fold a - gain. While
He whis-pered to as - sure me, "I've found thee, thou art Mine;" I
A mock - ing crown so thorn - y Was placed up - on His head: I
While with a - dor - ing won - der His bless - ings I re - trace. It
I'm wait - ing for the morn - ing, The bright - est and the best, When
an - gels in His pres-ence sang Un - til the courts of heav - en rang.
nev - er heard a sweet-er voice; It made my ach - ing heart re - joice!
won-dered what He saw in me, To suf - fer such deep ag - o - ny.
seems as if e - ter - nal days Are far too short to sound His praise.
He will call us to His side, To be with Him, His spot - less bride.
Refrain
Oh, the love that sought me! Oh, the blood that bought me! Oh, the grace that
brought me to the fold, Won-drous grace that brought me to the fold!

122

I've Found a Friend

FRIEND. 8 7 8 7 D.

James G. Small

George C. Stebbins

1. I've found a Friend, oh, such a Friend! He loved me ere I knew Him;
2. I've found a Friend, oh, such a Friend! He bled, He died to save me;
3. I've found a Friend, oh, such a Friend! All power to Him is giv - en,
4. I've found a Friend, oh, such a Friend! So kind, and true, and ten - der,
He drew me with the cords of love, And thus He bound me to Him.
And not a - lone the gift of life, But His own self He gave me.
To guard me on my on-ward course, And bring me safe to heav - en.
So wise a Coun - sel - lor and Guide, So might - y a De - fend - er!
And round my heart still close - ly twine Those ties which naught can sev - er,
Naught that I have my own I call, I hold it for the Giv - er;
Th' e - ter - nal glo - ries gleam a - far, To nerve my faint en - deav - or;
From Him who loves me now so well, What power my soul can sev - er?
For I am His, and He is mine, For - ev - er and for - ev - er.
My heart, my strength, my life, my all, Are His, and His for - ev - er.
So now to watch, to work, to war, And then to rest for - ev - er.
Shall life or death, or earth or hell? No; I am His for - ev - er.

I Know Whom I Have Believed

EL NATHAN. C.M. Ref.

Daniel W. Whittle — James McGranahan

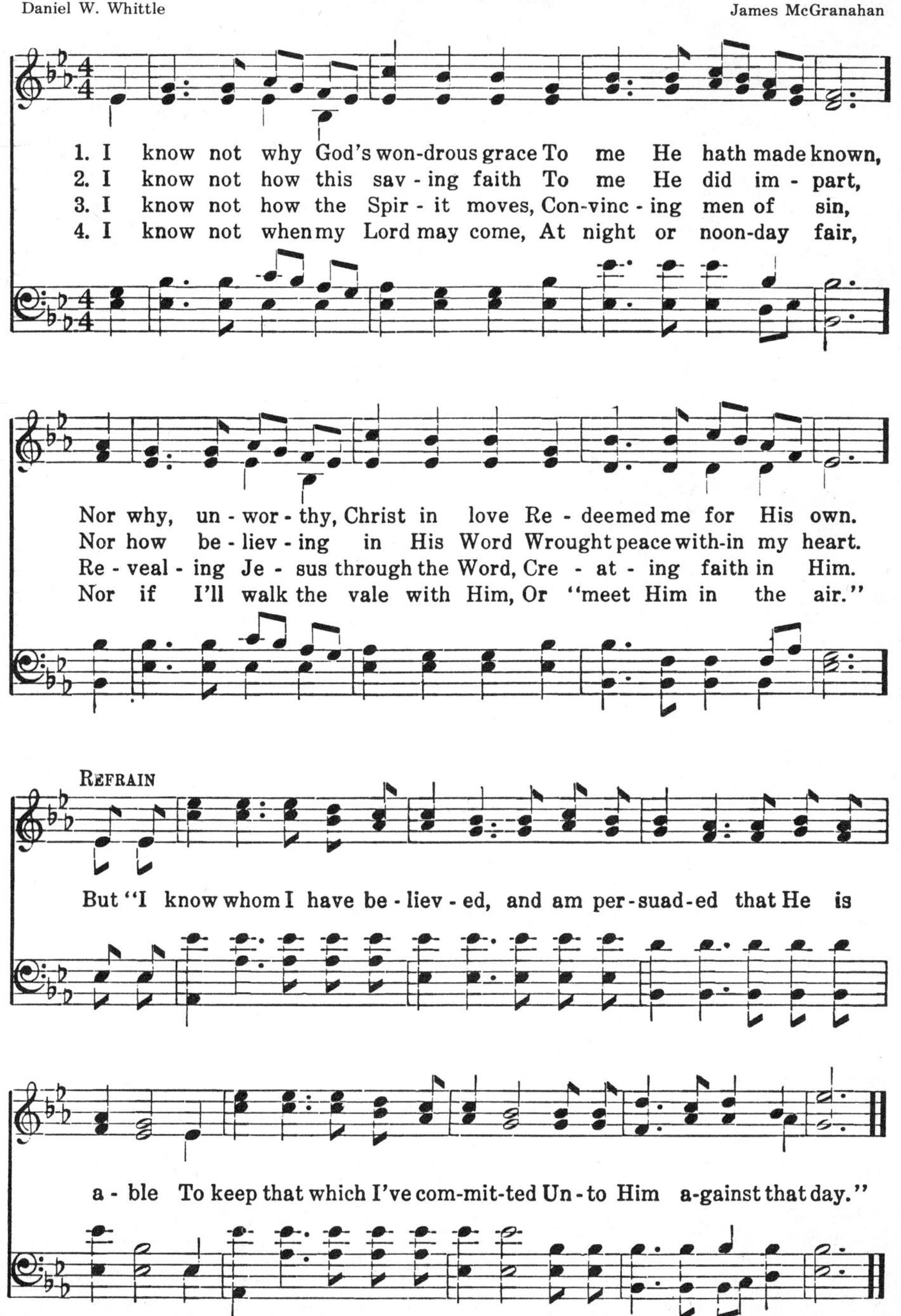
1. I know not why God's won-drous grace To me He hath made known,
2. I know not how this sav - ing faith To me He did im - part,
3. I know not how the Spir - it moves, Con-vinc - ing men of sin,
4. I know not when my Lord may come, At night or noon-day fair,
Nor why, un - wor - thy, Christ in love Re - deemed me for His own.
Nor how be - liev - ing in His Word Wrought peace with-in my heart.
Re - veal - ing Je - sus through the Word, Cre - at - ing faith in Him.
Nor if I'll walk the vale with Him, Or "meet Him in the air."
Refrain
But "I know whom I have be - liev - ed, and am per - suad - ed that He is
a - ble To keep that which I've com-mit-ted Un - to Him a-gainst that day."

124 Wounded for Me

FOR ME. 8 10 10 10

W. G. Ovens and Gladys Watkin Roberts — W. G. Ovens

1. Wound-ed for me, wound-ed for me, There on the cross
2. Dy - ing for me, dy - ing for me, There on the cross
3. Ris - en for me, ris - en for me, Up from the grave
4. Liv - ing for me, liv - ing for me, Up in the skies
5. Com - ing for me, com - ing for me, One day to earth

He was wound - ed for me; Gone my trans - gres - sions, and
He was dy - ing for me; Now in His death my re-
He has ris - en for me; Now ev - er - more from death's
He is liv - ing for me; Dai - ly He's plead - ing and
He is com - ing for me; Then with what joy His dear

now I am free, All be-cause Je - sus was wound-ed for me.
demp-tion I see, All be-cause Je - sus was dy - ing for me.
sting I am free, All be-cause Je - sus has ris - en for me.
pray-ing for me, All be-cause Je - sus is liv - ing for me.
face I shall see, Oh, how I praise Him, He's com - ing for me.

125 Not What These Hands Have Done

ST. ANDREW. 6 6 8 6

Horatius Bonar — Joseph Barnby

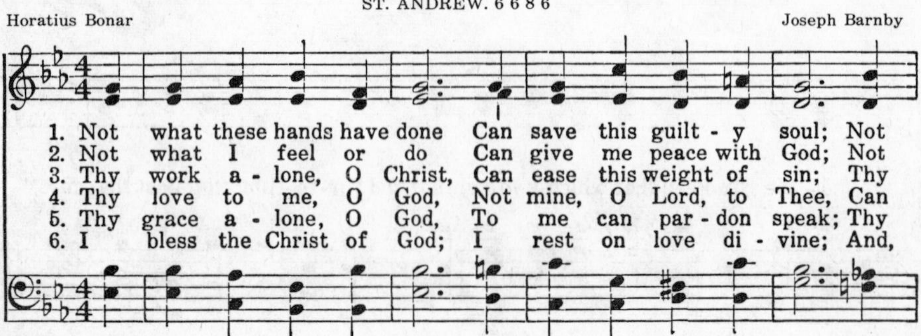
1. Not what these hands have done Can save this guilt - y soul; Not
2. Not what I feel or do Can give me peace with God; Not
3. Thy work a - lone, O Christ, Can ease this weight of sin; Thy
4. Thy love to me, O God, Not mine, O Lord, to Thee, Can
5. Thy grace a - lone, O God, To me can par - don speak; Thy
6. I bless the Christ of God; I rest on love di - vine; And,

what this toil - ing flesh has borne Can make my spir - it whole.
all my prayers and sighs and tears Can bear my aw - ful load.
blood a - lone, O Lamb of God, Can give me peace with - in.
rid me of this dark un - rest, And set my spir - it free.
power a - lone, O Son of God, Can this sore bon - dage break.
with un - fal - tering lip and heart, I call this Sav - iour mine. A-MEN.
Christ Liveth in Me
126
CHRIST LIVETH. C.M. Ref.
Daniel W. Whittle
James McGranahan
1. Once far from God and dead in sin, No light my heart could see;
2. As rays of light from yon - der sun, The flow'rs of earth set free,
3. As lives the flow'r with - in the seed, As in the cone the tree,
4. With long - ing all my heart is filled, That like Him I may be,
But in God's Word the light I found, Now Christ liv - eth in me.
So life and light and love came forth From Christ liv - ing in me.
So, praise the God of truth and grace, His Spir-it dwell-eth in me.
As on the won-drous thought I dwell That Christ liv - eth in me.
Refrain
Christ liv - eth in me, Christ liv - eth in me,
Christ liv - eth in me, Christ liv - eth in
Oh! what a sal - va - tion this, That Christ liv - eth in me.
me, Oh,

127 Near the Cross

NEAR THE CROSS. 7 6 7 6 Ref.

Fanny J. Crosby | William H. Doane

1. Je - sus, keep me near the cross, There a pre-cious foun-tain Free to all— a
2. Near the cross, a trembling soul, Love and mer-cy found me; There the Bright and
3. Near the cross! O Lamb of God, Bring its scenes be-fore me; Help me walk from
4. Near the cross I'll watch and wait, Hop-ing, trust-ing ev - er, Till I reach the

Refrain

heal-ing stream, Flows from Calvary's mountain.
Morn-ing Star Sheds its beams a-round me. In the cross, in the cross, Be my
day to day, With its shad-ows o'er me.
gold - en strand, Just be-yond the riv - er.

glo - ry ev - er; Till my rap-tured soul shall find Rest be-yond the riv - er.

128 O Happy Day, That Fixed My Choice

HAMBURG. L.M.

Philip Doddridge | From a Gregorian Melody Arr. by Lowell Mason

1. O hap-py day, that fixed my choice On Thee, my Sav - iour and my God!
2. O hap-py bond, that seals my vows To Him Who mer - its all my love!
3. 'Tis done, the great trans - ac - tion's done! I am my Lord's and He is mine;
4. Now rest, my long-di - vid - ed heart, Fixed on this bliss - ful cen - ter, rest!
5. High heav'n, that heard the sol-emn vow, That vow re-newed shall dai - ly hear,

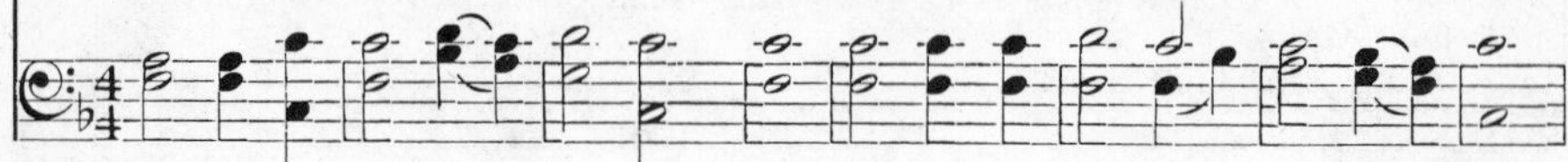

Well may this glow-ing heart re - joice And tell its rap-tures all a - broad.
Let cheer-ful an - thems fill His house, While to that sa - cred shrine I move.
He drew me, and I fol - lowed on, Charmed to confess the voice di - vine.
With ash-es who would grudge to part, When called on an - gels' bread to feast?
Till in life's lat-est hour I bow, And bless in death a bond so dear.
my hope is in the lord
129
WAKEFIELD. 6 6 8 4 Ref.
Norman J. Clayton
Norman J. Clayton
1. My hope is in the Lord Who gave Him - self for me, And paid the price of all my sin at Cal - va - ry.
2. No mer - it of my own His an - ger to sup - press. My on - ly hope is found in Je - sus' right-eous-ness.
3. And now for me He stands Be - fore the Fa-ther's throne. He shows His wounded hands, and names me as His own.
4. His grace has planned it all, 'Tis mine but to be - lieve, And rec - og-nize His work of love and Christ re - ceive.
Refrain
For me He died, For me He lives, And ev - er - last - ing life and light He free - ly gives.
For me He died, For me He lives,

130 JESUS, I WILL TRUST THEE

GOSHEN. 6 5 6 5 D.

Mary Jane Walker — *Bible Class Magazine*, 1860

131 I BELONG TO JESUS

DEDICATION. 6 5 7 5

M. Fraser — M. A. Sea

1. Je - sus, I will trust Thee, Trust Thee with my soul; Guilt - y, lost, and
2. Je - sus, I must trust Thee, Pon - der - ing Thy ways, Full of love and
3. Je - sus, I can trust Thee, Trust Thy writ-ten Word, Though Thy voice of
4. Je - sus, I do trust Thee, Trust with-out a doubt; Who - so-ev - er
help-less, Thou canst make me whole. There is none in heav - en Or on earth like
mer - cy All Thine earth - ly days; Sinners gathered round Thee, Lep-ers sought Thy
pit - y I have nev - er heard. When Thy Spir-it teach-eth, To my taste how
com - eth Thou wilt not cast out. Faith-ful is Thy prom-ise, Pre-cious is Thy
Thee; Thou hast died for sin - ners—There-fore, Lord, for me.
face; None too vile or loath-some For a Sav-iour's grace.
sweet! On - ly may I heark - en Sit - ting at Thy feet.
blood; These my soul's sal - va - tion, Thou my Sav - iour God. A-MEN.
1. I be - long to Je - sus; I am not my own;
2. I be - long to Je - sus; He is Lord and King,
3. I be - long to Je - sus; Bless - ed, bless - ed thought!
4. I be - long to Je - sus; He has died for me;
5. I be - long to Je - sus; He will keep my soul,
6. I be - long to Je - sus; And ere long I'll stand

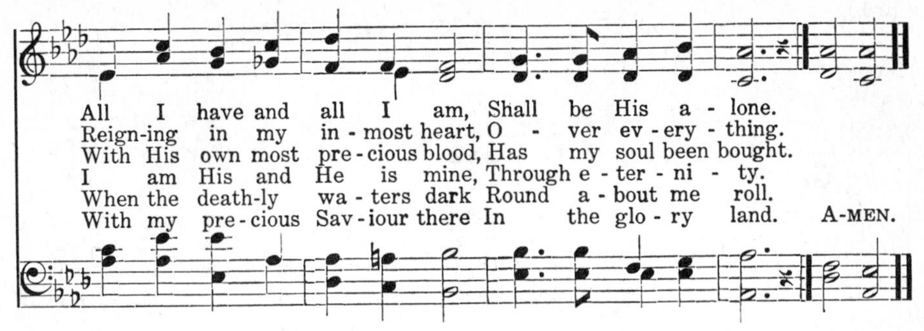
All I have and all I am, Shall be His a - lone.
Reign-ing in my in - most heart, O - ver ev - ery - thing.
With His own most pre - cious blood, Has my soul been bought.
I am His and He is mine, Through e - ter - ni - ty.
When the death-ly wa - ters dark Round a - bout me roll.
With my pre - cious Sav - iour there In the glo - ry land. A-MEN.

JESUS ONLY, LET ME SEE 132

BRINK. 7 7 7 6 Ref.

Oswald J. Smith

Daniel B. Towner

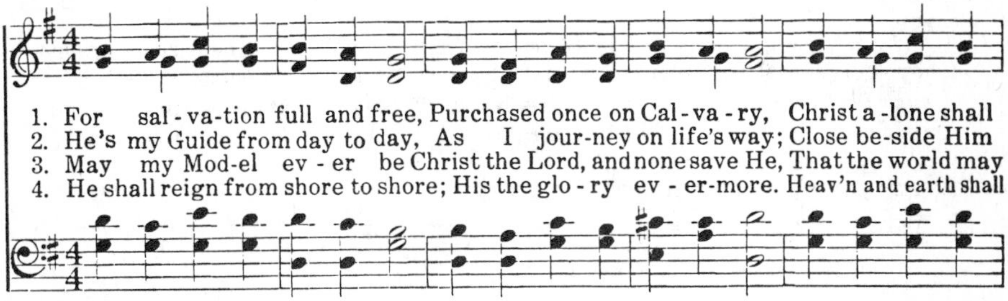

1. For sal - va - tion full and free, Purchased once on Cal - va - ry, Christ a - lone shall be my plea—Je - sus! Je - sus on - ly!
2. He's my Guide from day to day, As I jour - ney on life's way; Close be - side Him let me stay—Je - sus! Je - sus on - ly!
3. May my Mod - el ev - er be Christ the Lord, and none save He, That the world may see in me—Je - sus! Je - sus on - ly!
4. He shall reign from shore to shore; His the glo - ry ev - er - more. Heav'n and earth shall bow be - fore—Je - sus! Je - sus on - ly!

REFRAIN

Je - sus on - ly, let me see, Je - sus on - ly, none save He, Then my song shall ev - er be— Je - sus! Je - sus on - ly!

133 I Was a Wandering Sheep

LEBANON. S.M.D.

Horatius Bonar

John Zundel

1. I was a wan-d'ring sheep, I did not love the fold;
I did not love my Shep-herd's voice, I would not be con-trolled.
I was a way-ward child, I did not love my home;
I did not love my Fa-ther's voice, I loved a-far to roam.

2. The Shep-herd sought His sheep, The Fa-ther sought His child;
They fol-lowed me o'er vale and hill, O'er des-erts waste and wild;
They found me nigh to death, Fam-ished and faint and lone;
They bound me with the bands of love, They saved the wan-d'ring one.

3. Je-sus my Shep-herd is; T'was He that loved my soul,
'Twas He that washed me in His blood, 'Twas He that made me whole;
'Twas He that sought the lost, That found the wan-d'ring sheep,
'Twas He that brought me to the fold, 'Tis He that still doth keep.

4. I was a wan-d'ring sheep, I would not be con-trolled;
But now I love my Shep-herd's voice, I love, I love the fold.
I was a way-ward child, I once pre-ferred to roam;
But now I love my Fa-ther's voice, I love, I love His home.

hymns of the christian life

poets and musicians have given us music that speaks to and interprets the whole range of the christian life.

here are words that lead us to a more complete consecration of ourselves to jesus christ—hymns that encourage us to trust the faithfulness of god's word—and songs that reflect the serenity of a life of faith and commitment.

both in public worship and in private prayer, these pages reflect today's christian experience and speak our deepest hopes and highest aspirations for tomorrow.

134 Fully Surrendered

SNEAD. 9 9 6 6 6 4

Alfred C. Snead — George C. Stebbins

1. Ful - ly sur - ren - dered, Lord, I would be, Ful - ly sur - ren - dered,
2. Ful - ly sur - ren - dered—life, time, and all, All Thou hast giv'n me
3. Ful - ly sur - ren - dered—sil - ver and gold, His, who hath giv'n me
4. Ful - ly sur - ren - dered—Lord, I am Thine; Ful - ly sur - ren - dered,

dear Lord, to Thee. All on the al - tar laid, Sur - ren - der
held at Thy call. Speak but the word to me, Glad - ly I'll
rich - es un - told. All, all be - long to Thee, For Thou didst
Sav - iour di - vine! Live Thou Thy life in me, All full - ness

ful - ly made, Thou hast my ran - som paid; I yield to Thee.
fol - low Thee, Now and e - ter - nal - ly O - bey my Lord.
pur - chase me, Thine ev - er - more to be, Je - sus, my Lord.
dwells in Thee; Not I, but Christ in me, Christ all in all.

135 May the Mind of Christ, My Saviour

ST. LEONARDS. 8 7 8 5

Kate B. Wilkinson — A. Cyril Barham-Gould

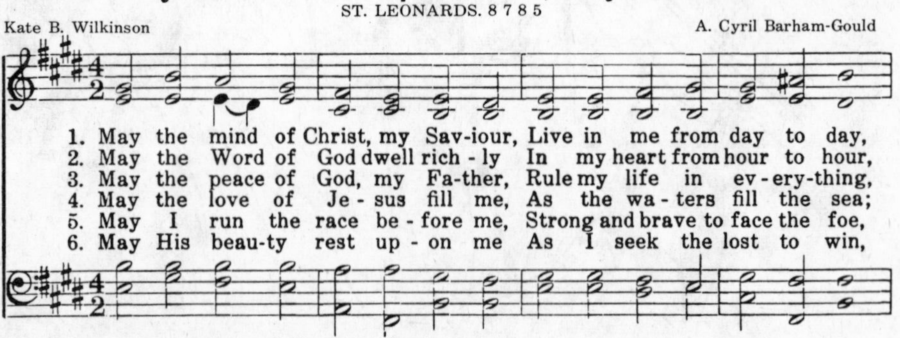
1. May the mind of Christ, my Sav-iour, Live in me from day to day,
2. May the Word of God dwell rich - ly In my heart from hour to hour,
3. May the peace of God, my Fa-ther, Rule my life in ev-ery-thing,
4. May the love of Je - sus fill me, As the wa - ters fill the sea;
5. May I run the race be - fore me, Strong and brave to face the foe,
6. May His beau-ty rest up - on me As I seek the lost to win,

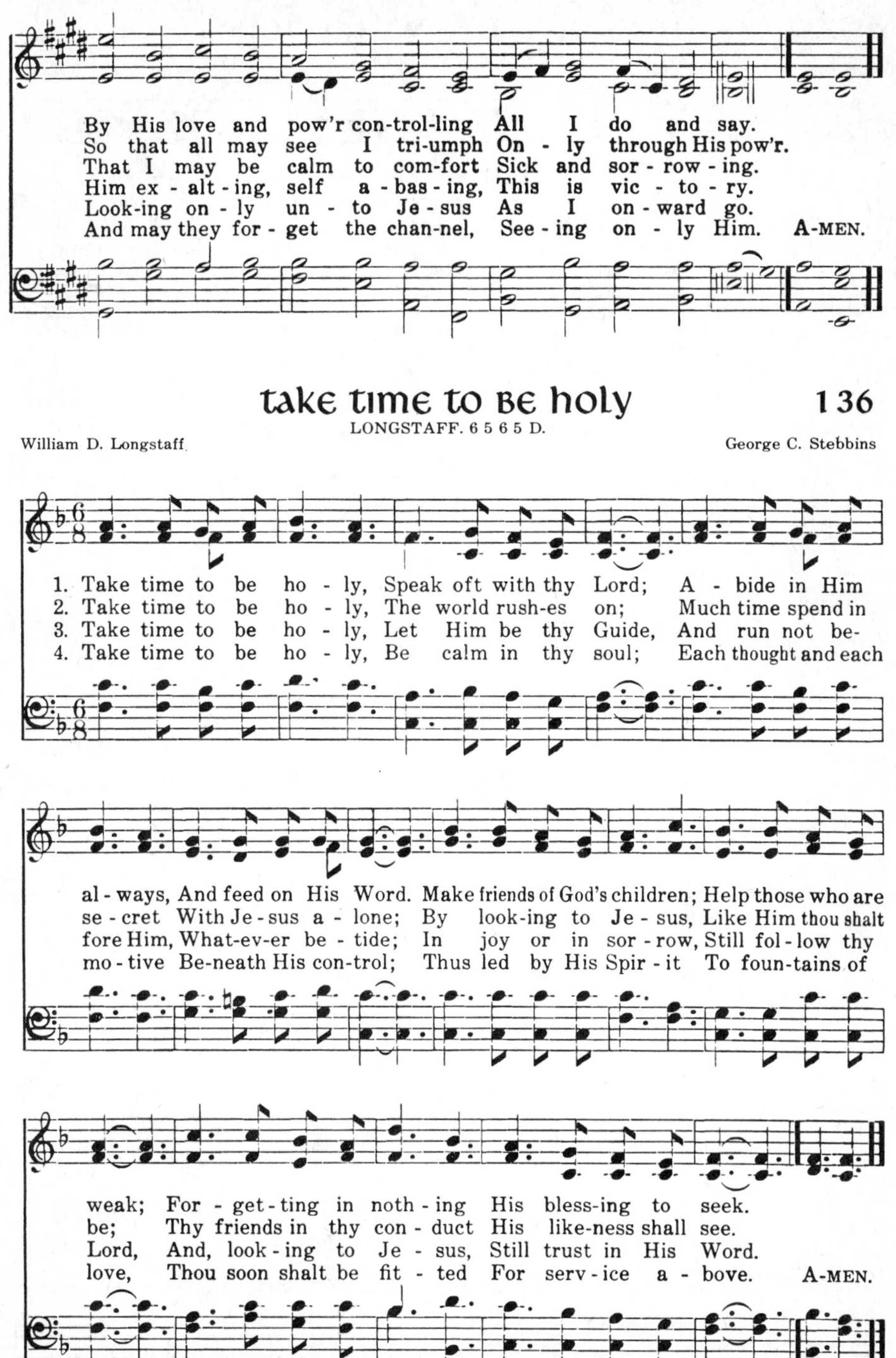
By His love and pow'r con-trol-ling All I do and say.
So that all may see I tri-umph On - ly through His pow'r.
That I may be calm to com-fort Sick and sor - row - ing.
Him ex - alt - ing, self a - bas - ing, This is vic - to - ry.
Look-ing on - ly un - to Je - sus As I on - ward go.
And may they for - get the chan-nel, See - ing on - ly Him. A-MEN.
Take Time to Be Holy
136
LONGSTAFF. 6 5 6 5 D.
William D. Longstaff
George C. Stebbins
1. Take time to be ho - ly, Speak oft with thy Lord; A - bide in Him
2. Take time to be ho - ly, The world rush-es on; Much time spend in
3. Take time to be ho - ly, Let Him be thy Guide, And run not be-
4. Take time to be ho - ly, Be calm in thy soul; Each thought and each
al - ways, And feed on His Word. Make friends of God's children; Help those who are
se - cret With Je - sus a - lone; By look-ing to Je - sus, Like Him thou shalt
fore Him, What-ev-er be - tide; In joy or in sor - row, Still fol - low thy
mo - tive Be-neath His con-trol; Thus led by His Spir - it To foun-tains of
weak; For - get-ting in noth - ing His bless-ing to seek.
be; Thy friends in thy con - duct His like-ness shall see.
Lord, And, look - ing to Je - sus, Still trust in His Word.
love, Thou soon shalt be fit - ted For serv - ice a - bove. A-MEN.

137 teach me thy will, o lord

TEACH ME. 10 10 12 10

Katherine A. Grimes — William M. Runyan

1. Teach me Thy will, O Lord, Teach me Thy way; Teach me to
2. Teach me Thy won-drous grace, Bound-less and free; Lord, let Thy
3. Teach me by pain Thy power, Teach me by love; Teach me to
4. Teach Thou my lips to sing, My heart to praise; Be Thou my

know Thy word, Teach me to pray. What-e'er seems best to Thee, That be my
bless - ed face Shine up - on me. Heal Thou sin's ev-ery smart, Dwell Thou with-
know, each hour, Thou art a - bove. Teach me as seem - eth best In Thee to
Lord and King Through all my days. Teach Thou my soul to cry, "Be Thou, dear

ear - nest plea, So that Thou draw-est me Clos - er each day.
in my heart; Grant that I nev - er part, Sav - iour, from Thee.
find sweet rest; Lean-ing up - on Thy breast, All doubt re - move.
Sav - iour, nigh, Teach me to live, to die, Saved by Thy grace." A - MEN.

138 let me come closer to thee, jesus

LLANTHONY ABBEY. 9 6 9 6

J. L. Lyne — John H. Lester

1. Let me come clos - er to Thee, Je - sus, Oh, clos - er day by day;
2. Let me show forth Thy beau-ty, Je - sus, Like sun-shine on the hills!
3. Yes, like a foun-tain, pre-cious Je - sus, Make me and let me be;
4. In all my heart and will, O Je - sus, Be al - to-geth - er King!
5. Thirsting and hung-'ring for Thee, Je - sus, With bless - ed hun - ger here,

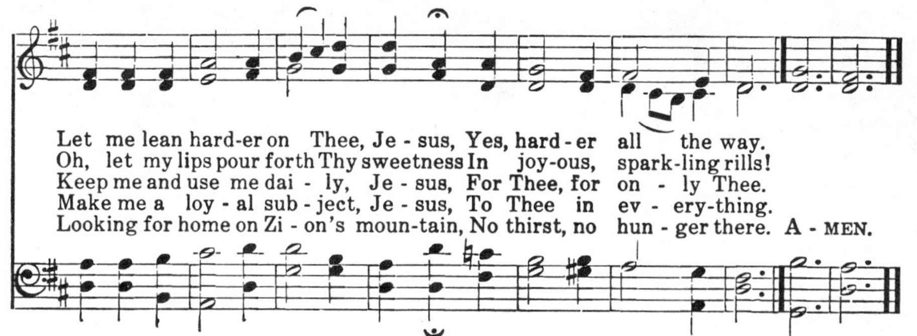
Let me lean hard-er on Thee, Je - sus, Yes, hard - er all the way.
Oh, let my lips pour forth Thy sweetness In joy-ous, spark-ling rills!
Keep me and use me dai - ly, Je - sus, For Thee, for on - ly Thee.
Make me a loy - al sub - ject, Je - sus, To Thee in ev - ery-thing.
Looking for home on Zi - on's moun-tain, No thirst, no hun - ger there. A - MEN.

O Love That Wilt Not Let Me Go **139**

ST. MARGARET. 8 8 8 8 6

George Matheson — Albert L. Peace

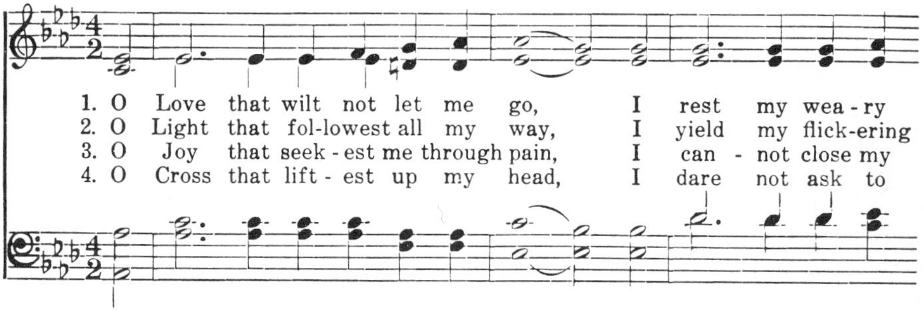

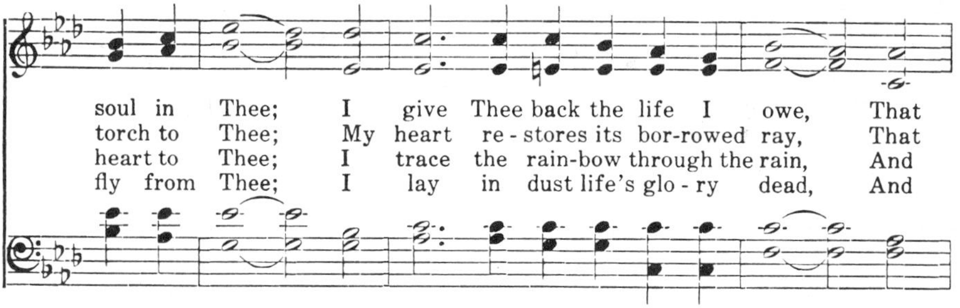

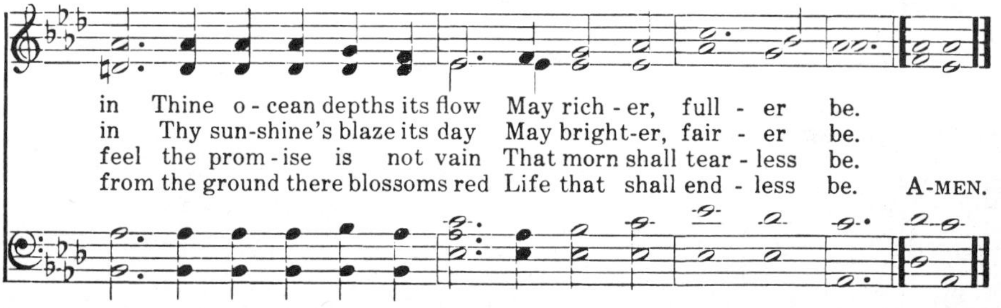

1. O Love that wilt not let me go,
I rest my wea - ry soul in Thee;
I give Thee back the life I owe,
That in Thine o - cean depths its flow
May rich - er, full - er be.

2. O Light that fol-lowest all my way,
I yield my flick-ering torch to Thee;
My heart re - stores its bor-rowed ray,
That in Thy sun-shine's blaze its day
May bright-er, fair - er be.

3. O Joy that seek - est me through pain,
I can - not close my heart to Thee;
I trace the rain-bow through the rain,
And feel the prom - ise is not vain
That morn shall tear - less be.

4. O Cross that lift - est up my head,
I dare not ask to fly from Thee;
I lay in dust life's glo - ry dead,
And from the ground there blossoms red
Life that shall end - less be.

A-MEN.

140 Jesus, Master, Whose I Am

ST. PETERSBURG. 7 7 7 7 7 7

Frances R. Havergal | Dimitri S. Bortniansky

1. Je - sus, Mas - ter, whose I am, Pur - chased Thine a-
2. Oth - er lords have long held sway; Now Thy name a-
3. Je - sus, Mas - ter, I am Thine. Keep me faith - ful,
lone to be By Thy blood, O spot - less Lamb,
lone to bear, Thy dear voice a - lone o - bey,
keep me near; Let Thy pres - ence in me shine,
Shed so will - ing - ly for me, Let my heart be
Is my dai - ly, hour - ly pray'r; Whom have I in
All my home - ward way to cheer. Je - sus, at Thy
all Thine own, Let me live to Thee a - lone.
heav'n but Thee? Noth - ing else my joy can be.
feet I fall; Oh, be Thou my all in all.

Make Me a Captive, Lord 141

PARADOXY. S.M.D.
George Matheson
Donald P. Hustad
1. Make me a cap - tive, Lord, And then I shall be free;
2. My heart is weak and poor Un - til it mas - ter find;
3. My pow'r is faint and low Till I have learned to serve:
4. My will is not my own Till Thou hast made it Thine;
Force me to ren - der up my sword, And I shall con-queror be;
It has no spring of ac - tion sure— It va - ries with the wind;
It wants the need - ed fire to glow, It wants the breeze to nerve;
If it would reach the monarch's throne It must its crown re - sign:
mp
I sink in life's a - larms When by my - self I stand;
It can - not free - ly move Till Thou has wrought its chain;
It can - not drive the world Un - til it - self be driv'n;
It on - ly stands un - bent, A - mid the clash - ing strife,
Im - pris - on me with - in Thine arms, And strong shall be my hand.
En-slave it with Thy match-less love, And death-less it shall reign.
Its flag can on - ly be un-furled When Thou shalt breathe from heav'n.
When on Thy bos - om it has leaned, And found in Thee its life. A-MEN.

142
Lord, speak to me
CANONBURY. L.M.
Frances R. Havergal
Robert Schumann
1. Lord, speak to me, that I may speak In liv-ing ech-oes of Thy tone;
2. O teach me; Lord, that I may teach The pre-cious things Thou dost impart;
3. O fill me with Thy full-ness, Lord, Un-til my ver-y heart o'er-flow
4. O use me, Lord, use e-ven me, Just as Thou wilt, and when, and where;
As Thou hast sought, so let me seek Thy err-ing chil-dren lost and lone.
And wing my words, that they may reach The hid-den depths of many a heart.
In kindling thought and glow-ing word, Thy love to tell, Thy praise to show.
Un-til Thy bless-ed face I see, Thy rest, Thy joy, Thy glo-ry share. AMEN.
143
I'll live for Him
DUNBAR. 8 8 8 6 Ref.
Ralph E. Hudson
C. R. Dunbar
1. My life, my love I give to Thee, Thou Lamb of God who died for me;
2. I now be-lieve Thou dost re-ceive, For Thou hast died that I might live;
3. O Thou who died on Cal-va-ry, To save my soul and make me free,
REF. I'll live for Him who died for me, How hap-py then my life shall be!
D.C. Refrain
Oh, may I ev-er faith-ful be, My Sav-iour and my God!
And now hence-forth I'll trust in Thee, My Sav-iour and my God!
I'll con-se-crate my life to Thee, My Sav-iour and my God!
I'll live for Him who died for me, My Sav-iour and my God!

Take Thou Our Minds, Dear Lord 144

HALL. 10 10 10 10
William H. Foulkes
Calvin W. Laufer
1. Take Thou our minds, dear Lord, we hum - bly pray;
2. Take Thou our hearts, O Christ, they are Thine own;
3. Take Thou our wills, Most High! Hold Thou full sway;
4. Take Thou our - selves, O Lord, heart, mind, and will;
Give us the mind of Christ each pass - ing day;
Come Thou with - in our souls and claim Thy throne;
Have in our in - most souls Thy per - fect way;
Through our sur - ren - dered souls Thy plans ful - fill.
Teach us to know the truth that sets us free;
Help us to shed a - broad Thy death - less love;
Guard Thou each sa - cred hour from self - ish ease;
We yield our - selves to Thee— time, tal - ents, all!
Grant us in all our thoughts to hon - or Thee.
Use us to make the earth like heav'n a - bove.
Guide Thou our or - dered lives as Thou dost please.
We hear, and hence - forth heed, Thy sov - ereign call. A-MEN.

145 I Would Be Like Jesus

WINONA LAKE. C.M. Ref.

James Rowe — Bentley D. Ackley

1. Earth-ly pleas-ures vain-ly call me, I would be like Je - sus;
2. He has bro-ken ev-ery fet-ter, I would be like Je - sus;
3. All the way from earth to glo-ry, I would be like Je - sus;
4. That in heav-en He may meet me, I would be like Je - sus;
would be like Je-sus;
Noth-ing world-ly shall en-thrall me, I would be like Je - sus.
That my soul may serve Him bet-ter, I would be like Je - sus.
Tell-ing o'er and o'er the sto-ry, I would be like Je - sus.
That His words "Well done" may greet me, I would be like Je - sus.
would be like Je-sus.
Refrain
Be like Je-sus, this my song, In the home and in the throng;
Be like Je-sus, all day long! I would be like Je-sus.

Oh, to Be Like Thee

RONDINELLA. 10 9 10 9 Ref.

Thomas O. Chisholm — William J. Kirkpatrick

1. Oh, to be like Thee! bless-ed Re-deem-er, This is my con-stant long-ing and prayer. Glad-ly I'll for-feit all of earth's treas-ures, Je-sus, Thy per-fect like-ness to wear.
2. Oh, to be like Thee! full of com-pas-sion, Lov-ing, for-giv-ing, ten-der and kind, Help-ing the help-less, cheer-ing the faint-ing, Seek-ing the wan-dering sin-ner to find.
3. Oh, to be like Thee! low-ly in spir-it, Ho-ly and harm-less, pa-tient and brave; Meek-ly en-dur-ing cru-el re-proach-es, Will-ing to suf-fer oth-ers to save.
4. Oh, to be like Thee! while I am plead-ing, Pour out Thy Spir-it, fill with Thy love; Make me a tem-ple meet for Thy dwell-ing, Fit me for life and heav-en a-bove.

REFRAIN

Oh, to be like Thee! Oh, to be like Thee, bless-ed Re-deem-er, pure as Thou art! Come in Thy sweet-ness, come in Thy full-ness; Stamp Thine own im-age deep on my heart.

147 Be Thou My Vision

SLANE. 10 10 10 10

Ancient Irish
Trans. by Mary E. Byrne
Versified by Eleanor H. Hull

Traditional Irish Melody
Harm. by David Evans

Unison

1. Be Thou my Vi - sion, O Lord of my heart;
2. Be Thou my Wis - dom, and Thou my true Word;
3. Rich - es I heed not, nor man's emp - ty praise,
4. High King of heav - en, my vic - to - ry won,

Nought be all else to me, save that Thou art—
I ev - er with Thee and Thou with me, Lord;
Thou mine in - her - it - ance, now and al - ways:
May I reach heav - en's joys, O bright heaven's Sun!

Thou my best thought, by day or by night,
Thou my great Fa - ther, I Thy true son;
Thou and Thou on - ly, first in my heart,
Heart of my own heart, what - ev - er be - fall,

Wak - ing or sleep - ing, Thy pres - ence my light.
Thou in me dwell - ing, and I with Thee one.
High King of heav - en, my Treas - ure Thou art.
Still be my Vi - sion, O Rul - er of all. A - MEN.

SEARCH ME, O GOD

MAORI. 10 10 10 10
J. Edwin Orr
Maori Melody
Arr. by Donald P. Hustad
1. Search me, O God, and know my heart to - day;
2. I praise Thee, Lord, for cleans - ing me from sin:
3. Lord, take my life, and make it whol - ly Thine:
4. O Ho - ly Ghost, re - vi - val comes from Thee:
Try me, O Sav - iour, know my thoughts, I pray:
Ful - fill Thy Word, and make me pure with - in;
Fill my poor heart with Thy great love di - vine;
Send a re - vi - val, start the work in me:
See if there be some wick - ed way in me:
Fill me with fire, where once I burned with shame:
Take all my will, my pas - sion, self and pride;
Thy Word de - clares Thou wilt sup - ply our need:
Cleanse me from ev - ery sin, And set me free.
Grant my de - sire to mag - ni - fy Thy name.
I now sur - ren - der: Lord, in me a - bide.
For bless - ing now, O Lord, I hum - bly plead.

149 I need thee every hour

NEED. 6 4 6 4 Ref.

Annie S. Hawks and Robert Lowry

Robert Lowry

1. I need Thee ev - ery hour, Most gra - cious Lord; No ten - der voice like
2. I need Thee ev - ery hour, Stay Thou near by; Temp-ta-tions lose their
3. I need Thee ev - ery hour, In joy or pain; Come quick-ly and a-
4. I need Thee ev - ery hour, Most Ho - ly One; O make me Thine in-

Refrain

Thine Can peace af - ford.
power When Thou art nigh. I need Thee, O I need Thee; Ev - ery hour I
bide, Or life is vain.
deed, Thou bless - ed Son!

need Thee; O bless me now, my Sav - iour, I come to Thee!

150 more love to thee

MORE LOVE TO THEE. 6 4 6 4 6 6 4 4

Elizabeth P. Prentiss

William H. Doane

1. More love to Thee, O Christ, More love to Thee! Hear Thou the
2. Once earth - ly joy I craved, Sought peace and rest; Now Thee a-
3. Let sor - row do its work, Send grief and pain; Sweet are Thy
4. Then shall my lat - est breath Whis - per Thy praise; This be the

prayer I make On bend - ed knee; This is my ear - nest plea:
lone I seek, Give what is best; This all my prayer shall be:
mes - sen-gers, Sweet their re - frain, When they can sing with me:
part - ing cry My heart shall raise; This still its prayer shall be:

More love, O Christ, to Thee, More love to Thee, More love to Thee! A-MEN.
Beneath the Cross of Jesus
151
ST. CHRISTOPHER. 7 6 8 6 8 6 8 6
Elizabeth C. Clephane
Frederick C. Maker
1. Be - neath the cross of Je - sus I fain would take my stand—
2. Up - on that cross of Je - sus Mine eye at times can see
3. I take, O cross, thy shad - ow For my a - bid - ing - place;
The shad - ow of a might - y Rock With - in a wea - ry land;
The ver - y dy - ing form of One Who suf - fered there for me;
I ask no oth - er sun-shine than The sun - shine of His face;
A home with - in the wil - der - ness, A rest up - on the way,
And from my smit - ten heart with tears Two won - ders I con - fess—
Con - tent to let the world go by, To know no gain nor loss,
From the burn-ing of the noon-tide heat, And the bur-den of the day.
The won - ders of re - deem - ing love And my un - wor - thi - ness.
My sin - ful self my on - ly shame, My glo - ry all the cross. A-MEN.

152 LIVING FOR JESUS

LIVING. 10 10 10 10 Ref.

Thomas O. Chisholm — C. Harold Lowden

1. Liv-ing for Je-sus a life that is true, Striv-ing to please Him in all that I do; Yield-ing al-le-giance, glad-heart-ed and free, This is the path-way of bless-ing for me.
2. Liv-ing for Je-sus who died in my place, Bear-ing on Cal-vary my sin and dis-grace; Such love con-strains me to an-swer His call, Fol-low His lead-ing and give Him my all.
3. Liv-ing for Je-sus wher-ev-er I am, Do-ing each du-ty in His ho-ly name; Will-ing to suf-fer af-flic-tion and loss, Deem-ing each tri-al a part of my cross.
4. Liv-ing for Je-sus through earth's little while, My dear-est treas-ure, the light of His smile; Seek-ing the lost ones He died to re-deem, Bring-ing the wea-ry to find rest in Him.
REFRAIN
O Je-sus, Lord and Sav-iour, I give my-self to Thee, For Thou, in Thy a-tone-ment, Didst give Thy-self for me; I own no oth-er Mas-ter, My heart shall be Thy

plore, Wash me and keep me Thine for - ev - er - more.
now im-plore, Wash and keep, O wash and keep me Thine for - ev - er - more.

SAVIOUR, MY HEART IS THINE 158

ORLEANS. 6 4 6 4 4 4 6 4

Source Unknown
Alt. by George C. Stebbins

George C. Stebbins

1. Sav - iour, my heart is Thine, Keep it for me; May ev - ery thought of mine Glo - ri - fy Thee. Glo - ri - fy Thee, Glo - ri - fy Thee; May ev-ery thought of mine Glo - ri - fy Thee.
2. Sav - iour, my will is Thine, Keep it for me; May ev - ery act of mine Be done for Thee. Be done for Thee, Be done for Thee; May ev-ery act of mine Be done for Thee.
3. Sav - iour, my life is Thine, Keep it for me; May ev - ery hour of mine Be lived for Thee. Be lived for Thee, Be lived for Thee; May ev-ery hour of mine Be lived for Thee.
4. Sav - iour, my all is Thine, Keep it for me; May all I have, O Lord, Be used for Thee. Be used for Thee, Be used for Thee; May all I have, O Lord, Be used for Thee. A-MEN.

159 IS YOUR ALL ON THE ALTAR?

HOFFMAN. 12 9 12 9 Ref.

Elisha A. Hoffman — Elisha A. Hoffman

1. You have longed for sweet peace and for faith to in-crease, And have earn-est-ly, fer-vent-ly prayed; But you can-not have rest, or be per-fect-ly blest, Un-til all on the al-tar is laid.
2. Would you walk with the Lord in the light of His Word, And have peace and con-tent-ment al-way? You must do His sweet will to be free from all ill, On the al-tar your all you must lay.
3. Oh, we nev-er can know what the Lord will be-stow Of the bless-ings for which we have prayed, Till our bod-y and soul He doth ful-ly con-trol, And our all on the al-tar is laid.
4. Who can tell all the love He will send from a-bove, And how hap-py our hearts will be made, Of the fel-low-ship sweet we shall share at His feet, When our all on the al-tar is laid.
REFRAIN
Is your all on the al-tar of sac-ri-fice laid? Your heart, does the Spir-it con-trol? You can on-ly be blest and have peace and sweet rest, As you yield Him your bod-y and soul.

Draw Me Nearer

I AM THINE. 10 7 10 7 Ref.

Fanny J. Crosby

William H. Doane

1. I am Thine, O Lord, I have heard Thy voice, And it told Thy love to me; But I long to rise in the arms of faith, And be clos - er drawn to Thee.
2. Con - se - crate me now to Thy serv - ice, Lord, By the power of grace di - vine; Let my soul look up with a stead-fast hope, And my will be lost in Thine.
3. Oh, the pure de - light of a sin - gle hour That be- fore Thy throne I spend, When I kneel in prayer, and with Thee, my God, I com-mune as friend with friend!
4. There are depths of love that I can - not know Till I cross the nar - row sea; There are heights of joy that I may not reach Till I rest in peace with Thee.
Refrain
Draw me near - er, near - er, near - er, near - er, bless - ed Lord, To the cross where Thou hast died; Draw me near - er, near - er, near-er, bless-ed Lord, To Thy pre-cious, bleed-ing side.

161 SAVIOUR, THY DYING LOVE

SOMETHING FOR THEE. 10 10 12 10

Sylvanus D. Phelps — Robert Lowry

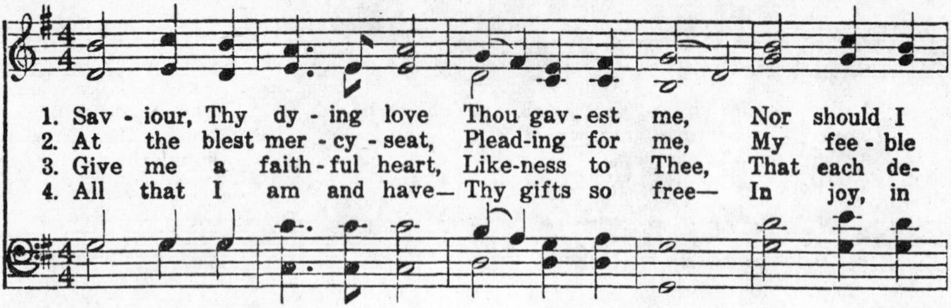

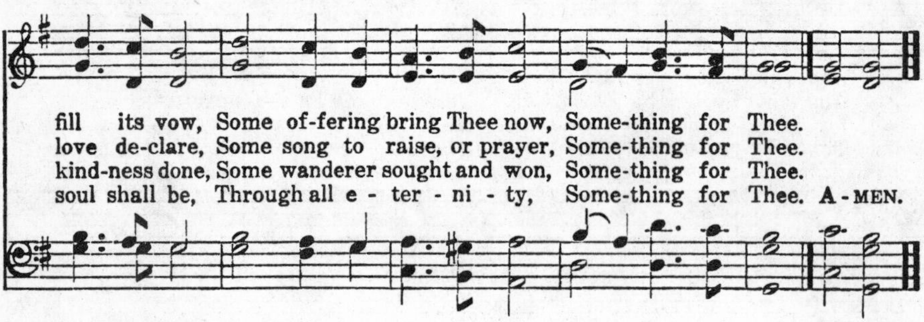

1. Sav - iour, Thy dy - ing love Thou gav - est me, Nor should I aught with-hold, Dear Lord, from Thee: In love my soul would bow, My heart ful-fill its vow, Some of-fering bring Thee now, Some-thing for Thee.
2. At the blest mer - cy - seat, Plead-ing for me, My fee - ble faith looks up, Je - sus, to Thee: Help me the cross to bear, Thy won-drous love de-clare, Some song to raise, or prayer, Some-thing for Thee.
3. Give me a faith - ful heart, Like-ness to Thee, That each de-part - ing day Henceforth may see Some work of love be - gun, Some deed of kind-ness done, Some wanderer sought and won, Some-thing for Thee.
4. All that I am and have— Thy gifts so free— In joy, in grief, through life, Dear Lord, for Thee! And when Thy face I see, My ran-somed soul shall be, Through all e - ter - ni - ty, Some-thing for Thee. A - MEN.

162 TAKE MY LIFE, AND LET IT BE

HENDON. 7 7 7 7 7

Frances R. Havergal, alt. — H. A. César Malan

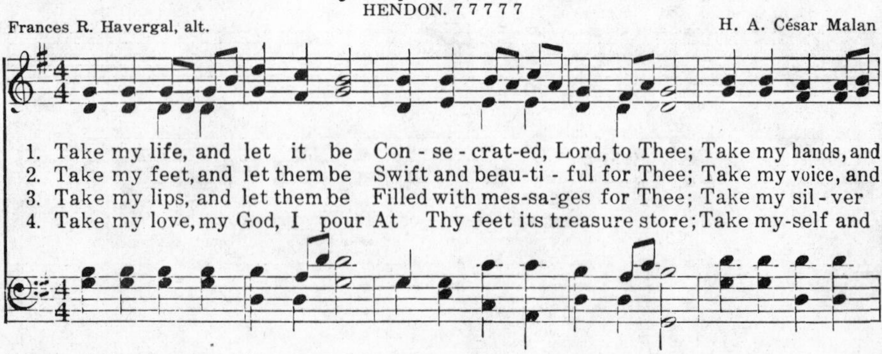

1. Take my life, and let it be Con - se - crat-ed, Lord, to Thee; Take my hands, and
2. Take my feet, and let them be Swift and beau-ti - ful for Thee; Take my voice, and
3. Take my lips, and let them be Filled with mes-sa-ges for Thee; Take my sil - ver
4. Take my love, my God, I pour At Thy feet its treasure store; Take my-self and

let them move At the im-pulse of Thy love, At the im-pulse of Thy love.
let me sing Al-ways, on-ly, for my King, Al-ways, on-ly, for my King.
and my gold, Not a mite would I with-hold, Not a mite would I with-hold.
I will be Ev-er, on-ly, all for Thee, Ev-er, on-ly, all for Thee. A-MEN.

MY JESUS, I LOVE THEE 163

CARITAS. 11 11 11 11

William R. Featherstone — Adoniram J. Gordon

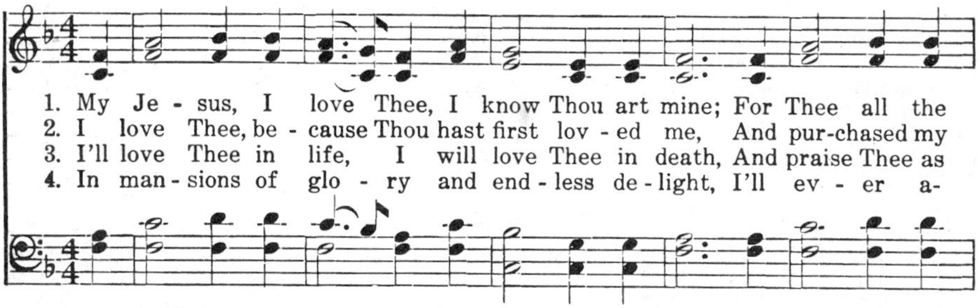

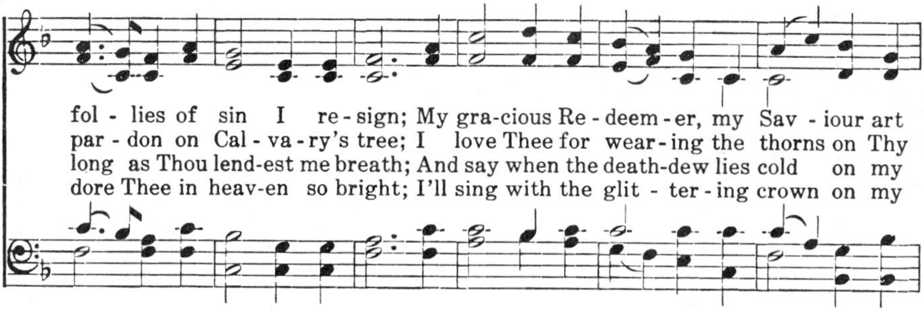

1. My Je - sus, I love Thee, I know Thou art mine; For Thee all the fol - lies of sin I re - sign; My gra-cious Re - deem - er, my Sav - iour art Thou; If ev - er I loved Thee, my Je - sus, 'tis now.

2. I love Thee, be - cause Thou hast first lov - ed me, And pur-chased my par - don on Cal - va - ry's tree; I love Thee for wear - ing the thorns on Thy brow; If ev - er I loved Thee, my Je - sus, 'tis now.

3. I'll love Thee in life, I will love Thee in death, And praise Thee as long as Thou lend-est me breath; And say when the death-dew lies cold on my brow, If ev - er I loved Thee, my Je - sus, 'tis now.

4. In man - sions of glo - ry and end - less de - light, I'll ev - er a - dore Thee in heav-en so bright; I'll sing with the glit - ter - ing crown on my brow, If ev - er I loved Thee, my Je - sus, 'tis now. A - MEN.

164 Lord, I Have Shut the Door

SANCTUARY. 6 4 6 4 D.

William M. Runyan — William M. Runyan

1. Lord, I have shut the door, Speak now the word Which in the din and throng Could not be heard; Hushed now my in - ner heart, Whis-per Thy will, While I have come a-part, While all is still.

2. Lord, I have shut the door, Here do I bow; Speak, for my soul at - tent Turns to Thee now. Re - buke Thou what is vain, Coun-sel my soul, Thy ho - ly will re-veal, My will con - trol.

3. In this blest qui - et - ness Clam - or - ings cease; Here in Thy pres - ence dwells In - fi - nite peace; Yon - der, the strife and cry, Yon - der, the sin: Lord, I have shut the door, Thou art with - in!

4. Lord, I have shut the door, Strength-en my heart; Yon - der a - waits the task— I share a part. On - ly through grace be-stowed May I be true; Here, while alone with Thee, My strength re - new. A - MEN.

165 A Charge to Keep I Have

BOYLSTON. S.M.

Charles Wesley — Lowell Mason

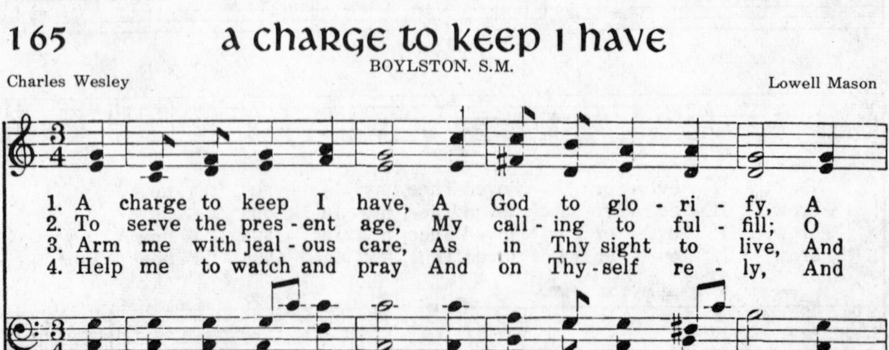
1. A charge to keep I have, A God to glo - ri - fy, A
2. To serve the pres - ent age, My call - ing to ful - fill; O
3. Arm me with jeal - ous care, As in Thy sight to live, And
4. Help me to watch and pray And on Thy - self re - ly, And

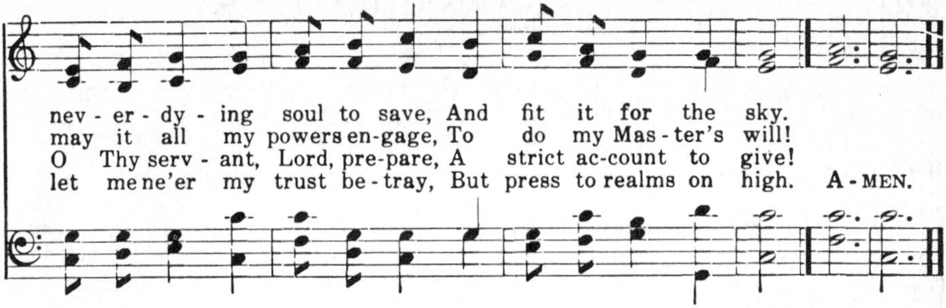

nev - er - dy - ing soul to save, And fit it for the sky.
may it all my powers en-gage, To do my Mas - ter's will!
O Thy serv - ant, Lord, pre-pare, A strict ac-count to give!
let me ne'er my trust be - tray, But press to realms on high. A - MEN.

NEARER, STILL NEARER 166

MORRIS. 9 10 9 10

Leila N. Morris — Leila N. Morris

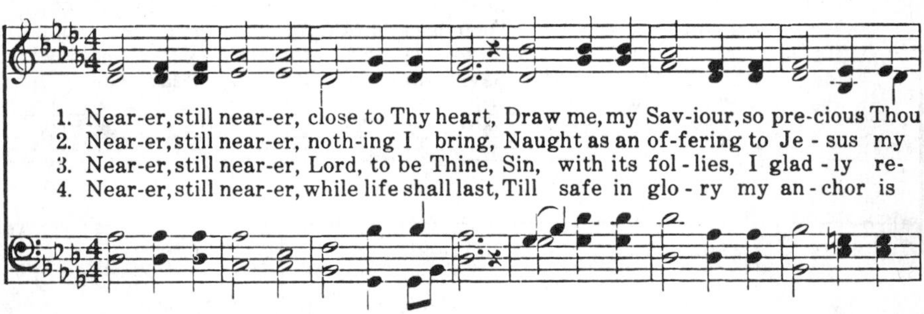

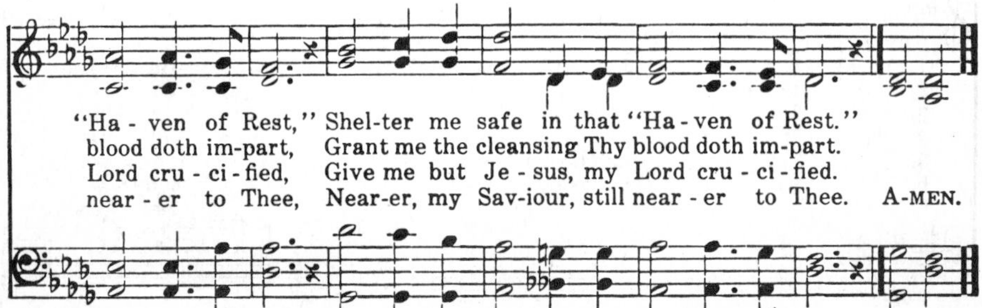

1. Near-er, still near-er, close to Thy heart, Draw me, my Sav-iour, so pre-cious Thou
2. Near-er, still near-er, noth-ing I bring, Naught as an of-fering to Je - sus my
3. Near-er, still near-er, Lord, to be Thine, Sin, with its fol - lies, I glad - ly re-
4. Near-er, still near-er, while life shall last, Till safe in glo - ry my an - chor is

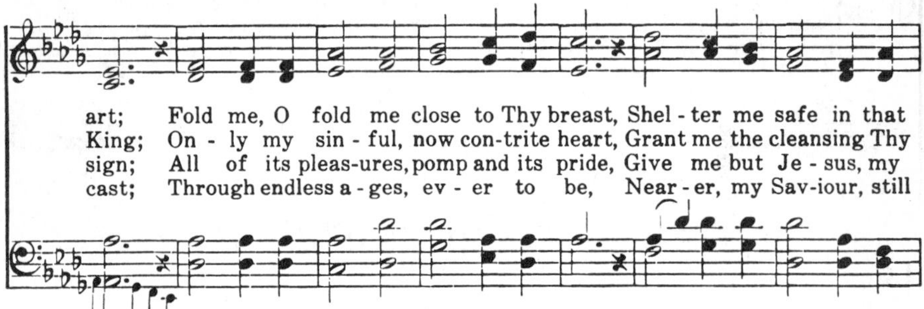

art; Fold me, O fold me close to Thy breast, Shel - ter me safe in that
King; On - ly my sin - ful, now con-trite heart, Grant me the cleansing Thy
sign; All of its pleas-ures, pomp and its pride, Give me but Je - sus, my
cast; Through endless a - ges, ev - er to be, Near - er, my Sav-iour, still

"Ha - ven of Rest," Shel-ter me safe in that "Ha - ven of Rest."
blood doth im-part, Grant me the cleansing Thy blood doth im-part.
Lord cru - ci - fied, Give me but Je - sus, my Lord cru - ci - fied.
near - er to Thee, Near-er, my Sav-iour, still near - er to Thee. A-MEN.

167 My Faith Looks Up to Thee

OLIVET. 6 6 4 6 6 6 4

Ray Palmer — Lowell Mason

1. My faith looks up to Thee, Thou Lamb of Cal - va - ry, Sav - iour di - vine! Now hear me while I pray, Take all my guilt a - way, O let me from this day Be whol - ly Thine!
2. May Thy rich grace im - part Strength to my faint - ing heart, My zeal in - spire; As Thou hast died for me, O may my love to Thee Pure, warm, and changeless be, A liv - ing fire!
3. While life's dark maze I tread, And griefs a - round me spread, Be Thou my Guide; Bid dark - ness turn to day, Wipe sor - row's tears a - way, Nor let me ev - er stray From Thee a - side.
4. When ends life's tran - sient dream, When death's cold, sul - len stream Shall o'er me roll; Blest Sav - iour, then, in love, Fear and dis- trust re-move; O bear me safe a - bove, A ran-somed soul! A-MEN.

168 Speak, Lord, in the Stillness

QUIETUDE. 6 5 6 5

E. May Grimes — Harold Green

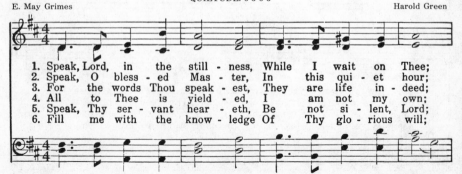

1. Speak, Lord, in the still - ness, While I wait on Thee;
2. Speak, O bless - ed Mas - ter, In this qui - et hour;
3. For the words Thou speak - est, They are life in - deed;
4. All to Thee is yield - ed, I am not my own;
5. Speak, Thy ser - vant hear - eth, Be not si - lent, Lord;
6. Fill me with the know - ledge Of Thy glo - rious will;

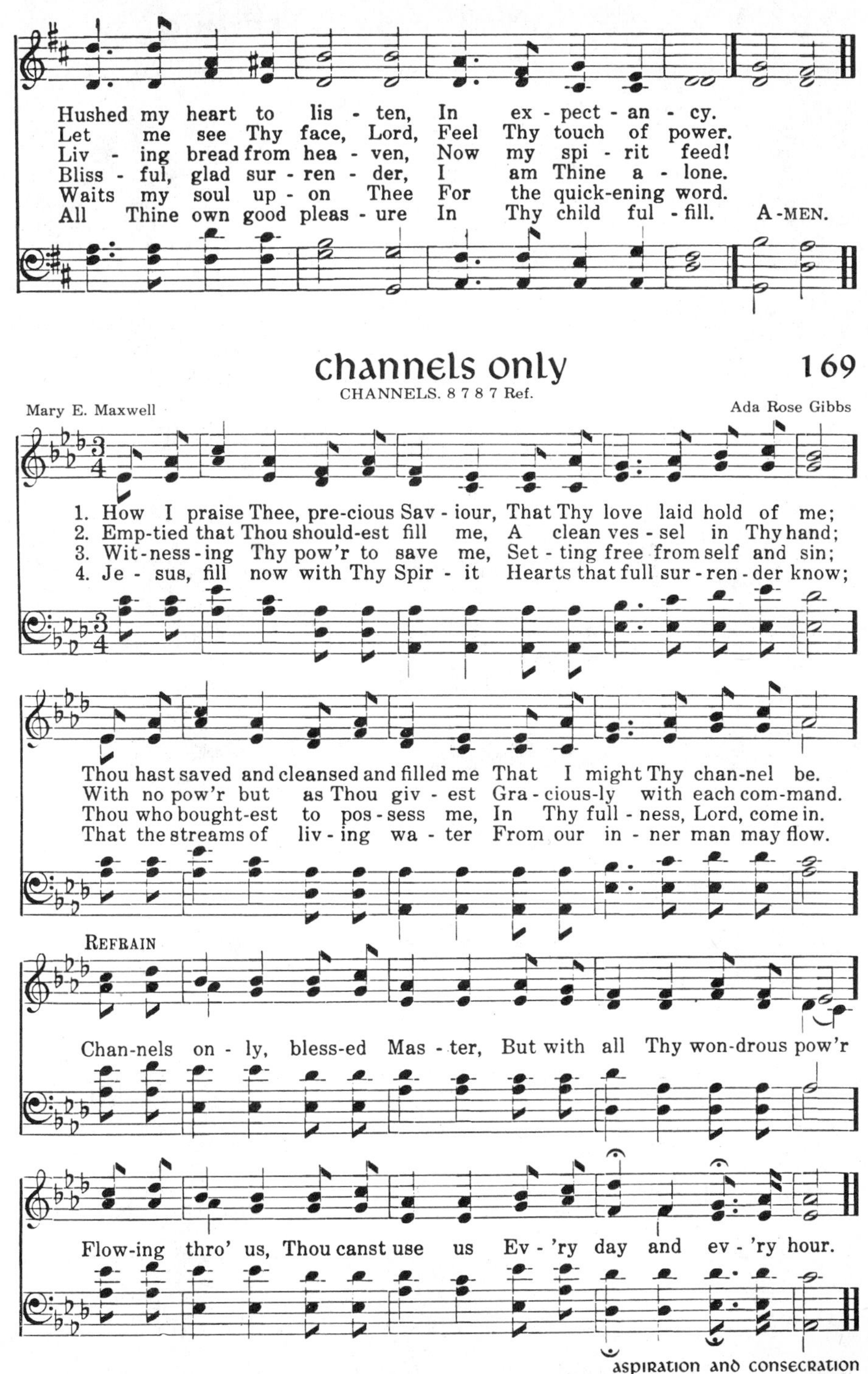

Hushed my heart to lis - ten, In ex - pect - an - cy.
Let me see Thy face, Lord, Feel Thy touch of power.
Liv - ing bread from hea - ven, Now my spi - rit feed!
Bliss - ful, glad sur - ren - der, I am Thine a - lone.
Waits my soul up - on Thee For the quick-ening word.
All Thine own good pleas - ure In Thy child ful - fill. A-MEN.
channels only
169
CHANNELS. 8 7 8 7 Ref.
Mary E. Maxwell
Ada Rose Gibbs
1. How I praise Thee, pre-cious Sav - iour, That Thy love laid hold of me;
2. Emp-tied that Thou should-est fill me, A clean ves - sel in Thy hand;
3. Wit-ness-ing Thy pow'r to save me, Set - ting free from self and sin;
4. Je - sus, fill now with Thy Spir - it Hearts that full sur - ren - der know;
Thou hast saved and cleansed and filled me That I might Thy chan-nel be.
With no pow'r but as Thou giv - est Gra - cious-ly with each com-mand.
Thou who bought-est to pos - sess me, In Thy full - ness, Lord, come in.
That the streams of liv - ing wa - ter From our in - ner man may flow.
Refrain
Chan-nels on - ly, bless-ed Mas - ter, But with all Thy won-drous pow'r
Flow-ing thro' us, Thou canst use us Ev - 'ry day and ev - 'ry hour.

170 Love Divine, All Loves Excelling

BLAENWERN. 8 7 8 7 D.

Charles Wesley — William Penfro Rowlands

1. Love Di - vine, all loves ex - cel - ling, Joy of heav'n, to earth come down;
2. Breathe, O breathe Thy lov - ing Spir - it In - to ev - ery troub - led breast!
3. Come, al - might - y to de - liv - er, Let us all Thy life re - ceive;
4. Fin - ish then Thy new cre - a - tion, Pure and spot - less let us be;
Fix in us Thy hum - ble dwell - ing, All Thy faith - ful mer - cies crown:
Let us all in Thee in - her - it, Let us find that sec - ond rest.
Sud - den - ly re - turn, and nev - er, Nev - er - more Thy tem - ples leave:
Let us see Thy great sal - va - tion Per - fect - ly re - stored in Thee:
Je - sus, Thou art all com - pas - sion, Pure, un - bound - ed love Thou art:
Take a - way our bent to sin - ning, Al - pha and O - me - ga be;
Thee we would be al - ways bless - ing, Serve Thee as Thy hosts a - bove,
Changed from glo - ry in - to glo - ry, Till in heav'n we take our place,
Vis - it us with Thy sal - va - tion; En - ter ev - ery trem - bling heart.
End of faith, as its be - gin - ning, Set our hearts at lib - er - ty.
Pray and praise Thee with - out ceas - ing, Glo - ry in Thy per - fect love.
Till we cast our crowns before Thee, Lost in won - der, love and praise. A - MEN.

See alternate tune on opposite page

Lord, Thou Lov'st the Cheerful Giver

BEECHER. 8 7 8 7 D.

Robert Murray

John Zundel

1. Lord, Thou lov'st the cheer-ful giv - er, Who with o - pen heart and hand
2. We are Thine, Thy mer - cy sought us, Found us in death's dread-ful way,
3. Blest by Thee with gifts and gra - ces, May we heed Thy church's call;
4. Sav - iour, Thou hast free - ly giv - en All the bless-ings we en - joy,
Bless-es free - ly, as a riv - er That re - fresh - es all the land.
To the fold in safe - ty brought us, Nev - er - more from Thee to stray.
Glad - ly in all times and pla - ces Give to Thee who giv - est all.
Earth-ly store and bread of heav - en, Love and peace with - out al - loy;
Grant us then the grace of giv - ing With a spir - it large and free,
Thine own life Thou free - ly gav - est As an off - 'ring on the cross,
Thou hast bought us, and no long - er Can we claim to be our own;
Hum - bly now we bow be - fore Thee, And our all to Thee re - sign;
That our life and all our liv - ing We may con - se - crate to Thee.
For each sin - ner whom Thou sav - est From e - ter - nal shame and loss.
Ev - er free and ev - er strong-er, We shall serve Thee, Lord, a - lone.
For the king-dom, pow'r and glo - ry Are, O Lord, for - ev - er Thine. A-MEN.

172 O Jesus, I Have Promised

ANGEL'S STORY. 7 6 7 6 D.

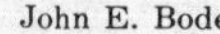

John E. Bode — Arthur H. Mann

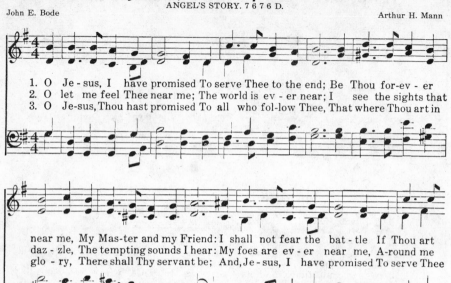

1. O Je-sus, I have promised To serve Thee to the end; Be Thou for-ev-er
2. O let me feel Thee near me; The world is ev-er near; I see the sights that
3. O Je-sus, Thou hast promised To all who fol-low Thee, That where Thou art in

near me, My Mas-ter and my Friend: I shall not fear the bat-tle If Thou art
daz-zle, The tempting sounds I hear: My foes are ev-er near me, A-round me
glo-ry, There shall Thy servant be; And, Je-sus, I have promised To serve Thee

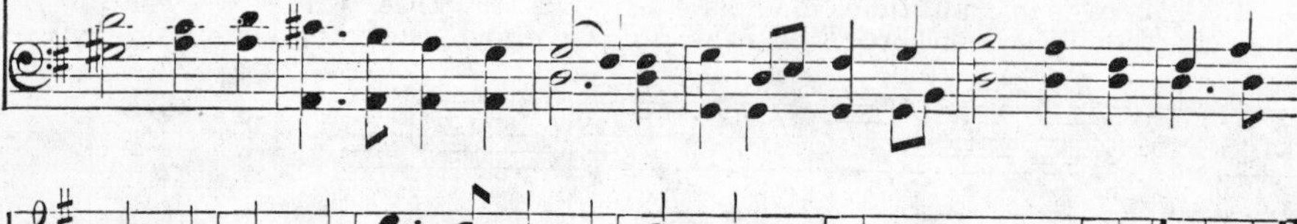

by my side, Nor wan-der from the path-way If Thou wilt be my guide.
and with-in; But, Je-sus, draw Thou near-er, And shield my soul from sin.
to the end; O give me grace to fol-low, My Mas-ter and my Friend. A-MEN.

Music used by permission of E. R. Goodliffe.

173 Holy Ghost, with Light Divine

MERCY. 7 7 7 7

Andrew Reed — Louis M. Gottschalk, Arr. by Edwin P. Parker

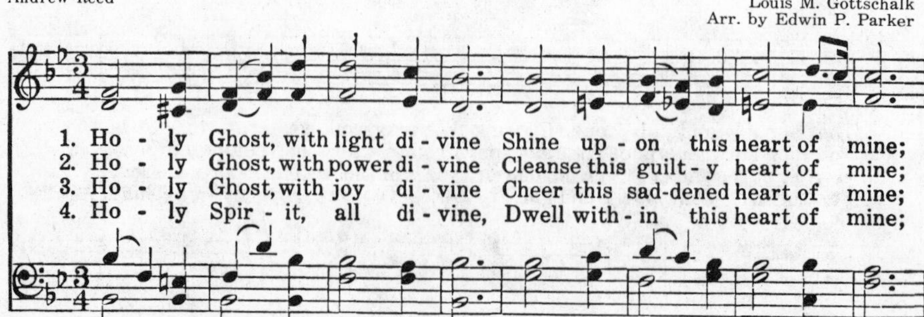
1. Ho-ly Ghost, with light di-vine Shine up-on this heart of mine;
2. Ho-ly Ghost, with power di-vine Cleanse this guilt-y heart of mine;
3. Ho-ly Ghost, with joy di-vine Cheer this sad-dened heart of mine;
4. Ho-ly Spir-it, all di-vine, Dwell with-in this heart of mine;

Chase the shades of night a - way, Turn my dark-ness in - to day.
Long hath sin, with-out con-trol, Held do - min - ion o'er my soul.
Bid my man - y woes de - part, Heal my wound-ed, bleed-ing heart.
Cast down ev - ery i - dol-throne, Reign su - preme, and reign a-lone. A-MEN.
thy will, not mine, be done
174
VOLUNTAS DEI. 10 10 10 11
Joseph C. Macaulay
Joseph C. Macaulay
1. "Thy will, not mine, be done, Fa - ther, I pray," Deep in Geth-
2. "Thy will, not mine, be done," teach me to say, Not as un-
3. Thy will, not mine, be done, in life and death! Thy sov-'reign
4. Thy will, not mine, be done! Je - sus, my Lord, Bind now my
sem - a - ne hear Je - sus say, Fac - ing the cross of shame, an-guish and
will - ing - ly, 'neath ty-rant's sway, But in sweet vas - sal-age, drawn by Thy
right I own, Who giv-est breath. Choose Thou my way, O Lord, Thou know-est
heart to Thee with love's strong cord; Teach me to self to die, to Thee to
woe, Drain - ing the cup of sor - row, life to be - stow.
grace, Glad - ly o - bey - ing till I look on Thy face.
best; On - ly in Thy blest will my soul finds its rest.
live, Help me, in glad sur - ren - der, my all to give. A-MEN.

175 Spirit of God, descend upon my heart

MORECAMBE. 10 10 10 10

George Croly — Frederick C. Atkinson

1. Spir - it of God, de - scend up - on my heart;
2. I ask no dream, no proph - et ec - sta - sies,
3. Hast Thou not bid us love Thee, God and King?
4. Teach me to feel that Thou art al - ways nigh;
5. Teach me to love Thee as Thine an - gels love,
Wean it from earth, through all its puls - es move;
No sud - den rend - ing of the veil of clay,
All, all Thine own, soul, heart and strength and mind.
Teach me the strug - gles of the soul to bear,
One ho - ly pas - sion fill - ing all my frame;
Stoop to my weak - ness, might - y as Thou art,
No an - gel vis - it - ant, no o - pening skies;
I see Thy cross— there teach my heart to cling:
To check the ris - ing doubt, the reb - el sigh;
The bap - tism of the heaven - de - scend - ed Dove,
And make me love Thee as I ought to love.
But take the dim - ness of my soul a - way.
O let me seek Thee, and O let me find.
Teach me the pa - tience of un - an - swered prayer.
My heart an al - tar, and Thy love the flame. A-MEN.

Holy Spirit, Breathe on Me

TRUETT. 7 6 8 6 Ref.

Edwin Hatch
Alt. by B. B. McKinney

B. B. McKinney

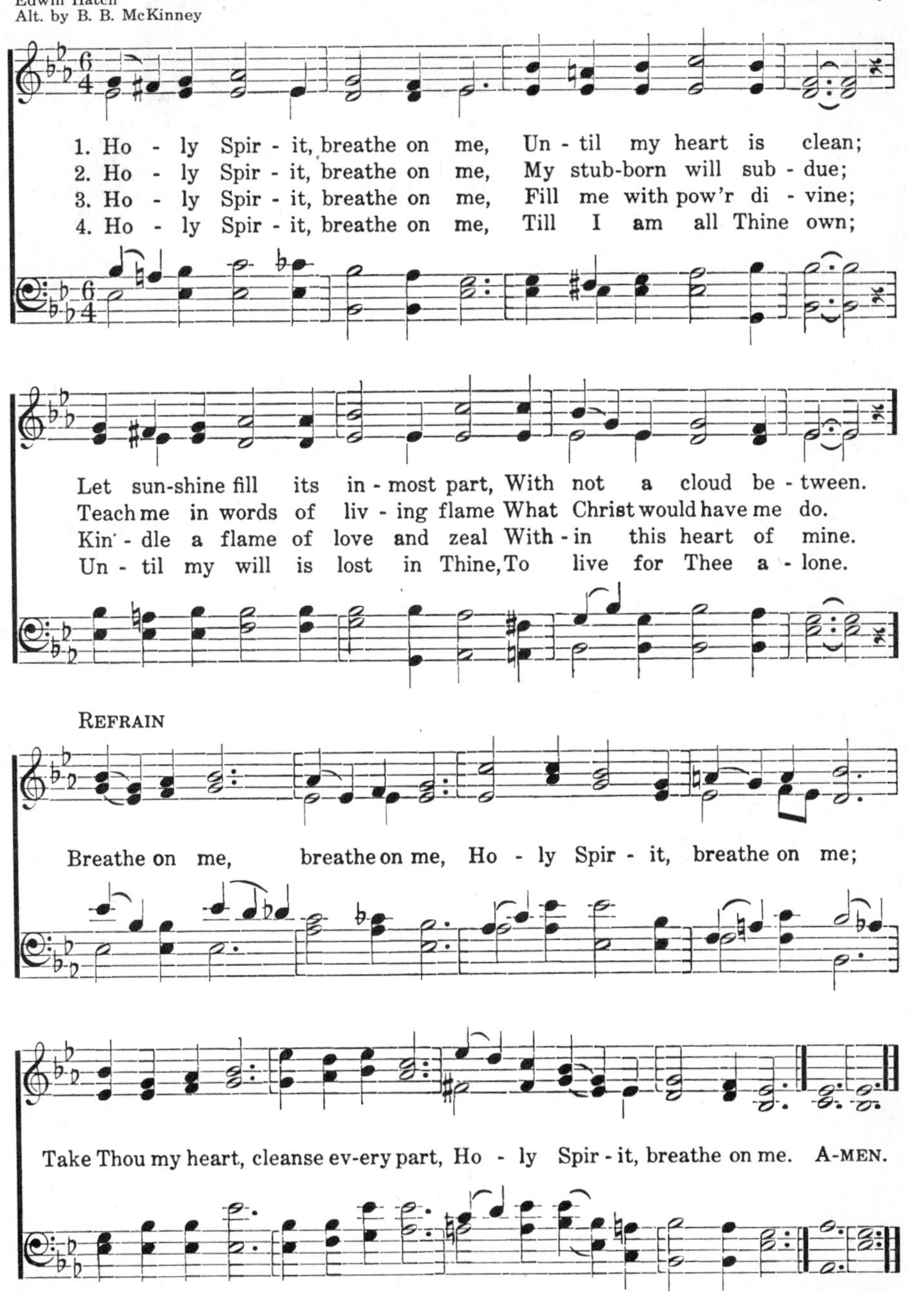
1. Ho - ly Spir - it, breathe on me, Un - til my heart is clean;
2. Ho - ly Spir - it, breathe on me, My stub-born will sub - due;
3. Ho - ly Spir - it, breathe on me, Fill me with pow'r di - vine;
4. Ho - ly Spir - it, breathe on me, Till I am all Thine own;
Let sun-shine fill its in - most part, With not a cloud be - tween.
Teach me in words of liv - ing flame What Christ would have me do.
Kin - dle a flame of love and zeal With - in this heart of mine.
Un - til my will is lost in Thine, To live for Thee a - lone.
Refrain
Breathe on me, breathe on me, Ho - ly Spir - it, breathe on me;
Take Thou my heart, cleanse ev-ery part, Ho - ly Spir - it, breathe on me. A-men.

177 I SURRENDER ALL

SURRENDER. 8 7 8 7 Ref.

Judson W. VanDeVenter

Winfield S. Weeden
Arr. by Donald P. Hustad

1. All to Je - sus I sur - ren - der, All to Him I free - ly give;
2. All to Je - sus I sur - ren - der, Hum-bly at His feet I bow,
3. All to Je - sus I sur - ren - der, Make me, Sav - iour, whol - ly Thine;
4. All to Je - sus I sur - ren - der, Lord, I give my - self to Thee;
I will ev - er love and trust Him, In His pres-ence dai - ly live.
World-ly pleas-ures all for - sak - en, Take me, Je - sus, take me now.
Let me feel the Ho - ly Spir - it, Tru - ly know that Thou art mine.
Fill me with Thy love and pow - er, Let Thy bless - ing fall on me.
Refrain
I sur - ren - der all, I sur - ren - der all.
I sur-ren-der all, I sur-ren-der all.
All to Thee, my bless - ed Sav - iour, I sur - ren - der all.

ALL IS WELL!

178

ALL IS WELL. 10 6 10 6 8 8 8 6

William Clayton
Alt. by Avis B. Christiansen

Adapted from J. T. White
The Sacred Harp, 1844

1. Come, come, ye saints, no toil nor la - bor fear, But with joy wend your way;
2. What though the path you tread be rough and steep? Have no fear, He is near!
3. God hath pre-pared a glo-rious Home a - bove Round His throne, for His own,
4. With long-ing hearts we wait the prom-ised day When the trump we shall hear,

Though hard to you life's jour-ney may ap - pear, Grace shall be as your day.
His might-y arm un - to the end will keep; Soon His call you shall hear.
Where they may rest for - ev - er in His love, Toil and tears all un-known.
That sum-mons us from earth-ly cares a - way, At His side to ap - pear!

God's hand of love shall be your guide, And all your need He will pro-vide;
Then fol - low on, fresh cour-age take, For God His own will ne'er for-sake,
There they shall sing e - ter-nal praise To Him who saved them by His grace.
But un - til then we'll la - bor on In pa-tience till our course is run,

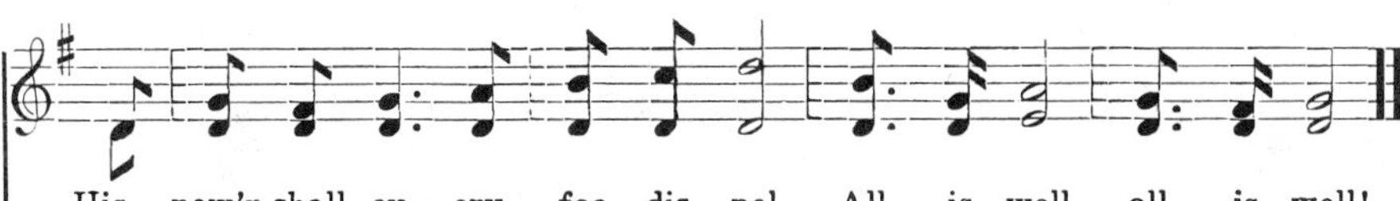

His pow'r shall ev - ery foe dis - pel, All is well, all is well!
Till in His pres - ence they shall dwell! All is well, all is well!
Through heaven's courts the song shall swell, All is well, all is well!
Al - though the hour we may not tell, All is well, all is well!

179 He Hideth My Soul

KIRKPATRICK. 11 8 11 8 Ref.

Fanny J. Crosby

William J. Kirkpatrick

1. A won-der-ful Sav-iour is Je-sus my Lord, A won-der-ful Sav-iour to me; He hid-eth my soul in the cleft of the rock, Where riv-ers of pleas-ure I see.
2. A won-der-ful Sav-iour is Je-sus my Lord, He tak-eth my bur-den a-way; He hold-eth me up, and I shall not be moved, He giv-eth me strength as my day.
3. With num-ber-less bless-ings each mo-ment He crowns, And, filled with His full-ness di-vine, I sing in my rap-ture, oh, glo-ry to God For such a Re-deem-er as mine!
4. When clothed in His bright-ness, trans-port-ed I rise To meet Him in clouds of the sky, His per-fect sal-va-tion, His won-der-ful love, I'll shout with the millions on high.
Refrain
He hid-eth my soul in the cleft of the rock That shadows a dry, thirst-y land; He hid-eth my life in the depths of His love, And cov-ers me there with His hand, And cov-ers me there with His hand.

How Firm a Foundation 180

FOUNDATION. 11 11 11 11

K. in Rippon's
A Selection of Hymns, 1787; alt.

Early American Melody

1. How firm a foun - da - tion, ye saints of the Lord,
2. "Fear not, I am with thee; O be not dis - mayed,
3. "When through fier - y tri - als thy path - way shall lie,
4. "The soul that on Je - sus hath leaned for re - pose,
Is laid for your faith in His ex - cel - lent Word;
For I am thy God, and will still give thee aid;
My grace, all - suf - fi - cient, shall be thy sup - ply;
I will not, I will not de - sert to his foes;
What more can He say than to you He hath said,
I'll strength - en thee, help thee, and cause thee to stand,
The flame shall not hurt thee; I on - ly de - sign
That soul, though all hell should en - deav - or to shake,
To you who for ref - uge to Je - sus have fled?
Up - held by my right - eous, om - nip - o - tent hand.
Thy dross to con - sume, and thy gold to re - fine.
I'll nev - er, no, nev - er, no, nev - er for - sake!" A - MEN.

For alternate tune, see No. 265

181 TRUST AND OBEY

TRUST AND OBEY. 6 6 9 D. Ref.

John H. Sammis — Daniel B. Towner

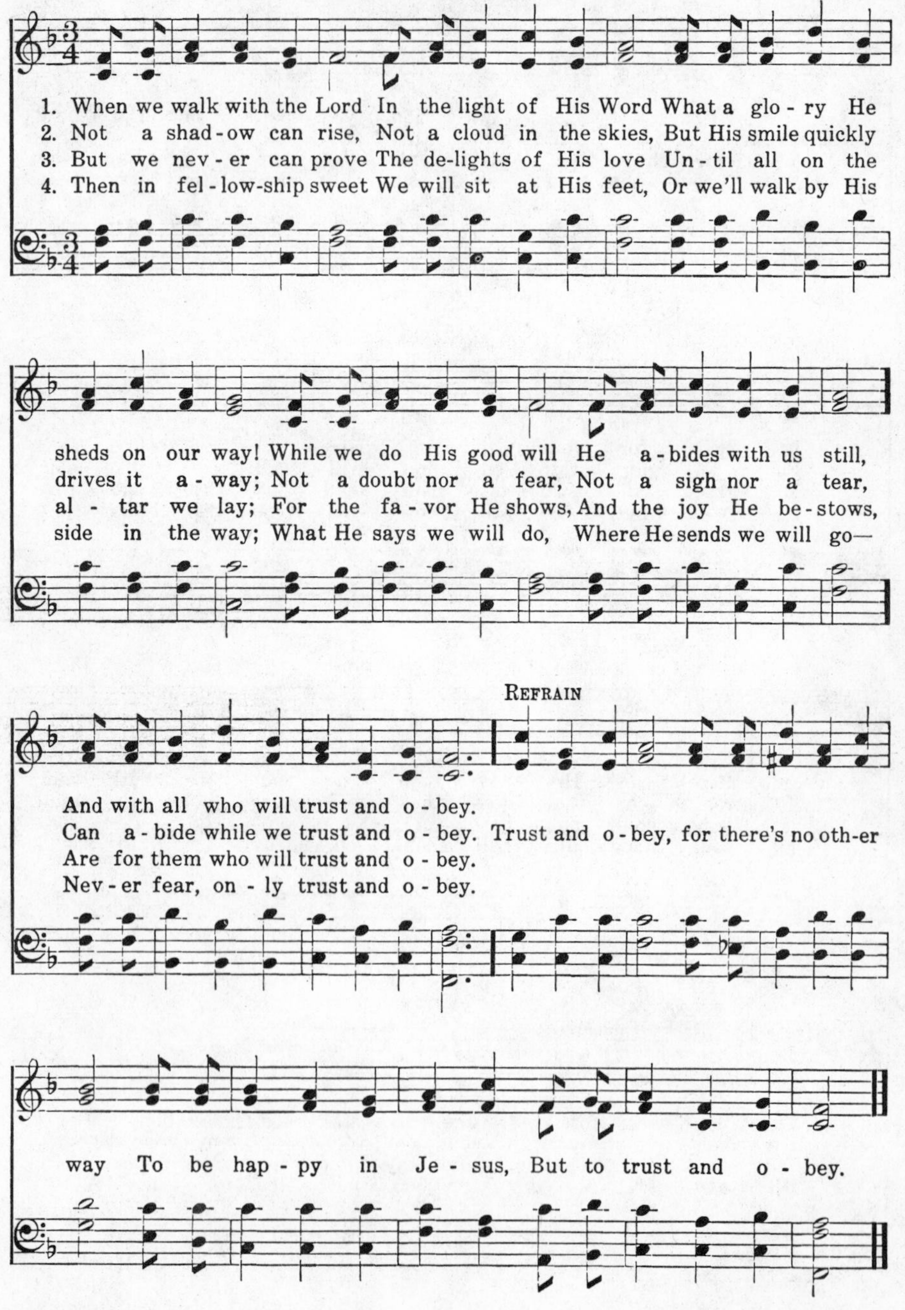
1. When we walk with the Lord In the light of His Word What a glo - ry He sheds on our way! While we do His good will He a - bides with us still, And with all who will trust and o - bey.
2. Not a shad - ow can rise, Not a cloud in the skies, But His smile quickly drives it a - way; Not a doubt nor a fear, Not a sigh nor a tear, Can a - bide while we trust and o - bey.
3. But we nev - er can prove The de-lights of His love Un - til all on the al - tar we lay; For the fa - vor He shows, And the joy He be - stows, Are for them who will trust and o - bey.
4. Then in fel - low-ship sweet We will sit at His feet, Or we'll walk by His side in the way; What He says we will do, Where He sends we will go— Nev - er fear, on - ly trust and o - bey.
Refrain
Trust and o - bey, for there's no oth-er way To be hap - py in Je - sus, But to trust and o - bey.

God Will Take Care of You

GOD CARES. C.M. Ref.

Civilla D. Martin

W. Stillman Martin

1. Be not dis - mayed what-e'er be - tide, God will take care of you;
2. Through days of toil when heart doth fail, God will take care of you;
3. All you may need He will pro - vide, God will take care of you;
4. No mat - ter what may be the test, God will take care of you;
Be - neath His wings of love a - bide, God will take care of you.
When dan-gers fierce your path as - sail, God will take care of you.
Noth - ing you ask will be de - nied, God will take care of you.
Lean, wea - ry one, up - on His breast, God will take care of you.
Refrain
God will take care of you, Through ev-ery day, O'er all the way;
He will take care of you, God will take care of you..........
take care of you.

183 TRUSTING JESUS

TRUSTING JESUS. 7 7 7 7 Ref.

Edgar P. Stites — Ira D. Sankey

1. Sim - ply trust - ing ev - ery day, Trust - ing through a storm - y way;
2. Bright - ly doth His Spir - it shine In - to this poor heart of mine;
3. Sing - ing if my way is clear; Pray - ing if the path be drear;
4. Trust - ing Him while life shall last, Trust - ing Him till earth be past;
E - ven when my faith is small, Trust - ing Je - sus, that is all.
While He leads I can - not fall; Trust - ing Je - sus, that is all.
If in dan - ger, for Him call; Trust - ing Je - sus, that is all.
Till with - in the jas - per wall: Trust - ing Je - sus, that is all.
Refrain
Trust - ing as the mo - ments fly, Trust - ing as the days go by;
Trust - ing Him what - e'er be - fall, Trust - ing Je - sus, that is all.

Moment by Moment

WHITTLE. 10 10 10 10 Ref.

Daniel W. Whittle

May Whittle Moody

1. Dy - ing with Je - sus, by death reck-oned mine; Liv - ing with Je - sus, a
2. Nev - er a tri - al that He is not there, Nev - er a bur - den that
3. Nev - er a heart-ache and nev - er a groan, Nev - er a tear-drop and
4. Nev - er a weak-ness that He doth not feel, Nev - er a sick-ness that
new life di - vine; Look-ing to Je - sus till glo - ry doth shine, Mo-ment by
He doth not bear, Nev - er a sor - row that He doth not share, Mo-ment by
nev - er a moan; Nev - er a dan - ger, but there on the throne, Mo-ment by
He can - not heal; Mo - ment by mo-ment, in woe or in weal, Je - sus, my
Refrain
mo-ment, O Lord, I am Thine.
mo-ment I'm un - der His care; Mo-ment by mo-ment I'm kept in His love;
mo-ment, He thinks of His own.
Sav-iour, a-bides with me still.
Mo-ment by mo-ment I've life from a - bove; Look - ing to Je - sus till
glo - ry doth shine; Mo - ment by mo - ment, O Lord, I am Thine.

185 What a Friend We Have in Jesus

CONVERSE. 8 7 8 7 D.

Joseph Scriven — Charles C. Converse

1. What a Friend we have in Je - sus, All our sins and griefs to bear!
2. Have we tri - als and temp-ta - tions? Is there trou-ble an - y - where?
3. Are we weak and heav - y - la - den, Cum-bered with a load of care?

FINE

What a priv - i - lege to car - ry Ev - ery-thing to God in prayer!
We should nev - er be dis - cour-aged, Take it to the Lord in prayer.
Pre - cious Sav-iour, still our ref - uge— Take it to the Lord in prayer.

D.S.—*All be - cause we do not car - ry Ev - ery-thing to God in prayer!*
D.S.—*Je - sus knows our ev - ery weak - ness, Take it to the Lord in prayer.*
D.S.—*In His arms He'll take and shield thee, Thou wilt find a sol - ace there.*

D. S.

O what peace we oft - en for - feit, O what need-less pain we bear,
Can we find a friend so faith - ful Who will all our sor-rows share?
Do thy friends de-spise, for-sake thee? Take it to the Lord in prayer;

186 Come, My Soul, Thy Suit Prepare

HENDON. 7 7 7 7 7

John Newton — H. A. César Malan

1. Come, my soul, thy suit pre-pare, Je - sus loves to an-swer prayer; He Him-self has
2. Thou art com-ing to a King; Large pe-ti-tions with thee bring; For His grace and
3. Lord, I come to Thee for rest; Take pos-ses-sion of my breast; There Thy blood-bought
4. While I am a pil-grim here, Let Thy love my spir-it cheer: As my guide, my
5. Show me what I have to do; Ev - ery hour my strength renew; Let me live a

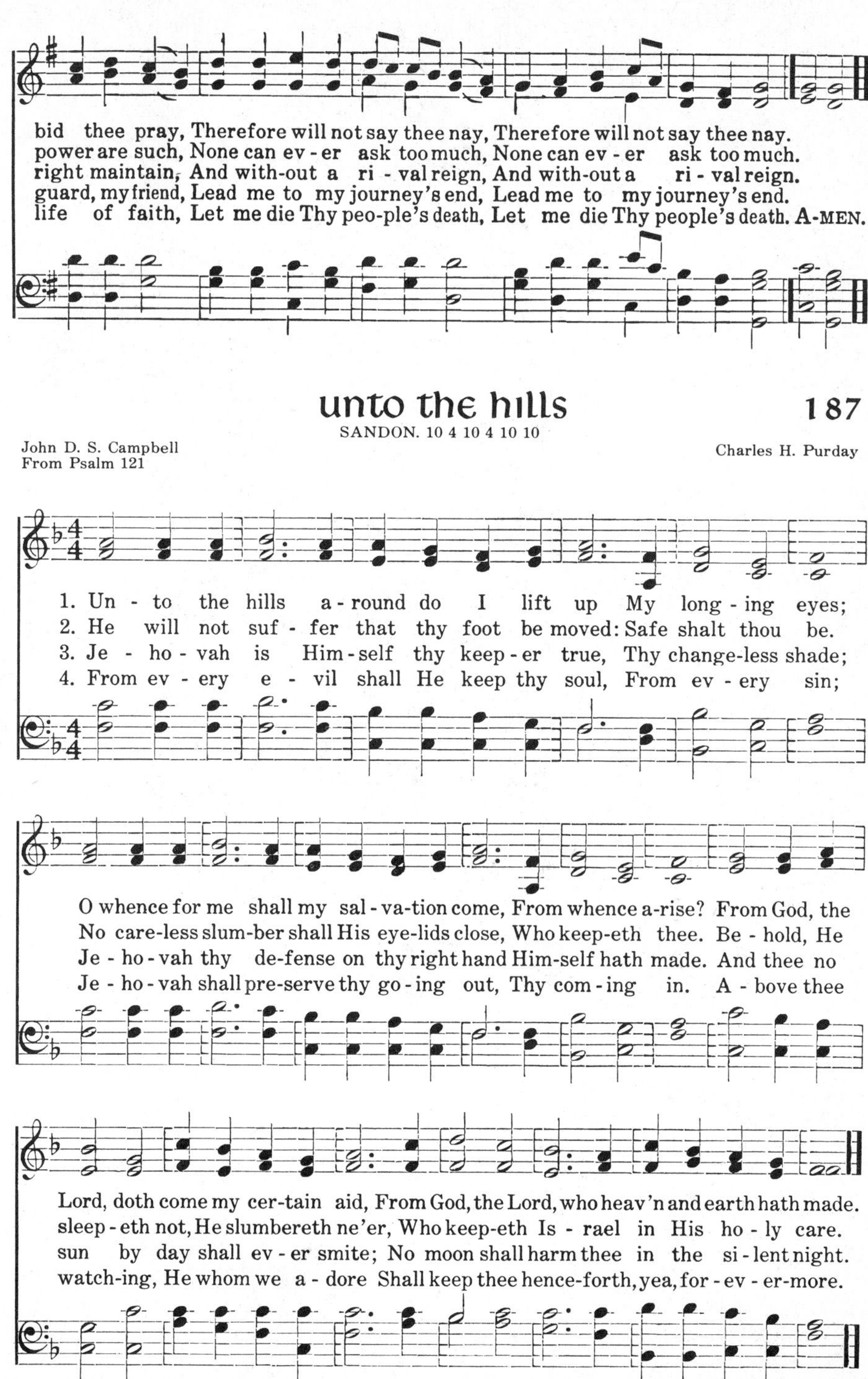
bid thee pray, Therefore will not say thee nay, Therefore will not say thee nay.
power are such, None can ev - er ask too much, None can ev - er ask too much.
right maintain, And with-out a ri - val reign, And with-out a ri - val reign.
guard, my friend, Lead me to my journey's end, Lead me to my journey's end.
life of faith, Let me die Thy peo-ple's death, Let me die Thy people's death. A-MEN.
unto the hills
187
SANDON. 10 4 10 4 10 10
John D. S. Campbell
From Psalm 121
Charles H. Purday
1. Un - to the hills a - round do I lift up My long - ing eyes;
2. He will not suf - fer that thy foot be moved: Safe shalt thou be.
3. Je - ho - vah is Him - self thy keep - er true, Thy change-less shade;
4. From ev - ery e - vil shall He keep thy soul, From ev - ery sin;
O whence for me shall my sal - va-tion come, From whence a-rise? From God, the
No care-less slum-ber shall His eye-lids close, Who keep-eth thee. Be - hold, He
Je - ho - vah thy de-fense on thy right hand Him-self hath made. And thee no
Je - ho - vah shall pre-serve thy go - ing out, Thy com - ing in. A - bove thee
Lord, doth come my cer-tain aid, From God, the Lord, who heav'n and earth hath made.
sleep - eth not, He slumbereth ne'er, Who keep-eth Is - rael in His ho - ly care.
sun by day shall ev - er smite; No moon shall harm thee in the si - lent night.
watch-ing, He whom we a - dore Shall keep thee hence-forth, yea, for - ev - er-more.

188 Like a River Glorious

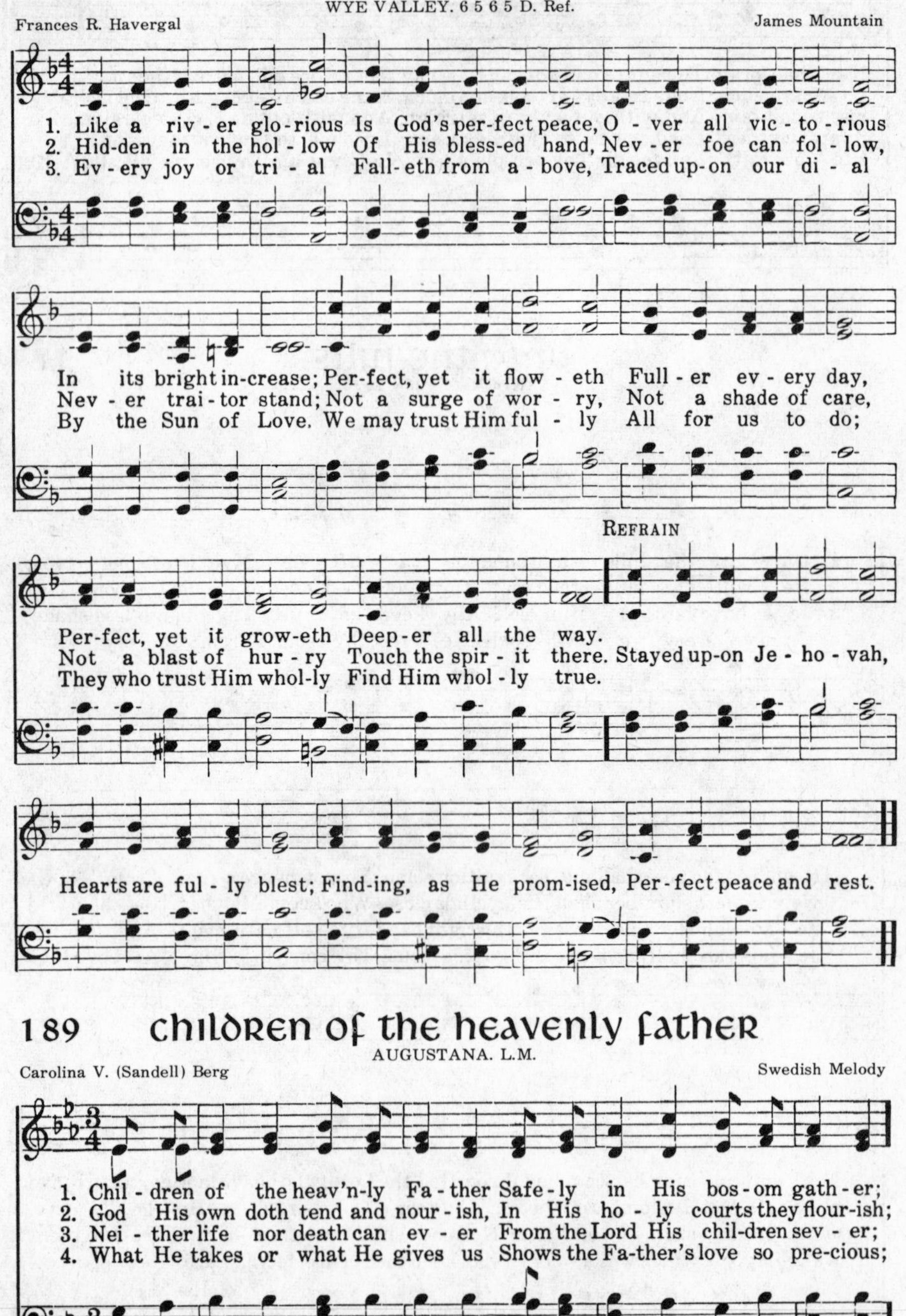
WYE VALLEY. 6 5 6 5 D. Ref.
Frances R. Havergal
James Mountain
1. Like a riv - er glo-rious Is God's per-fect peace, O - ver all vic - to - rious
2. Hid-den in the hol - low Of His bless-ed hand, Nev - er foe can fol - low,
3. Ev-ery joy or tri - al Fall-eth from a - bove, Traced up-on our di - al
In its bright in-crease; Per-fect, yet it flow - eth Full - er ev - ery day,
Nev - er trai - tor stand; Not a surge of wor - ry, Not a shade of care,
By the Sun of Love. We may trust Him ful - ly All for us to do;
Refrain
Per-fect, yet it grow-eth Deep-er all the way.
Not a blast of hur - ry Touch the spir - it there. Stayed up-on Je - ho - vah,
They who trust Him whol-ly Find Him whol - ly true.
Hearts are ful - ly blest; Find-ing, as He prom-ised, Per-fect peace and rest.
189 Children of the Heavenly Father
AUGUSTANA. L.M.
Carolina V. (Sandell) Berg
Swedish Melody
1. Chil - dren of the heav'n-ly Fa-ther Safe - ly in His bos-om gath - er;
2. God His own doth tend and nour - ish, In His ho - ly courts they flour-ish;
3. Nei - ther life nor death can ev - er From the Lord His chil-dren sev - er;
4. What He takes or what He gives us Shows the Fa-ther's love so pre-cious;

Nest-ling bird nor star in heav-en Such a ref-uge e'er was giv-en.
Like a fa-ther kind He spares them, In His lov-ing arms He bears them.
For His love and deep com-pas-sion Com-forts them in trib-u-la-tion.
We may trust His pur-pose whol-ly—'Tis His chil-dren's wel-fare sole-ly.
LEANING ON THE EVERLASTING ARMS 190
SHOWALTER. 10 9 10 9 Ref.
Elisha A. Hoffman
Anthony J. Showalter
1. What a fel-low-ship, what a joy di-vine, Lean-ing on the ev-er-last-ing arms;
2. Oh, how sweet to walk in this pilgrim way, Lean-ing on the ev-er-last-ing arms;
3. What have I to dread, what have I to fear, Lean-ing on the ev-er-last-ing arms?
What a bless-ed-ness, what a peace is mine, Lean-ing on the ev-er-last-ing arms.
Oh, how bright the path grows from day to day, Lean-ing on the ev-er-last-ing arms.
I have bless-ed peace with my Lord so near, Lean-ing on the ev-er-last-ing arms.
REFRAIN
Lean-ing, lean-ing, Safe and se-cure from all a-larms;
Lean-ing on Je-sus, lean-ing on Je-sus,
Lean-ing, lean-ing, Lean-ing on the ev-er-last-ing arms.
Lean-ing on Je-sus, lean-ing on Je-sus,

191 Come, Ye Disconsolate

CONSOLATION (WEBBE). 11 10 11 10

Thomas Moore; 1, 2
Alt. by Thomas Hastings; 3

Samuel Webbe

1. Come, ye dis - con - so - late, wher - e'er ye lan - guish; Come to the mer - cy-seat, fer - vent-ly kneel; Here bring your wounded hearts, here tell your an - guish; Earth has no sor - row that heaven can-not heal.
2. Joy of the des - o - late, light of the stray - ing, Hope of the pen - i - tent, fade-less and pure, Here speaks the Com-fort-er, ten - der - ly say - ing, "Earth has no sor - row that heaven can-not cure."
3. Here see the bread of life; see wa - ters flow - ing Forth from the throne of God, pure from a - bove; Come to the feast of love; come, ev - er know-ing Earth has no sor - row but heaven can re - move. A - MEN.
192 Peace, Perfect Peace
PAX TECUM. 4 6 10
Edward H. Bickersteth
George T. Caldbeck
Arr. by Charles J. Vincent
1. Peace, per - fect peace, in this dark world of sin?
2. Peace, per - fect peace, by throng - ing du - ties pressed?
3. Peace, per - fect peace, with sor - rows surg - ing round?
4. Peace, per - fect peace, our fu - ture all un - known?
5. Peace, per - fect peace, death shad - owing us and ours?
6. It is e - nough: earth's strug - gles soon shall cease,

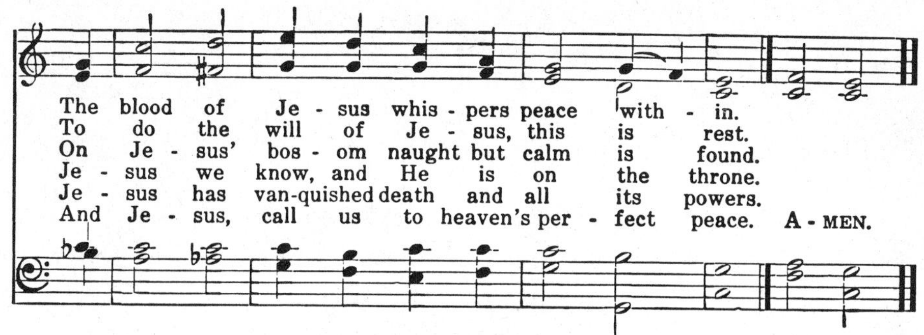
The blood of Je - sus whis - pers peace with - in.
To do the will of Je - sus, this is rest.
On Je - sus' bos - om naught but calm is found.
Je - sus we know, and He is on the throne.
Je - sus has van-quished death and all its powers.
And Je - sus, call us to heaven's per - fect peace. A - MEN.

NEAR TO THE HEART OF GOD 193

McAFEE. C.M. Ref.

Cleland B. McAfee | Cleland B. McAfee

1. There is a place of qui - et rest, Near to the heart of God,
2. There is a place of com - fort sweet, Near to the heart of God,
3. There is a place of full re - lease, Near to the heart of God,

A place where sin can - not mo - lest, Near to the heart of God.
A place where we our Sav - iour meet, Near to the heart of God.
A place where all is joy and peace, Near to the heart of God.

REFRAIN

O Je - sus, blest Re - deem - er, Sent from the heart of God,

Hold us, who wait be - fore Thee, Near to the heart of God.

194 JESUS, I AM RESTING, RESTING

TRANQUILLITY. 8 7 8 5 D. Ref.

Jean S. Pigott — James Mountain

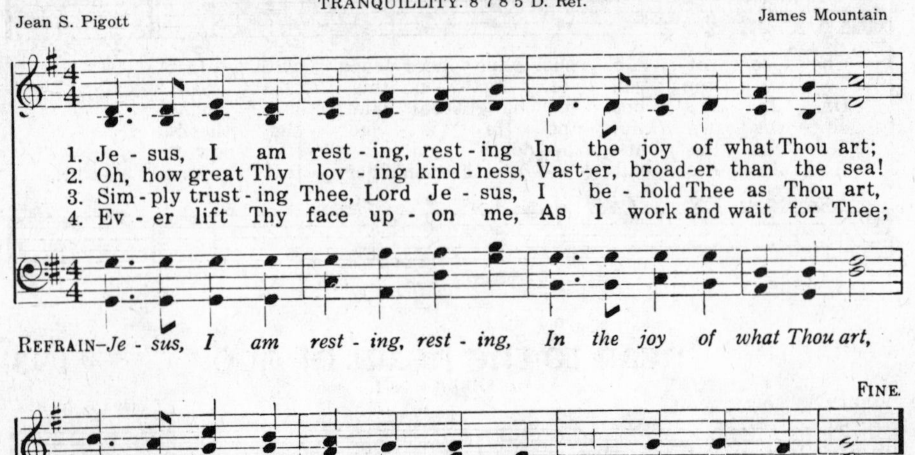

1. Je - sus, I am rest - ing, rest - ing In the joy of what Thou art;
2. Oh, how great Thy lov - ing kind - ness, Vast - er, broad - er than the sea!
3. Sim - ply trust - ing Thee, Lord Je - sus, I be - hold Thee as Thou art,
4. Ev - er lift Thy face up - on me, As I work and wait for Thee;

REFRAIN—*Je - sus, I am rest - ing, rest - ing, In the joy of what Thou art,*

FINE.

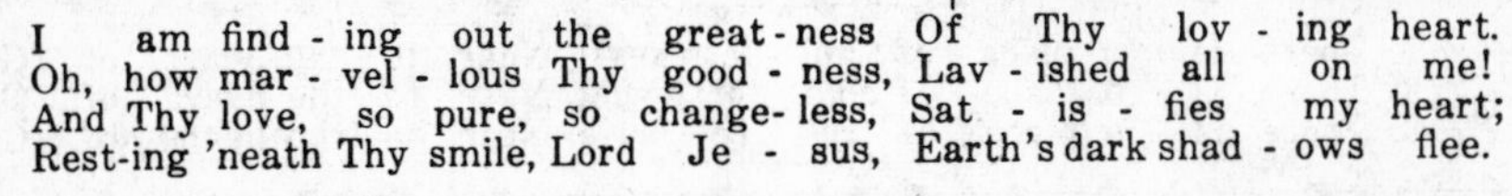

I am find - ing out the great - ness Of Thy lov - ing heart.
Oh, how mar - vel - lous Thy good - ness, Lav - ished all on me!
And Thy love, so pure, so change - less, Sat - is - fies my heart;
Rest - ing 'neath Thy smile, Lord Je - sus, Earth's dark shad - ows flee.

I am find - ing out the great - ness Of Thy lov - ing heart.

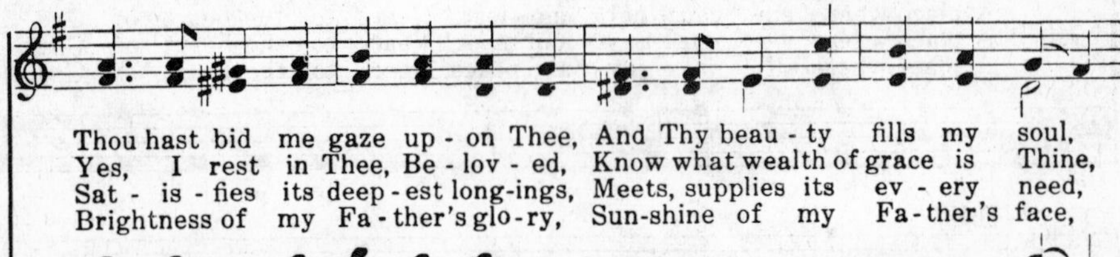

Thou hast bid me gaze up - on Thee, And Thy beau - ty fills my soul,
Yes, I rest in Thee, Be - lov - ed, Know what wealth of grace is Thine,
Sat - is - fies its deep - est long - ings, Meets, supplies its ev - ery need,
Brightness of my Fa - ther's glo - ry, Sun - shine of my Fa - ther's face,

D. C. Refrain

For by Thy trans - form - ing pow - er, Thou hast made me whole.
Know Thy cer - tain - ty of prom - ise, And have made it mine.
Com - pass - eth me round with bless - ings: Thine is love in - deed!
Keep me ev - er trust - ing, rest - ing, Fill me with Thy grace.

Under His Wings

HINGHAM. 11 10 11 10 Ref.

William O. Cushing

Ira D. Sankey

1. Under His wings I am safely abiding;
Though the night deepens and tempests are wild,
Still I can trust Him; I know He will keep me;
He has redeemed me, and I am His child.

2. Under His wings, what a refuge in sorrow!
How the heart yearningly turns to His rest!
Often when earth has no balm for my healing,
There I find comfort, and there I am blest.

3. Under His wings, O what precious enjoyment!
There will I hide till life's trials are o'er;
Sheltered, protected, no evil can harm me;
Resting in Jesus I'm safe evermore.

REFRAIN

Under His wings, under His wings,
Who from His love can sever?
Under His wings my soul shall abide,
Safely abide forever.

196 

In the Garden

GARDEN. Irregular. Ref.

C. Austin Miles — C. Austin Miles

1. I come to the gar - den a - lone, While the dew is still on the
2. He speaks, and the sound of His voice Is so sweet the birds hush their
3. I'd stay in the gar - den with Him Though the night a-round me be

ros - es; And the voice I hear, fall - ing on my ear; The
sing - ing, And the mel - o - dy that He gave to me, With-
fall - ing, But He bids me go; through the voice of woe, His

Refrain

Son of God dis - clos - es.
in my heart is ring - ing. And He walks with me, and He
voice to me is call - ing.

talks with me, And He tells me I am His own, And the

joy we share as we tar - ry there, None oth-er has ev - er known.

Be still, my soul

197

FINLANDIA. 10 10 10 10 10 10

Katharina von Schlegel
From Psalm 46
Trans. by Jane L. Borthwick

Jean Sibelius
Arr. for *The Hymnal*, 1933

1. Be still, my soul: the Lord is on thy side; Bear pa-tient-ly the
2. Be still, my soul: thy God doth un - der - take To guide the fu - ture
3. Be still, my soul: the hour is has-t'ning on When we shall be for-

cross of grief or pain; Leave to thy God to or - der and pro - vide;
as He has the past. Thy hope, thy con - fi - dence let noth-ing shake;
ev - er with the Lord, When dis - ap-point-ment, grief, and fear are gone,

In ev - ery change He faith - ful will re - main. Be still, my soul: thy
All now mys - te - rious shall be bright at last. Be still, my soul: the
Sor - row for - got, love's pur - est joys re - stored. Be still, my soul: when

best, thy heav'n-ly Friend Thro' thorn-y ways leads to a joy - ful end.
waves and winds still know His voice who ruled them while He dwelt be-low.
change and tears are past, All safe and bless - ed we shall meet at last. A-MEN.

198 He Leadeth Me

HE LEADETH ME. L.M. Ref.

Joseph H. Gilmore William B. Bradbury

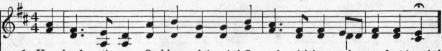

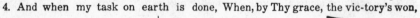

1. He lead - eth me, O bless-ed thought! O words with heavenly com-fort fraught!
2. Sometimes 'mid scenes of deep-est gloom, Sometimes where Eden's bowers bloom,
3. Lord, I would clasp Thy hand in mine, Nor ev - er mur - mur nor re - pine;
4. And when my task on earth is done, When, by Thy grace, the vic-tory's won,

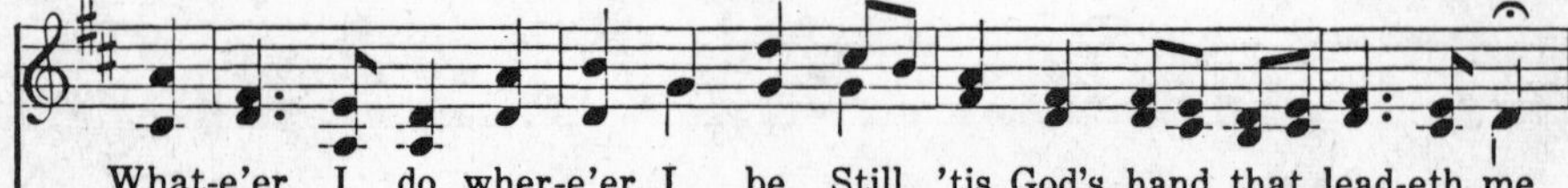

What-e'er I do, wher-e'er I be, Still 'tis God's hand that lead-eth me.
By wa - ters still, o'er troub-led sea, Still 'tis His hand that lead-eth me.
Con - tent, what-ev - er lot I see, Since 'tis my God that lead-eth me.
E'en death's cold wave I will not flee, Since God through Jor-dan lead-eth me.

REFRAIN

He lead-eth me, He lead-eth me! By His own hand He lead-eth me!
His faithful follower I would be, For by His hand He (*Omit....*) lead-eth me.

199 Jesus, My Saviour, Look on Me

HANFORD. 8 8 8 4

Charlotte Elliott Arthur S. Sullivan

1. Je - sus, my Sav - iour, look on me, For I am wea - ry and op-prest;
2. Look down on me, for I am weak; I feel the toil-some journey's length:
3. I am be - wil - dered on my way, Dark and tem-pest-uous is the night;
4. When Sa - tan flings his fi - ery darts, I look to Thee, my ter-rors cease;
5. Stand-ing a - lone on Jordan's brink, In that tre - men-dous, lat - est strife,
6. Thou wilt my ev - ery want sup - ply, E'en to the end, what-e'er be - fall;

I come to cast my-self on Thee: Thou art my Rest.
Thine aid om-nip-o-tent I seek: Thou art my Strength.
O send Thou forth some cheer-ing ray! Thou art my Light.
Thy Cross a hid-ing-place im-parts: Thou art my Peace.
Thou wilt not suf-fer me to sink: Thou art my Life.
Through life, in death, e-ter-nal-ly, Thou art my All. A-MEN.
It is well with my soul
200
VILLE DU HAVRE. 11 8 11 9 Ref.
Horatio G. Spafford
Philip P. Bliss
1. When peace, like a riv-er, at-tend-eth my way, When sor-rows like sea-bil-lows roll; What-ev-er my lot, Thou hast taught me to say, "It is well, it is well with my soul."
2. Though Sa-tan should buf-fet, tho' tri-als should come, Let this blest as-sur-ance con-trol, That Christ has re-gard-ed my help-less es-tate, And hath shed His own blood for my soul.
3. My sin—oh, the bliss of this glo-ri-ous thought, My sin—not in part, but the whole, Is nailed to the cross and I bear it no more, Praise the Lord, praise the Lord, O my soul!
4. And, Lord, haste the day when the faith shall be sight, The clouds be rolled back as a scroll, The trump shall re-sound and the Lord shall de-scend, "E-ven so"—it is well with my soul.
REFRAIN
It is well with my soul, It is well, it is well with my soul.
It is well with my soul,

201 Give to the winds thy fears

DIADEMATA. S.M.D.

Paul Gerhardt
Trans. by John Wesley

George J. Elvey

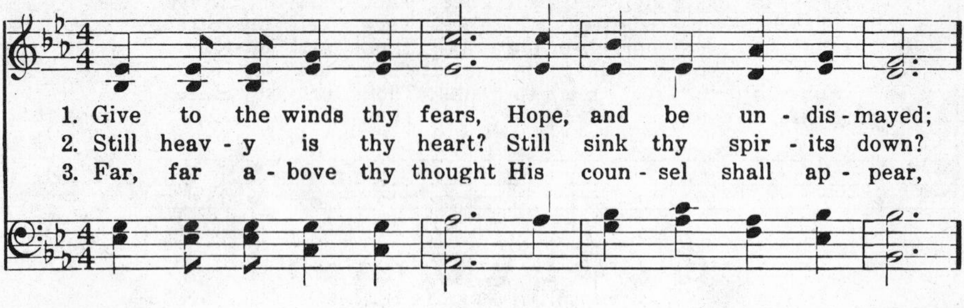

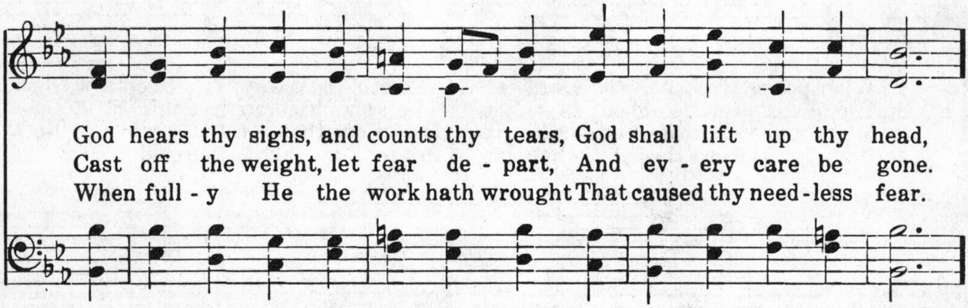

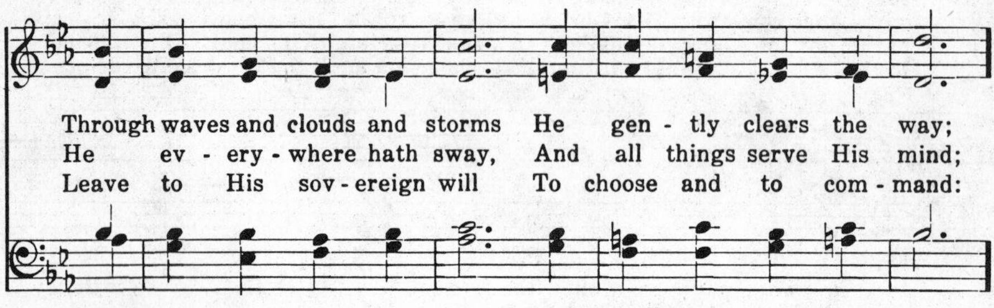

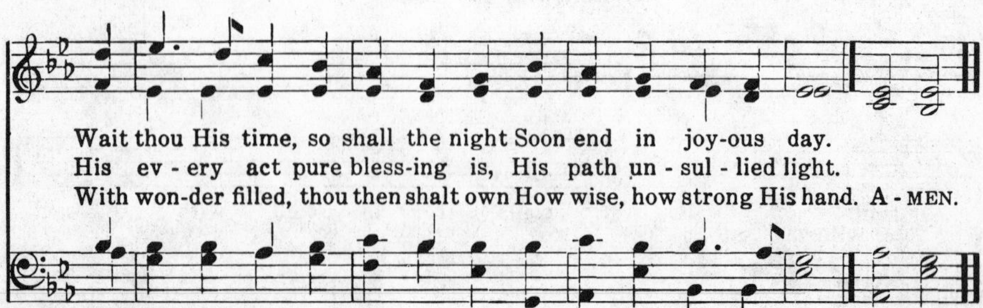

1. Give to the winds thy fears, Hope, and be un - dis - mayed;
God hears thy sighs, and counts thy tears, God shall lift up thy head,
Through waves and clouds and storms He gen - tly clears the way;
Wait thou His time, so shall the night Soon end in joy-ous day.

2. Still heav - y is thy heart? Still sink thy spir - its down?
Cast off the weight, let fear de - part, And ev - ery care be gone.
He ev - ery - where hath sway, And all things serve His mind;
His ev - ery act pure bless-ing is, His path un - sul - lied light.

3. Far, far a - bove thy thought His coun - sel shall ap - pear,
When full - y He the work hath wrought That caused thy need - less fear.
Leave to His sov - ereign will To choose and to com - mand:
With won-der filled, thou then shalt own How wise, how strong His hand. A - MEN.

Standing on the Promises

PROMISES. 11 11 11 9 Ref.

R. Kelso Carter — R. Kelso Carter

1. Stand-ing on the prom-is-es of Christ my King, Through e-ter-nal a-ges let His prais-es ring; Glo-ry in the high-est, I will shout and sing, Stand-ing on the prom-is-es of God.
2. Stand-ing on the prom-is-es that can-not fail, When the howl-ing storms of doubt and fear as-sail, By the liv-ing word of God I shall pre-vail, Stand-ing on the prom-is-es of God.
3. Stand-ing on the prom-is-es of Christ the Lord, Bound to Him e-ter-nal-ly by love's strong cord, O-ver-com-ing dai-ly with the Spir-it's sword, Stand-ing on the prom-is-es of God.
4. Stand-ing on the prom-is-es I can-not fall, Lis-tening ev-ery mo-ment to the Spir-it's call, Rest-ing in my Sav-iour as my all in all, Stand-ing on the prom-is-es of God.

REFRAIN

Stand-ing, stand-ing, (Standing on the promises, standing on the promises,)
Stand-ing on the prom-is-es of God my Sav-iour;
Stand-ing, stand-ing, (Standing on the prom-is-es, stand-ing on the prom-is-es,)
I'm stand-ing on the prom-is-es of God.

203 Thy Word Have I Hid in My Heart

EOLA. 8 7 8 7 Ref.

Adapted by Ernest O. Sellers
From Psalm 119

Ernest O. Sellers

1. Thy Word is a lamp to my feet, A light to my path al - way,
2. For - ev - er, O Lord, is Thy Word Es - tab-lished and fixed on high;
3. At morn - ing, at noon, and at night I ev - er will give Thee praise;
4. Thro' Him whom Thy Word hath foretold, The Sav-iour and Morn-ing Star,

To guide and to save me from sin, And show me the heav'n-ly way.
Thy faith-ful-ness un - to all men A - bid - eth for - ev - er nigh.
For Thou art my por - tion, O Lord, And shall be thro' all my days!
Sal - va - tion and peace have been bro't To those who have strayed a - far.

REFRAIN

Thy Word have I hid in my heart (in my heart), That I might not sin a-gainst Thee (a - gainst Thee); That I might not sin, that I might not sin, Thy Word have I hid in my heart.

Thy Word Is Like a Garden, Lord

SERAPH (BETHLEHEM). C.M.D.

Edwin Hodder | Gottfried W. Fink

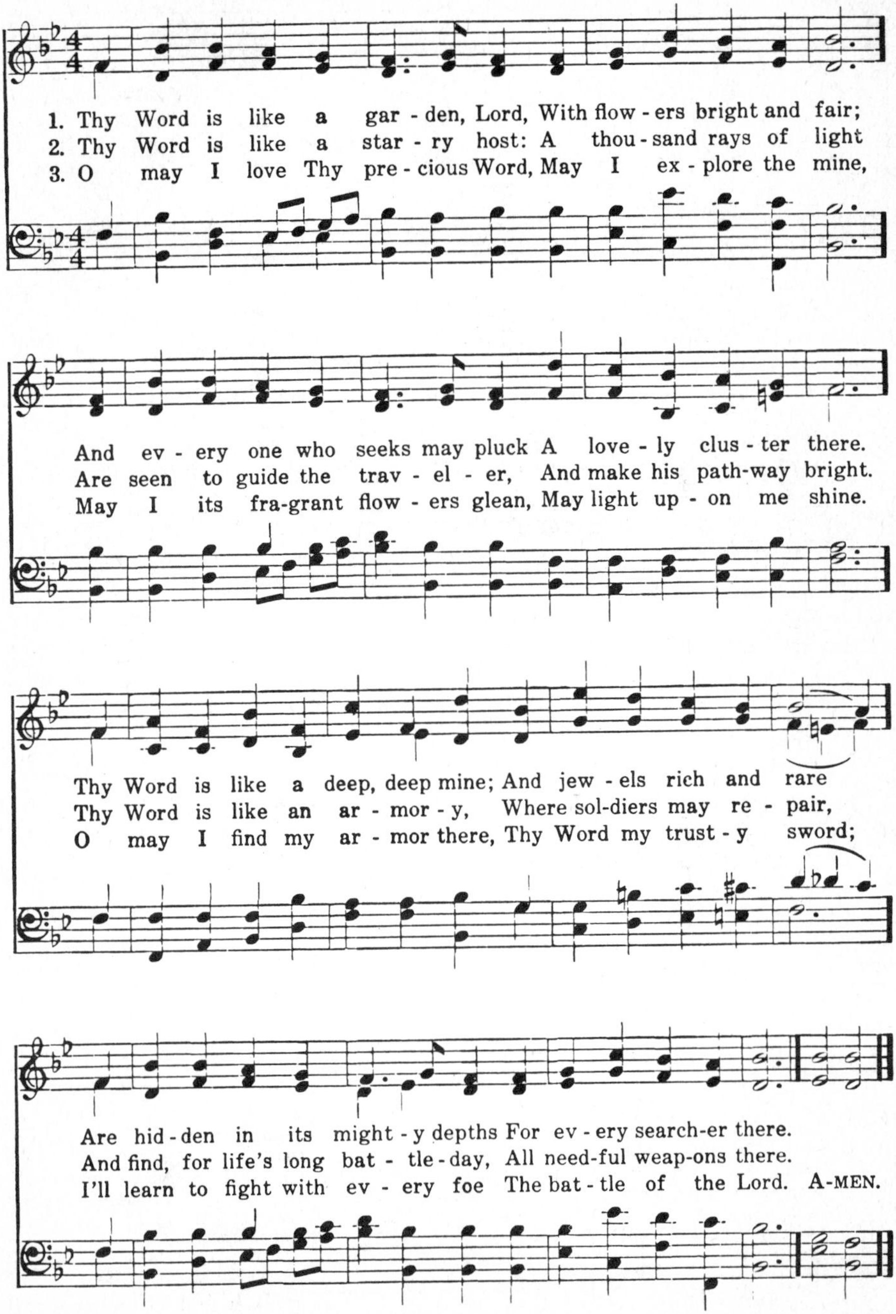

1. Thy Word is like a gar - den, Lord, With flow - ers bright and fair;
2. Thy Word is like a star - ry host: A thou - sand rays of light
3. O may I love Thy pre - cious Word, May I ex - plore the mine,

And ev - ery one who seeks may pluck A love - ly clus - ter there.
Are seen to guide the trav - el - er, And make his path-way bright.
May I its fra-grant flow - ers glean, May light up - on me shine.

Thy Word is like a deep, deep mine; And jew - els rich and rare
Thy Word is like an ar - mor - y, Where sol-diers may re - pair,
O may I find my ar - mor there, Thy Word my trust - y sword;

Are hid - den in its might - y depths For ev - ery search-er there.
And find, for life's long bat - tle-day, All need-ful weap-ons there.
I'll learn to fight with ev - ery foe The bat - tle of the Lord. A-MEN.

205 Break Thou the Bread of Life

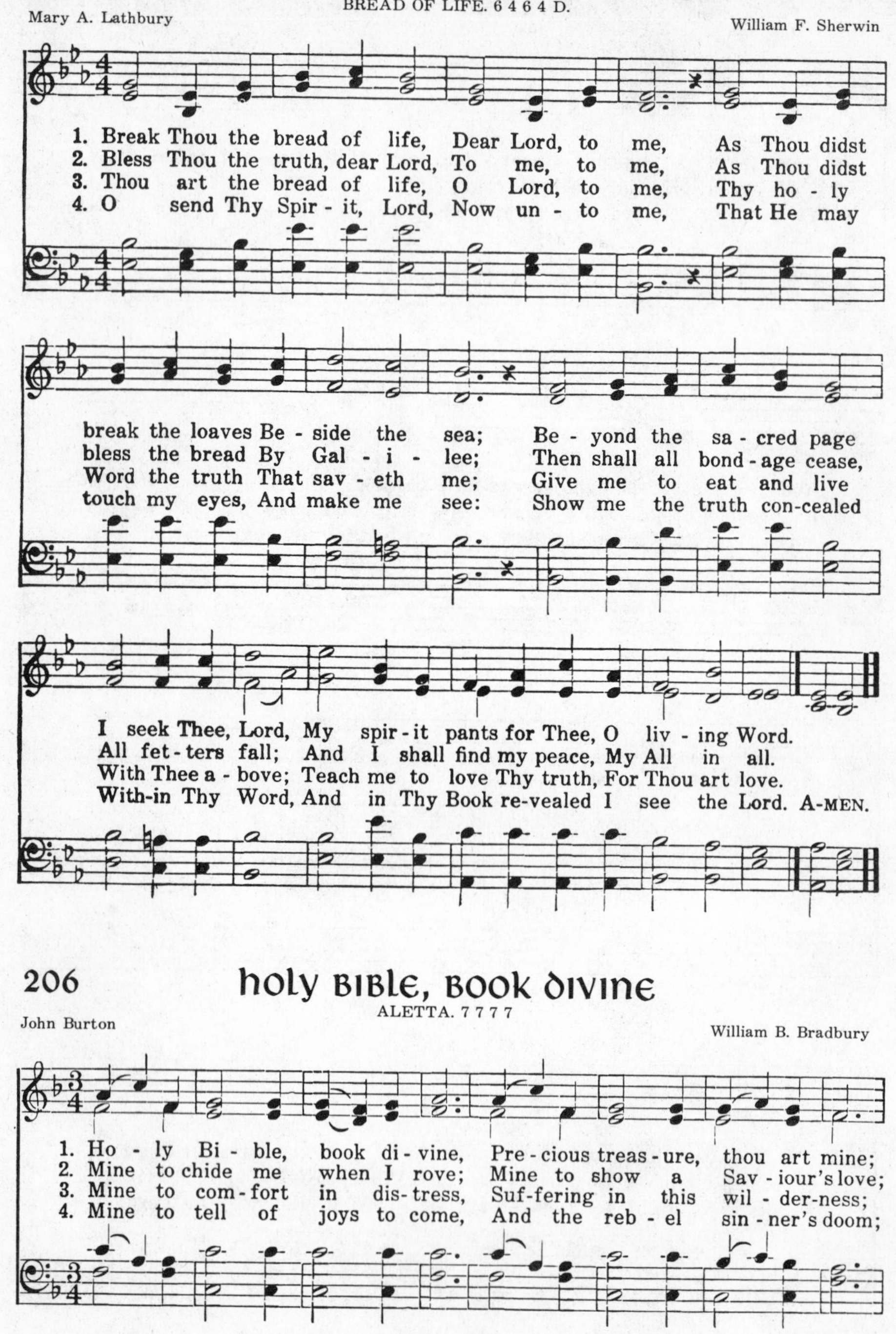
BREAD OF LIFE. 6 4 6 4 D.
Mary A. Lathbury
William F. Sherwin
1. Break Thou the bread of life, Dear Lord, to me, As Thou didst
2. Bless Thou the truth, dear Lord, To me, to me, As Thou didst
3. Thou art the bread of life, O Lord, to me, Thy ho - ly
4. O send Thy Spir - it, Lord, Now un - to me, That He may
break the loaves Be - side the sea; Be - yond the sa - cred page
bless the bread By Gal - i - lee; Then shall all bond - age cease,
Word the truth That sav - eth me; Give me to eat and live
touch my eyes, And make me see: Show me the truth con-cealed
I seek Thee, Lord, My spir - it pants for Thee, O liv - ing Word.
All fet - ters fall; And I shall find my peace, My All in all.
With Thee a - bove; Teach me to love Thy truth, For Thou art love.
With-in Thy Word, And in Thy Book re-vealed I see the Lord. A-MEN.
206
holy Bible, Book Divine
ALETTA. 7 7 7 7
John Burton
William B. Bradbury
1. Ho - ly Bi - ble, book di - vine, Pre - cious treas - ure, thou art mine;
2. Mine to chide me when I rove; Mine to show a Sav - iour's love;
3. Mine to com - fort in dis - tress, Suf - fering in this wil - der - ness;
4. Mine to tell of joys to come, And the reb - el sin - ner's doom;

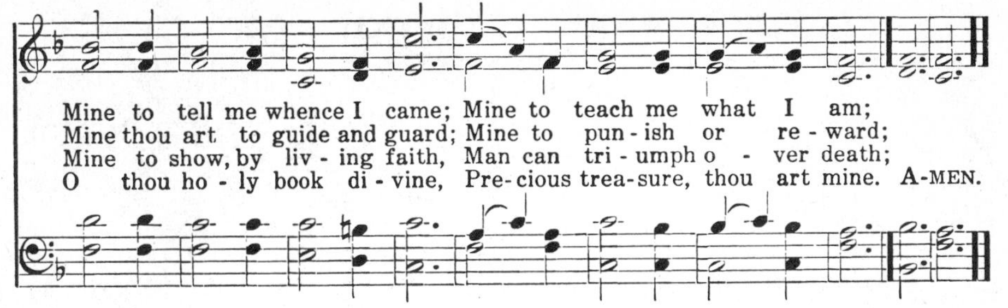
Mine to tell me whence I came; Mine to teach me what I am;
Mine thou art to guide and guard; Mine to pun - ish or re - ward;
Mine to show, by liv - ing faith, Man can tri - umph o - ver death;
O thou ho - ly book di - vine, Pre - cious trea - sure, thou art mine. A-MEN.

Faith of Our Fathers! 207

ST. CATHERINE. 8 8 8 8 8 8

Frederick W. Faber

Henri F. Hemy
Alt. by James G. Walton

1. Faith of our fa - thers! liv - ing still In spite of dun - geon, fire and sword:
2. Our fa-thers, chained in pris - ons dark, Were still in heart and conscience free:
3. Faith of our fa - thers! we will strive To win all na - tions un - to thee,
4. Faith of our fa - thers! we will love Both friend and foe in all our strife:

O how our hearts beat high with joy When-e'er we hear that glo - rious word!
How sweet would be their chil-dren's fate, If they, like them, could die for thee!
And through the truth that comes from God Mankind shall then be tru - ly free.
And preach thee, too, as love knows how, By kind - ly words and vir - tuous life:

Faith of our fa-thers, ho - ly faith! We will be true to thee till death!
Faith of our fa-thers, ho - ly faith! We will be true to thee till death!
Faith of our fa-thers, ho - ly faith! We will be true to thee till death!
Faith of our fa-thers, ho - ly faith! We will be true to thee till death! A-MEN.

208 Glorious things of thee are spoken

AUSTRIAN HYMN. 8.7 8 7 D.

John Newton — Franz Joseph Haydn

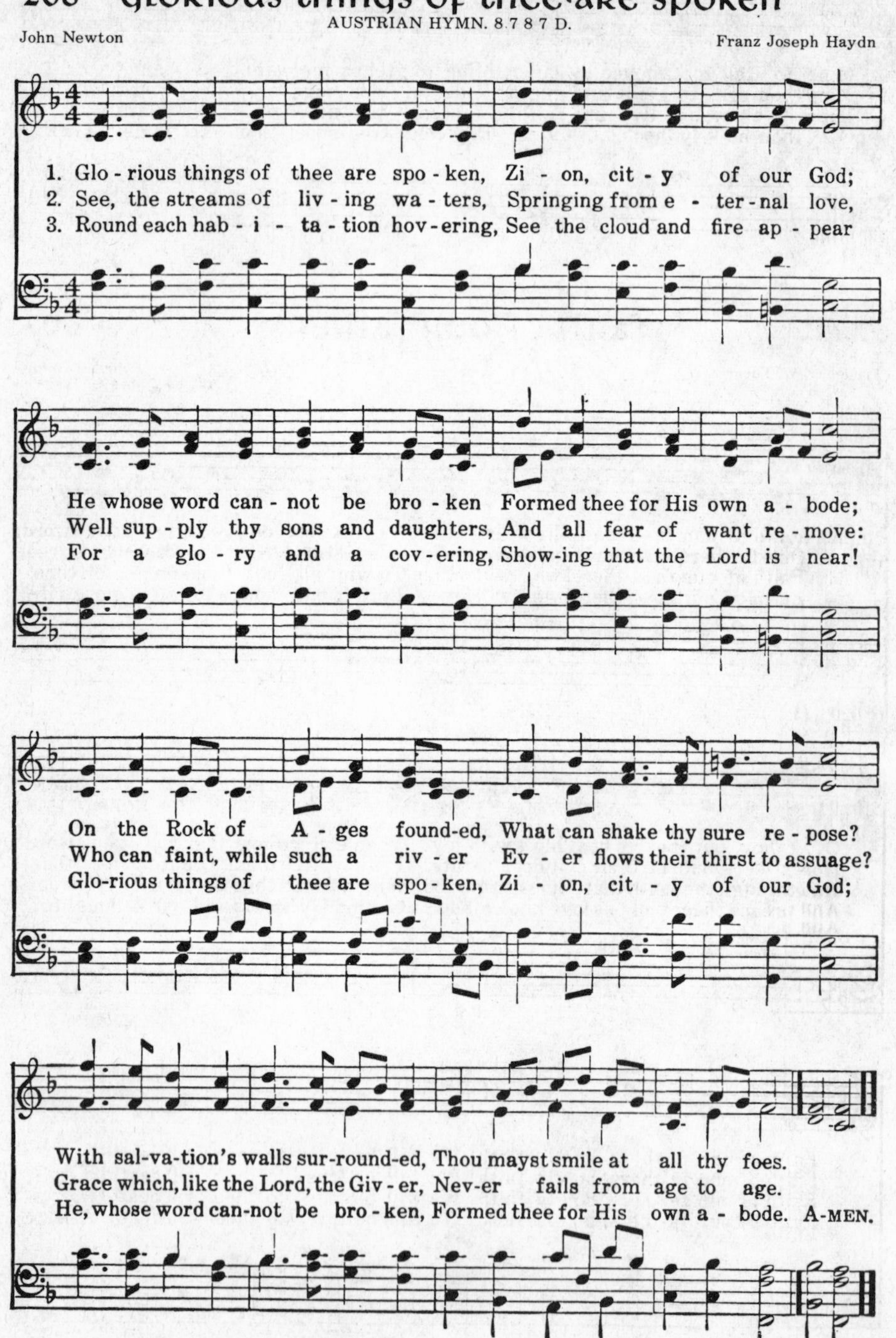
1. Glo - rious things of thee are spo - ken, Zi - on, cit - y of our God;
2. See, the streams of liv - ing wa - ters, Springing from e - ter - nal love,
3. Round each hab - i - ta - tion hov - ering, See the cloud and fire ap - pear
He whose word can - not be bro - ken Formed thee for His own a - bode;
Well sup - ply thy sons and daughters, And all fear of want re - move:
For a glo - ry and a cov - ering, Show-ing that the Lord is near!
On the Rock of A - ges found-ed, What can shake thy sure re - pose?
Who can faint, while such a riv - er Ev - er flows their thirst to assuage?
Glo-rious things of thee are spo - ken, Zi - on, cit - y of our God;
With sal-va-tion's walls sur-round-ed, Thou mayst smile at all thy foes.
Grace which, like the Lord, the Giv - er, Nev-er fails from age to age.
He, whose word can-not be bro - ken, Formed thee for His own a - bode. A-MEN.

The Church's One Foundation

AURELIA. 7 6 7 6 D.

Samuel J. Stone

Samuel S. Wesley

1. The Church's one Foun - da - tion Is Je - sus Christ her Lord;
2. E - lect from ev - ery na - tion, Yet one o'er all the earth,
3. 'Mid toil and trib - u - la - tion, And tu - mult of her war,
4. Yet she on earth hath un - ion With God the Three in One,

She is His new cre - a - tion, By wa - ter and the word:
Her char - ter of sal - va - tion, One Lord, one faith, one birth;
She waits the con - sum - ma - tion Of peace for - ev - er - more;
And mys - tic sweet com - mun - ion With those whose rest is won:

From heaven He came and sought her To be His ho - ly bride;
One ho - ly name she bless - es, Par - takes one ho - ly food,
Till with the vi - sion glo - rious Her long - ing eyes are blest,
O hap - py ones and ho - ly! Lord, give us grace that we,

With His own blood He bought her, And for her life He died.
And to one hope she press - es, With ev - ery grace en - dued.
And the great Church vic - to - rious Shall be the Church at rest.
Like them, the meek and low - ly, On high may dwell with Thee. A-MEN.

hymns of service and challenge

the apostle paul often describes the christian's daily life as a warfare against sin and the powers of darkness, not only in our own personalities but also in the social environment around us.

soldiers of the twelfth century left family and fortune to answer the call of the crusades. many lost their lives in those adventurous days.

"deus vult" —"god wills it" —was their eager response, and it is also ours today. these hymns express a joyful willingness to give ourselves and not to count the cost, in the service of our king.

RISE UP, O MEN OF GOD! 210

FESTAL SONG. S.M.

William P. Merrill — William H. Walter

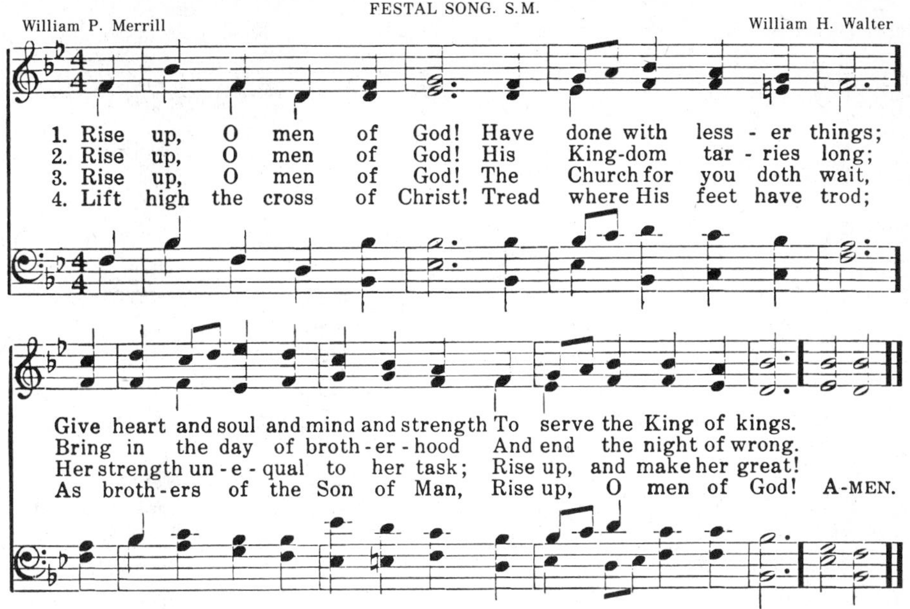

1. Rise up, O men of God! Have done with less - er things;
2. Rise up, O men of God! His King-dom tar - ries long;
3. Rise up, O men of God! The Church for you doth wait,
4. Lift high the cross of Christ! Tread where His feet have trod;
Give heart and soul and mind and strength To serve the King of kings.
Bring in the day of broth - er - hood And end the night of wrong.
Her strength un - e - qual to her task; Rise up, and make her great!
As broth - ers of the Son of Man, Rise up, O men of God! A-MEN.

Words used by permission of "The Presbyterian Outlook"

O MASTER, LET ME WALK WITH THEE 211

MARYTON. L.M.

Washington Gladden — H. Percy Smith

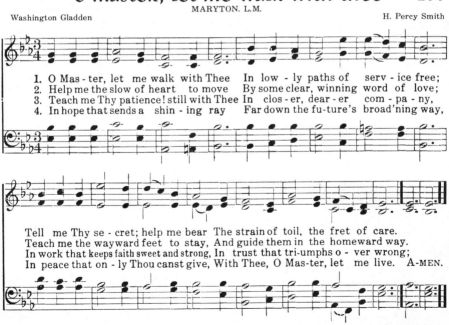

1. O Mas - ter, let me walk with Thee In low - ly paths of serv - ice free;
2. Help me the slow of heart to move By some clear, winning word of love;
3. Teach me Thy patience! still with Thee In clos - er, dear - er com - pa - ny,
4. In hope that sends a shin - ing ray Far down the fu - ture's broad'ning way,

Tell me Thy se - cret; help me bear The strain of toil, the fret of care.
Teach me the wayward feet to stay, And guide them in the homeward way.
In work that keeps faith sweet and strong, In trust that tri - umphs o - ver wrong;
In peace that on - ly Thou canst give, With Thee, O Mas - ter, let me live. A-MEN.

212 He Who Would Valiant Be

ST. DUNSTAN'S. 11 11 12 11

John Bunyan, alt. — Charles W. Douglas

1. He who would valiant be 'Gainst all disaster,
2. Whoso beset him round With dismal stories,
3. Since, Lord, thou dost defend Us with Thy Spirit,
Let him in constancy Follow the Master.
Do but themselves confound, His strength the more is.
We know we at the end Shall life inherit.
There's no discouragement Shall make him once relent His
No foes shall stay his might; Though he with giants fight, He
Then fancies, flee away! I'll fear not what men say, I'll
first avowed intent To be a pilgrim.
will make good his right To be a pilgrim.
labor night and day To be a pilgrim. A-MEN.

Guide Me, O Thou Great Jehovah

CWM RHONDDA. 8 7 8 7 8 7 7

From the Welsh
Trans. by Peter Williams and
William Williams

John Hughes

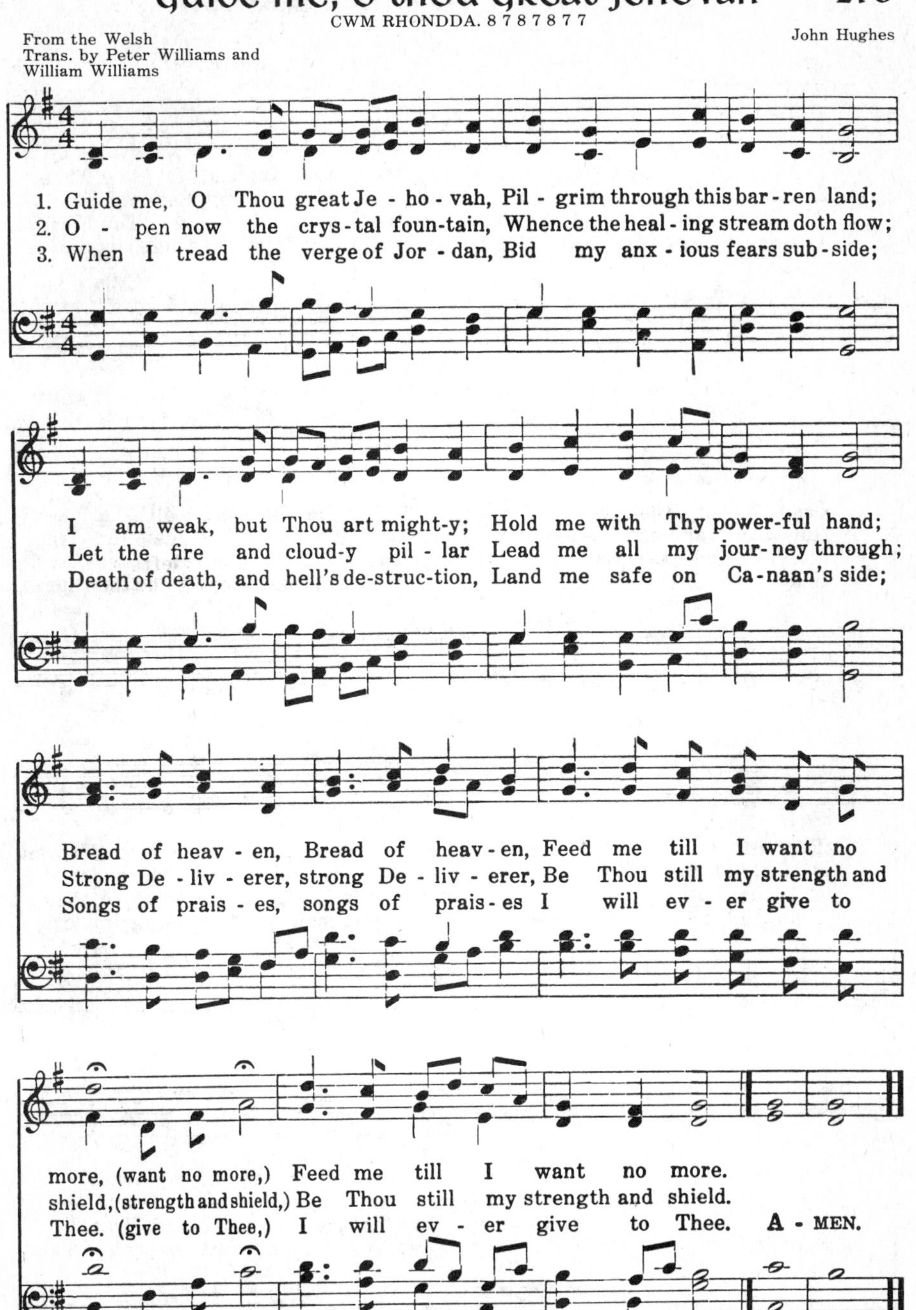
1. Guide me, O Thou great Je - ho - vah, Pil - grim through this bar - ren land;
2. O - pen now the crys - tal foun - tain, Whence the heal - ing stream doth flow;
3. When I tread the verge of Jor - dan, Bid my anx - ious fears sub - side;
I am weak, but Thou art might - y; Hold me with Thy power - ful hand;
Let the fire and cloud - y pil - lar Lead me all my jour - ney through;
Death of death, and hell's de - struc - tion, Land me safe on Ca - naan's side;
Bread of heav - en, Bread of heav - en, Feed me till I want no
Strong De - liv - erer, strong De - liv - erer, Be Thou still my strength and
Songs of prais - es, songs of prais - es I will ev - er give to
more, (want no more,) Feed me till I want no more.
shield, (strength and shield,) Be Thou still my strength and shield.
Thee. (give to Thee,) I will ev - er give to Thee. A - MEN.

214 Jesus, I my Cross Have Taken

ELLESDIE. 8 7 8 7 D.

Henry F. Lyte

Ascribed to Wolfgang A. Mozart
Arr. by Hubert P. Main

1. Je - sus, I my cross have tak - en, All to leave and fol - low Thee;
2. Let the world de-spise and leave me, They have left my Sav-iour, too;
3. Man may troub-le and dis - tress me, 'Twill but drive me to Thy breast;
4. Haste thee on from grace to glo - ry, Armed by faith and winged by prayer;
Des - ti - tute, de-spised, for - sak - en, Thou, from hence, my all shalt be:
Hu - man hearts and looks de - ceive me; Thou art not, like man, un - true;
Life with tri - als hard may press me, Heaven will bring me sweet - er rest.
Heaven's e-ter - nal day's be - fore thee, God's own hand shall guide thee there.
Per - ish ev - ery fond am - bi - tion, All I've sought, and hoped, and known;
And, while Thou shalt smile up - on me, God of wis - dom, love, and might,
O 'tis not in grief to harm me, While Thy love is left to me;
Soon shall close thy earth - ly mis - sion, Swift shall pass thy pil - grim days,
Yet how rich is my con-di - tion, God and heaven are still my own!
Foes may hate, and friends may shun me; Show Thy face, and all is bright.
O 'twere not in joy to charm me, Were that joy un-mixed with Thee.
Hope shall change to glad fru-i - tion, Faith to sight, and prayer to praise. AMEN.

Wherever He Leads I'll Go

FALLS CREEK. 8 6 8 7 Ref.

B. B. McKinney — B. B. McKinney

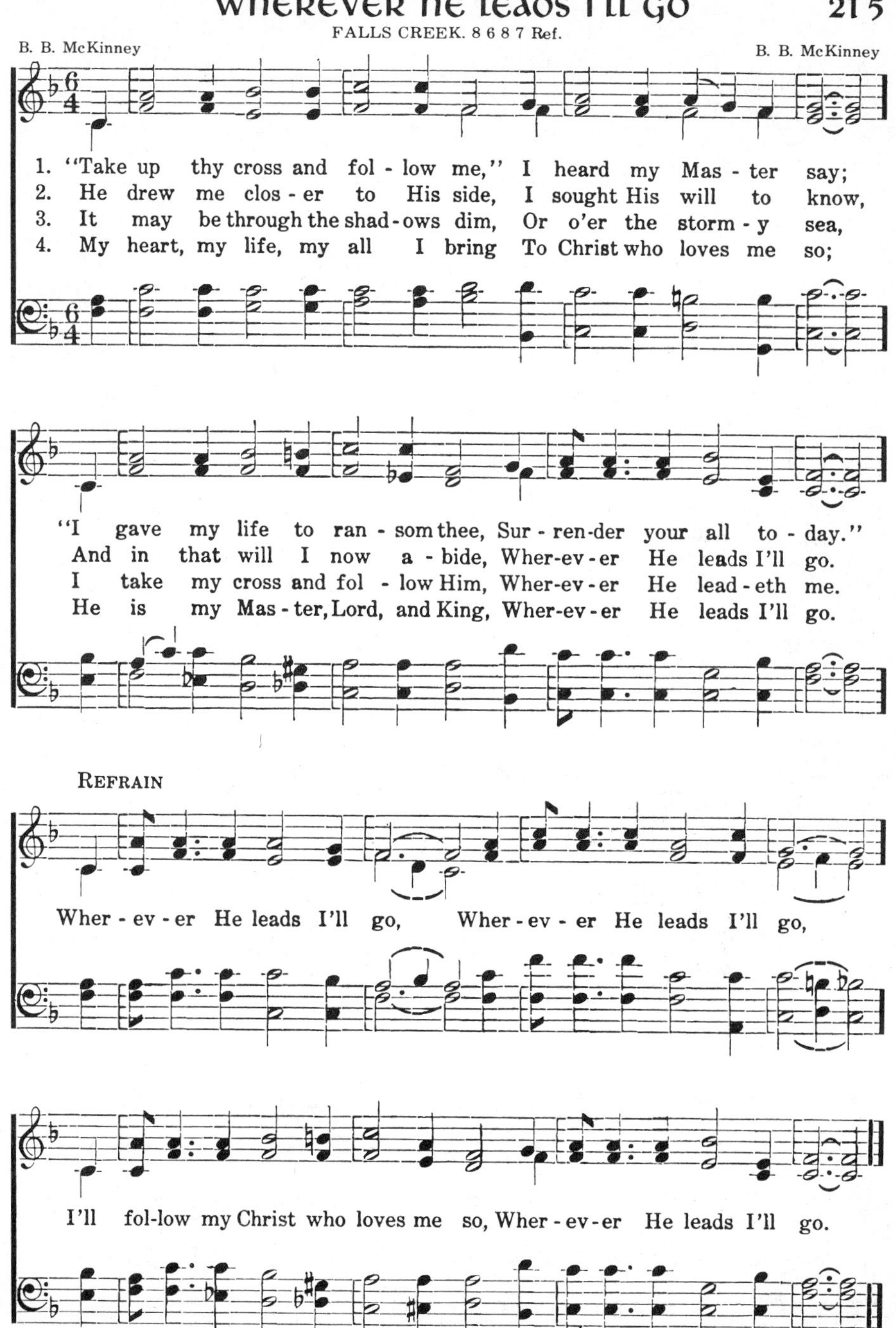
1. "Take up thy cross and fol - low me," I heard my Mas - ter say;
2. He drew me clos - er to His side, I sought His will to know,
3. It may be through the shad - ows dim, Or o'er the storm - y sea,
4. My heart, my life, my all I bring To Christ who loves me so;
"I gave my life to ran - som thee, Sur - ren - der your all to - day."
And in that will I now a - bide, Wher - ev - er He leads I'll go.
I take my cross and fol - low Him, Wher - ev - er He lead - eth me.
He is my Mas - ter, Lord, and King, Wher - ev - er He leads I'll go.
Refrain
Wher - ev - er He leads I'll go, Wher - ev - er He leads I'll go,
I'll fol - low my Christ who loves me so, Wher - ev - er He leads I'll go.

216 Soldiers of Christ, Arise

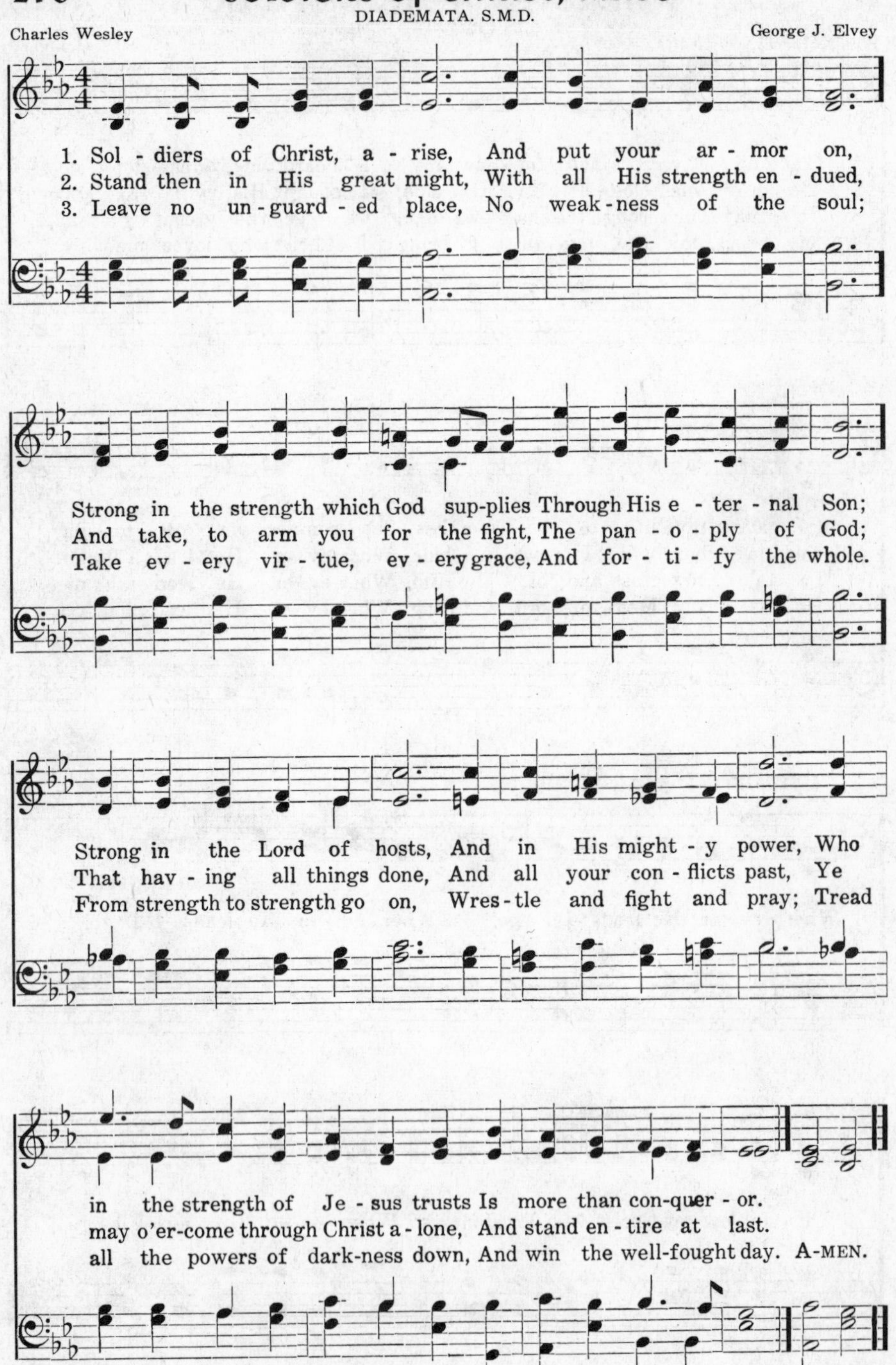
DIADEMATA. S.M.D.
Charles Wesley
George J. Elvey
1. Sol - diers of Christ, a - rise, And put your ar - mor on,
2. Stand then in His great might, With all His strength en - dued,
3. Leave no un - guard - ed place, No weak - ness of the soul;
Strong in the strength which God sup - plies Through His e - ter - nal Son;
And take, to arm you for the fight, The pan - o - ply of God;
Take ev - ery vir - tue, ev - ery grace, And for - ti - fy the whole.
Strong in the Lord of hosts, And in His might - y power, Who
That hav - ing all things done, And all your con - flicts past, Ye
From strength to strength go on, Wres - tle and fight and pray; Tread
in the strength of Je - sus trusts Is more than con - quer - or.
may o'er - come through Christ a - lone, And stand en - tire at last.
all the powers of dark - ness down, And win the well - fought day. A - MEN.

ONWARD, CHRISTIAN SOLDIERS 217

ST. GERTRUDE. 6 5 6 5 D. Ref.

Sabine Baring-Gould

Arthur S. Sullivan

1. On-ward, Christian sol-diers, March-ing as to war, With the cross of Je - sus
2. Like a might-y ar - my Moves the Church of God; Brothers, we are tread-ing
3. Crowns and thrones may perish, Kingdoms rise and wane, But the Church of Je - sus
4. On-ward, then, ye peo - ple, Join our hap-py throng, Blend with ours your voic-es

Go - ing on be-fore: Christ the roy - al Mas - ter Leads a-gainst the foe;
Where the saints have trod; We are not di - vid - ed, All one bod - y we,
Con-stant will re-main; Gates of hell can nev - er 'Gainst that Church prevail;
In the tri-umph song; Glo - ry, laud, and hon - or Un - to Christ the King;

For-ward in - to bat - tle, See, His banners go.
One in hope and doc - trine, One in char - i - ty.
We have Christ's own promise, And that cannot fail.
This through countless a - ges Men and an-gels sing.

REFRAIN

Onward, Christian sol - diers,
March-ing as to war, With the cross of Je - sus Go - ing on be - fore. A-MEN.

218 Lead On, O King Eternal

LANCASHIRE. 7 6 7 6 D.

Ernest W. Shurtleff — Henry Smart

1. Lead on, O King E - ter - nal, The day of march has come;
2. Lead on, O King E - ter - nal, Till sin's fierce war shall cease,
3. Lead on, O King E - ter - nal, We fol - low, not with fears;
Hence-forth in fields of con - quest Thy tents shall be our home.
And ho - li - ness shall whis - per The sweet A - men of peace;
For glad - ness breaks like morn - ing Wher-e'er Thy face ap - pears;
Through days of prep - a - ra - tion Thy grace has made us strong,
For not with swords loud clash - ing, Nor roll of stir - ring drums,
Thy cross is lift - ed o'er us; We jour - ney in its light:
And now, O King E - ter - nal, We lift our bat - tle song.
With deeds of love and mer - cy The heaven-ly king - dom comes.
The crown a - waits the con - quest; Lead on, O God of might. A-MEN.

AM I A SOLDIER OF THE CROSS? 219

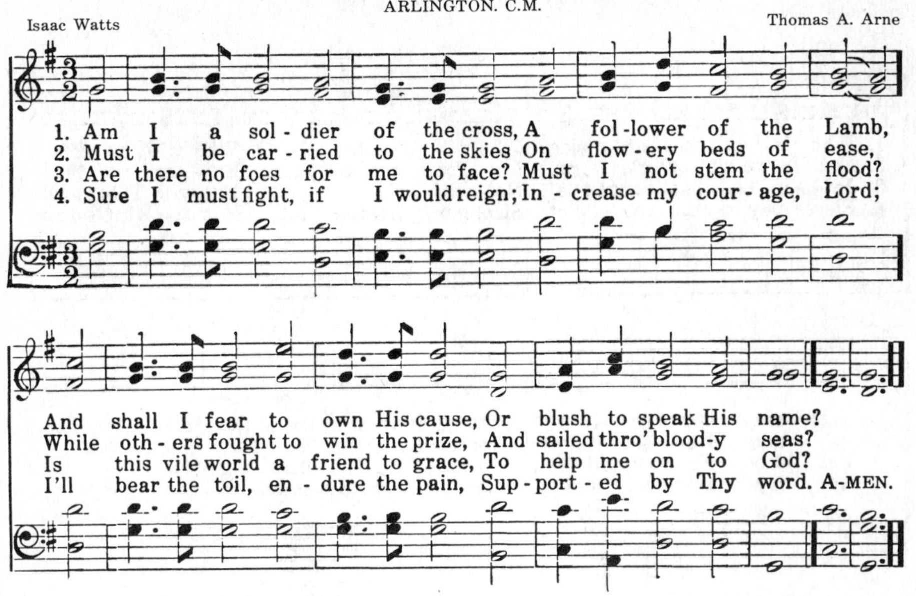
ARLINGTON. C.M.
Isaac Watts
Thomas A. Arne
1. Am I a sol-dier of the cross, A fol-lower of the Lamb,
2. Must I be car-ried to the skies On flow-ery beds of ease,
3. Are there no foes for me to face? Must I not stem the flood?
4. Sure I must fight, if I would reign; In-crease my cour-age, Lord;
And shall I fear to own His cause, Or blush to speak His name?
While oth-ers fought to win the prize, And sailed thro' blood-y seas?
Is this vile world a friend to grace, To help me on to God?
I'll bear the toil, en-dure the pain, Sup-port-ed by Thy word. A-MEN.

WHERE CROSS THE CROWDED WAYS OF LIFE 220

GERMANY. L.M.

Frank Mason North

William Gardiner's *Sacred Melodies*, 1815

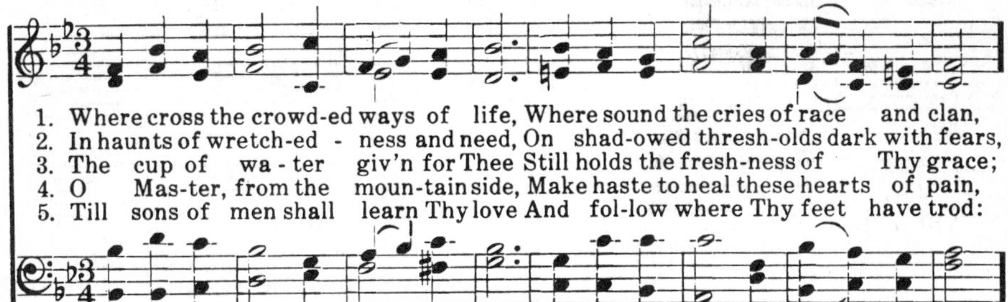

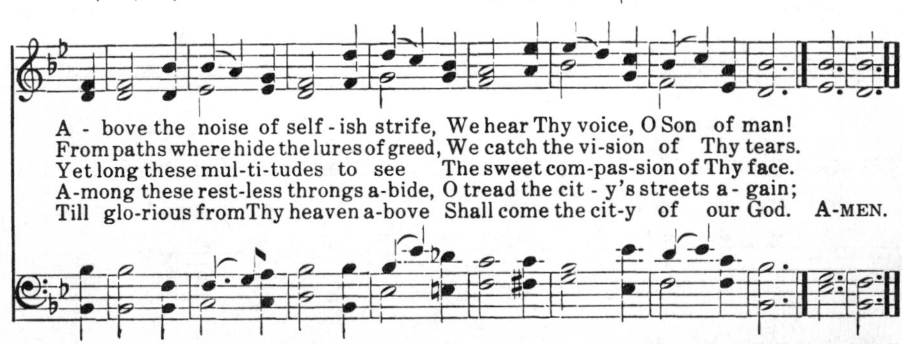

1. Where cross the crowd-ed ways of life, Where sound the cries of race and clan,
A-bove the noise of self-ish strife, We hear Thy voice, O Son of man!

2. In haunts of wretch-ed-ness and need, On shad-owed thresh-olds dark with fears,
From paths where hide the lures of greed, We catch the vi-sion of Thy tears.

3. The cup of wa-ter giv'n for Thee Still holds the fresh-ness of Thy grace;
Yet long these mul-ti-tudes to see The sweet com-pas-sion of Thy face.

4. O Mas-ter, from the moun-tain side, Make haste to heal these hearts of pain,
A-mong these rest-less throngs a-bide, O tread the cit-y's streets a-gain;

5. Till sons of men shall learn Thy love And fol-low where Thy feet have trod:
Till glo-rious from Thy heaven a-bove Shall come the cit-y of our God. A-MEN.

221 Who Is on the Lord's Side?

ARMAGEDDON. 6 5 6 5 D. Ref.

Frances R. Havergal

Traditional German Melody
Arr. by John Goss

1. Who is on the Lord's side? Who will serve the King? Who will be His
2. Not for weight of glo - ry, Not for crown and palm, En - ter we the
3. Je - sus, Thou hast bought us, Not with gold or gem, But with Thine own
4. Fierce may be the con - flict, Strong may be the foe, But the King's own

help - ers, Oth - er lives to bring? Who will leave the world's side?
ar - my, Raise the war - rior psalm; But for love that claim - eth
life - blood, For Thy di - a - dem. With Thy bless - ing fill - ing
ar - my None can o - ver - throw. Round His stand - ard rang - ing

Who will face the foe? Who is on the Lord's side? Who for
Lives for whom He died; He whom Je - sus nam - eth Must be
Each who comes to Thee, Thou hast made us will - ing, Thou hast
Vic - tory is se - cure; For His truth un - chang - ing Makes the

Him will go? By Thy call of mer - cy, By Thy grace di - vine,
on His side. By Thy love con - strain - ing, By Thy grace di - vine,
made us free. By Thy grand re - demp - tion, By Thy grace di - vine,
tri - umph sure. Joy - ful - ly en - list - ing By Thy grace di - vine,

We are on the Lord's side, Sav - iour, we are Thine. A - MEN.

See alternate tune on opposite page

ON OUR WAY REJOICING 222

HERMAS. 6 5 6 5 D. Ref.

John S. B. Monsell, alt. | Frances R. Havergal

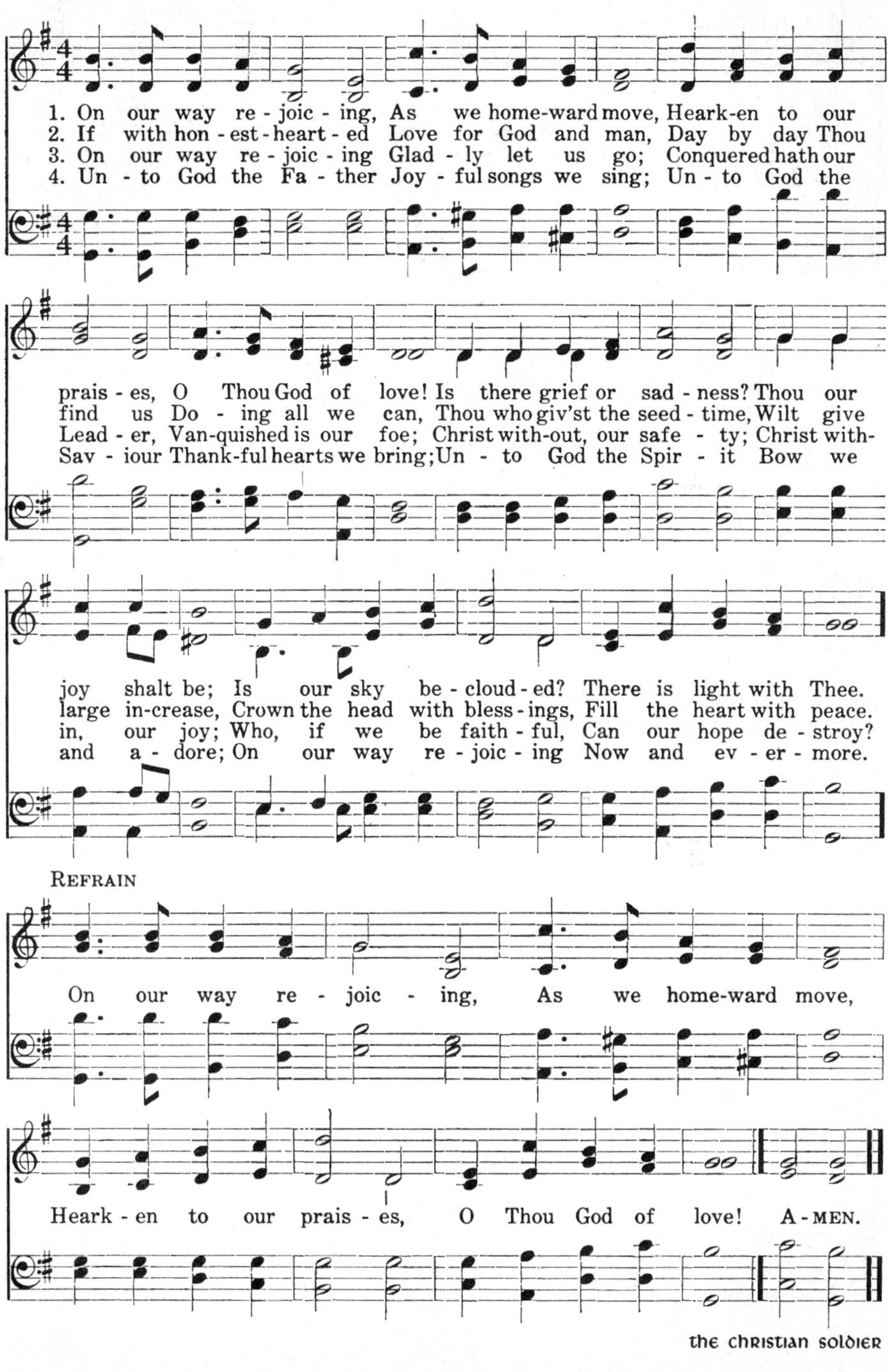

1. On our way re - joic - ing, As we home-ward move, Hear-ken to our
2. If with hon - est - heart - ed Love for God and man, Day by day Thou
3. On our way re - joic - ing Glad - ly let us go; Conquered hath our
4. Un - to God the Fa - ther Joy - ful songs we sing; Un - to God the

prais - es, O Thou God of love! Is there grief or sad - ness? Thou our
find us Do - ing all we can, Thou who giv'st the seed - time, Wilt give
Lead - er, Van-quished is our foe; Christ with-out, our safe - ty; Christ with-
Sav - iour Thank-ful hearts we bring; Un - to God the Spir - it Bow we

joy shalt be; Is our sky be - cloud - ed? There is light with Thee.
large in-crease, Crown the head with bless - ings, Fill the heart with peace.
in, our joy; Who, if we be faith - ful, Can our hope de - stroy?
and a - dore; On our way re - joic - ing Now and ev - er - more.

REFRAIN

On our way re - joic - ing, As we home-ward move,
Heark - en to our prais - es, O Thou God of love! A - MEN.

223 The Son of God Goes Forth to War

ALL SAINTS, NEW. C.M.D.

Reginald Heber

Henry S. Cutler

1. The Son of God goes forth to war, A king-ly crown to gain;
2. The mar-tyr first, whose ea-gle eye Could pierce be-yond the grave,
3. A glo-rious band, the cho-sen few On whom the Spir-it came,
4. A no-ble ar-my, men and boys, The ma-tron and the maid,
His blood-red ban-ner streams a-far: Who fol-lows in His train?
Who saw his Mas-ter in the sky, And called on Him to save:
Twelve va-liant saints, their hope they knew, And mocked the cross and flame:
A-round the Sav-iour's throne re-joice, In robes of light ar-rayed:
Who best can drink his cup of woe, Tri-um-phant o-ver pain,
Like Him, with par-don on his tongue In midst of mor-tal pain,
They met the ty-rant's brandished steel, The li-on's go-ry mane;
They climbed the steep as-cent of heaven Through per-il, toil, and pain;
Who pa-tient bears his cross be-low, He fol-lows in His train.
He prayed for them that did the wrong: Who fol-lows in his train?
They bowed their necks the death to feel: Who fol-lows in their train?
O God, to us may grace be given To fol-low in their train. A-MEN.

THE BATTLE IS THE LORD'S! 224

LEONI. 6 6 8 4 D.

E. Margaret Clarkson

Hebrew Melody
Arr. by Meyer Lyon

1. The bat - tle is the Lord's! The har - vest fields are white:
2. The bat - tle is the Lord's! Not ours is strength or skill,
3. The bat - tle is the Lord's! The Vic - tor cru - ci - fied
4. The bat - tle is the Lord's! Stand still, my soul, and see
How few the reap - ing hands ap - pear, Their strength how slight!
But His a - lone, in sov - ereign grace, To work His will.
Must with the tra - vail of His soul Be sat - is - fied.
The great sal - va - tion God hath wrought Re - vealed for thee.
Yet vic - to - ry is sure— We face a van-quished foe;
Ours, count - ing not the cost, Un - flinch - ing, to o - bey;
The pow'rs of hell shall fail, And all God's will be done,
Then, rest - ing in His might, Lift high His tri - umph song,
Then for - ward with the ris - en Christ To bat - tle go!
And in His time His ho - ly arm Shall win the day.
Till ev - ery soul whom He hath giv'n To Christ be won.
For pow'r, do - min - ion, king - dom, strength To Christ be - long!

By permission of Christian Publications, Inc., Harrisburg, Pa.

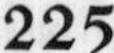

Stand Up, Stand Up for Jesus

GEIBEL. 7 6 7 6 D. Ref.

George Duffield — Adam Geibel

Unison

1. Stand up, stand up for Je - sus, Ye sol - diers of the cross;
2. Stand up, stand up for Je - sus, The trump-et call o - bey;
3. Stand up, stand up for Je - sus, The strife will not be long;

Lift high His roy - al ban - ner, It must not suf - fer loss:
Forth to the might - y con - flict, In this His glo - rious day:
This day the noise of bat - tle, The next, the vic - tor's song:

From vic - tory un - to vic - tory His ar - my shall He lead,
"Ye that are men, now serve Him" A - gainst un - num-bered foes;
To Him that o - ver - com - eth, A crown of life shall be:

rit.

Till ev - ery foe is van - quished, And Christ is Lord in - deed.
Let cour - age rise with dan - ger, And strength to strength op - pose.
He with the King of glo - ry Shall reign e - ter - nal - ly.

See alternate tune on opposite page

REFRAIN
Stand up for Je - sus, Ye sol - diers of the cross;. . .
Stand up, stand up for Je - sus,
Lift high His roy-al ban - ner, It must not, it must not suf - fer loss.
the morning light is breaking
226
WEBB. 7 6 7 6 D.
Samuel F. Smith
George J. Webb
1. The morn-ing light is break-ing, The dark-ness dis-ap-pears; The sons of earth are
2. See hea-then na-tions bend-ing Be-fore the God we love, And thousand hearts as-
3. Blest riv - er of sal - va - tion, Pur-sue thine on-ward way; Flow thou to ev - ery
wak - ing To pen - i-ten-tial tears! Each breeze that sweeps the o-cean Brings ti-dings
cend - ing In grat - i - tude a-bove; While sin-ners, now con-fess-ing, The gos - pel
na - tion, Nor in thy rich-ness stay; Stay not till all the low - ly Tri - um-phant
from a - far, Of na-tions in com-mo - tion, Pre-pared for Zi-on's war.
call o - bey, And seek the Saviour's blessing, A na-tion in a day.
reach their home; Stay not till all the ho - ly Proclaim, "The Lord is come!" A-MEN.

227 Rescue the Perishing

RESCUE. Irregular. Ref.

Fanny J. Crosby | William H. Doane

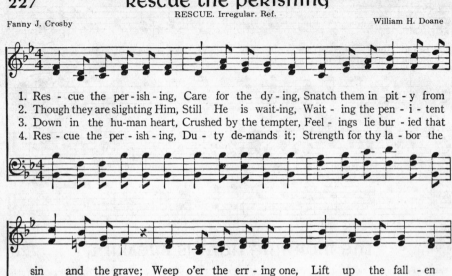

1. Res - cue the per - ish - ing, Care for the dy - ing, Snatch them in pit - y from
2. Though they are slighting Him, Still He is wait - ing, Wait - ing the pen - i - tent
3. Down in the hu - man heart, Crushed by the tempter, Feel - ings lie bur - ied that
4. Res - cue the per - ish - ing, Du - ty de - mands it; Strength for thy la - bor the

sin and the grave; Weep o'er the err - ing one, Lift up the fall - en
child to re - ceive; Plead with them ear - nest - ly, Plead with them gen - tly,
grace can re - store; Touched by a lov - ing heart, Wak - ened by kind - ness,
Lord will pro - vide; Back to the nar - row way Pa - tient - ly win them;

REFRAIN

Tell them of Je - sus the migh - ty to save.
He will for - give if they on - ly be - lieve. Res - cue the per - ish - ing,
Chords that were bro - ken will vi - brate once more.
Tell the poor wan - derer a Sav - iour has died.

Care for the dy - ing; Je - sus is mer - ci - ful, Je - sus will save.

Hark, the Voice of Jesus Calling 228

ELLESDIE. 8 7 8 7 D.

Daniel March

Ascribed to Wolfgang A. Mozart
Arr. by Hubert P. Main

1. Hark, the voice of Je - sus call - ing, "Who will go and work to - day?
2. If you can - not cross the o - cean And the heath - en lands ex - plore,
3. Let none hear you i - dly say - ing, "There is noth - ing I can do,"

Fields are white, and har - vests wait - ing, Who will bear the sheaves a - way?"
You can find the heath - en near - er, You can help them at your door:
While the souls of men are dy - ing, And the Mas - ter calls for you:

Loud and long the Mas - ter call - eth, Rich re - ward He of - fers thee;
If you can - not give your thousands, You can give the wid - ow's mite;
Glad - ly take the task He gives you; Let His work your pleas - ure be;

Who will an - swer, glad - ly say - ing, "Here am I; send me, send me"?
And the least you give for Je - sus Will be pre - cious in His sight.
An - swer quickly when He call - eth, "Here am I; send me, send me." A-MEN.

229 O Master of the Waking World

ST. PETERSBURG. 8 8 8 8 8 8
Frank Mason North
Dimitri S. Bortniansky
1. O Mas - ter of the wak - ing world, Who hast the
2. We hear the throb of surg - ing life, The clank of
3. Thy wit - ness in the souls of men, Thy Spir - it's
4. O Church of God! A - wake! A - wake! The wak - ing
na - tions in Thy heart— The heart that bled and broke to send
chains, the curse of greed, The moan of pain, the fu - tile cries
cease - less, brood-ing power, In lands where shad - ows hide the light,
world is call - ing thee. Lift up thine eyes! Hear thou once more
God's love to earth's re - mot - est part — Show us a - new in
Of su - per - sti - tion's cru - el creed; The peo - ples hun - ger
A - wait a new cre - a - tive hour. O might - y God, set
The chal - lenge of hu - man - i - ty! O Christ, we come! Our
Cal - va - ry The won - drous power that makes men free.
for Thee, Lord, The isles are wait - ing for Thy Word.
us a - flame To show the glo - ries of Thy name.
all we bring, To serve our world and Thee, our King. A - MEN.

We've a Story to Tell to the Nations 230

MESSAGE. Irregular. Ref.
H. Ernest Nichol
H. Ernest Nichol
1. We've a sto - ry to tell to the na - tions That shall turn their hearts to the right, A sto - ry of truth and mer - cy, A sto - ry of peace and light, A sto - ry of peace and light.
2. We've a song to be sung to the na - tions That shall lift their hearts to the Lord, A song that shall con - quer e - vil And shat - ter the spear and sword, And shat - ter the spear and sword.
3. We've a mes - sage to give to the na - tions That the Lord who reign-eth a - bove Hath sent us His Son to save us, And show us that God is love, And show us that God is love.
4. We've a Sav - iour to show to the na - tions Who the path of sor - row hath trod, That all of the world's great peo - ples Might come to the truth of God, Might come to the truth of God.
Refrain
For the dark-ness shall turn to dawn - ing, And the dawn-ing to noon-day bright,
And Christ's great king-dom shall come to earth, The king-dom of love and light.

231 The Call for Reapers

CLEMM. 8 7 8 7 Ref.

John O. Thompson | J.B.O. Clemm

1. Far and near the fields are teem-ing With the waves of ri - pened grain;
2. Send them forth with morn's first beaming, Send them in the noon-tide's glare;
3. O thou, whom thy Lord is send-ing, Gath - er now the sheaves of gold;

Far and near their gold is gleam-ing O'er the sun - ny slope and plain.
When the sun's last rays are gleam-ing, Bid them gath - er ev - ery-where.
Heavenward then at eve-ning wend- ing, Thou shalt come with joy un - told.

FINE

D.S.—*Send them now the sheaves to gath - er, Ere the har - vest - time pass by.*

REFRAIN
D.S.
Lord of har - vest, send forth reap - ers! Hear us, Lord, to Thee we cry;

232 Jesus Shall Reign

DUKE STREET. L.M.

Isaac Watts
From Psalm 72 | John Hatton

1. Je - sus shall reign wher-e'er the sun Does his suc - ces - sive jour-neys run;
2. From north to south the prin - ces meet To pay their hom-age at His feet;
3. To Him shall end - less prayer be made, And end- less prais-es crown His head;
4. Peo - ple and realms of ev - ery tongue Dwell on His love with sweet-est song,

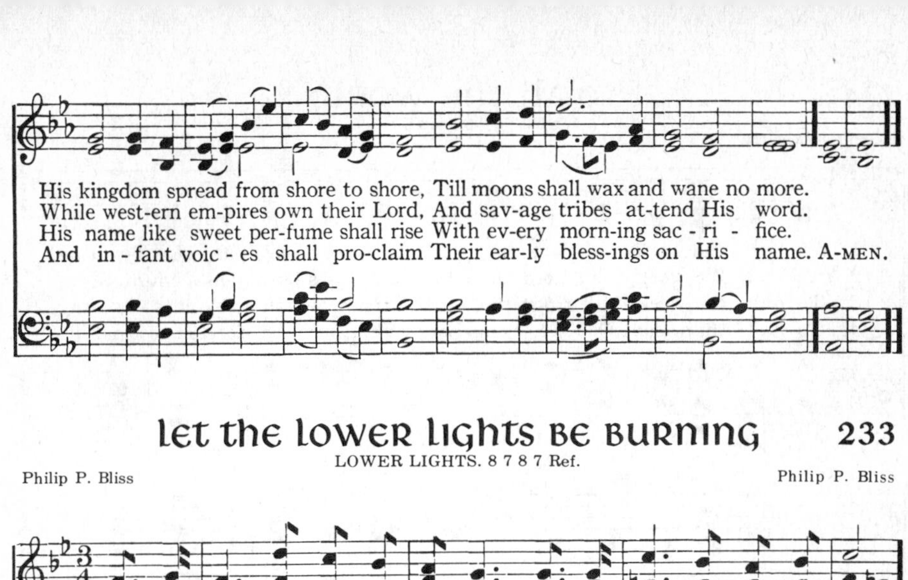
His kingdom spread from shore to shore, Till moons shall wax and wane no more.
While west-ern em-pires own their Lord, And sav-age tribes at-tend His word.
His name like sweet per-fume shall rise With ev-ery morn-ing sac - ri - fice.
And in - fant voic - es shall pro-claim Their ear-ly bless-ings on His name. A-MEN.

LET THE LOWER LIGHTS BE BURNING 233

LOWER LIGHTS. 8 7 8 7 Ref.

Philip P. Bliss — Philip P. Bliss

1. Bright-ly beams our Fa-ther's mer - cy From His light-house ev - er - more,
But to us He gives the keep - ing Of the lights a - long the shore.

2. Dark the night of sin has set - tled, Loud the an - gry bil - lows roar;
Ea - ger eyes are watch-ing, long - ing, For the lights a - long the shore.

3. Trim your fee - ble lamp, my broth - er; Some poor sail - or tem-pest tossed,
Try - ing now to make the har - bor, In the dark-ness may be lost.

REFRAIN

Let the low - er lights be burn - ing! Send a gleam a - cross the wave!
Some poor faint - ing, strug-gling sea-man You may res - cue, you may save.

234 TO ALL THE WORLD

WIMBY. 8 7 8 7 8 8 8 7 Ref.

Joseph C. Macaulay — Wendell P. Loveless

1. To all the world! the love of God, In sav-ing pas-sion flow-ing,
2. "To all the world!" our Lord de-creed, His mes-sen-gers com-mand-ing:
3. To all the world! still rings the call From men in dark-ness ly-ing,
4. To all the world! O Je-sus, Lord, While here be-fore Thee bend-ing,
Sent forth His Son to bear the rod, E-ter-nal life be-stow-ing;
To ev-ery clime this Gos-pel speed, Your wit-ness still ex-pand-ing,
Fast bound in Sa-tan's bane-ful thrall, In sin and an-guish dy-ing:
Strike in my heart love's mas-ter-chord, All low de-sires tran-scend-ing.
Not on-ly to the fa-vored race, And such as boast su-per-ior place,
Till earth re-ech-o with the sound, And ev-ery-where My grace a-bound;
No res-pite from their haunt-ing fears, No dry-ing of their bit-ter tears,
Here would I yield to Thee my all, And has-ten at Thy dear-est call
But un-to all who seek His face, His great sal-va-tion show-ing.
Nor fear, tho' foes be-set you round, Your on-ward march with-stand-ing.
Till Christ's am-bas-sa-dor ap-pears, The hosts of hell de-fy-ing.
To res-cue souls from sin's dark pall: Send me whilst Thou art send-ing.

Refrain
To all the world! O word of love di-vine! To all the world! This is Thy
blest de-sign; To all the world! and lo, the task is mine, Send me! O Lord, send me.
I gave my life for thee
235
KENOSIS. Irregular. Ref.
Frances R. Havergal
Philip P. Bliss
1. I gave My life for thee, My pre - cious blood I shed,
2. My Fa - ther's house of light, My glo - ry - cir - cled throne
3. I suf - fered much for thee, More than thy tongue can tell,
4. And I have brought to thee, Down from My home a - bove,
That thou might'st ran-somed be, And quick - ened from the dead;
I left for earth - ly night, For wan - derings sad and lone;
Of bit - terest ag - o - ny, To res - cue thee from hell;
Sal - va - tion full and free, My par - don and My love;
I gave, I gave My life for thee, What hast thou given for Me?
I left, I left it all for thee, Hast thou left aught for Me?
I've borne, I've borne it all for thee, What hast thou borne for Me?
I bring, I bring rich gifts to thee, What hast thou brought to Me?

236 MAKE ME A BLESSING

SCHULER. 10 7 10 7 Ref.

Ira B. Wilson | George S. Schuler

1. Out in the highways and byways of life, Man-y are weary and sad;
are wea-ry and sad;
2. Tell the sweet story of Christ and His love, Tell of His power to forgive;
His power to for-give;
3. Give as 'twas giv-en to you in your need, Love as the Master loved you;
the Mas-ter loved you;
Car-ry the sunshine where darkness is rife, Mak-ing the sor-row-ing glad.
Oth-ers will trust Him if on-ly you prove True, ev-ery mo-ment you live.
Be to the help-less a help-er in-deed, Un-to your mis-sion be true.
REFRAIN Men or Unison
Women
Make me a bless-ing, Make me a bless-ing, Out of my
Unison
life may Je-sus shine; Make me a bless-ing,
Out of my life
Men
Women
Parts
O Sav-iour, I pray, Make me a bless-ing to some-one to-day.
I pray Thee, my Saviour,
Tenors

O Zion, Haste

TIDINGS. 11 10 11 10 Ref.

Mary A. Thomson

James Walch

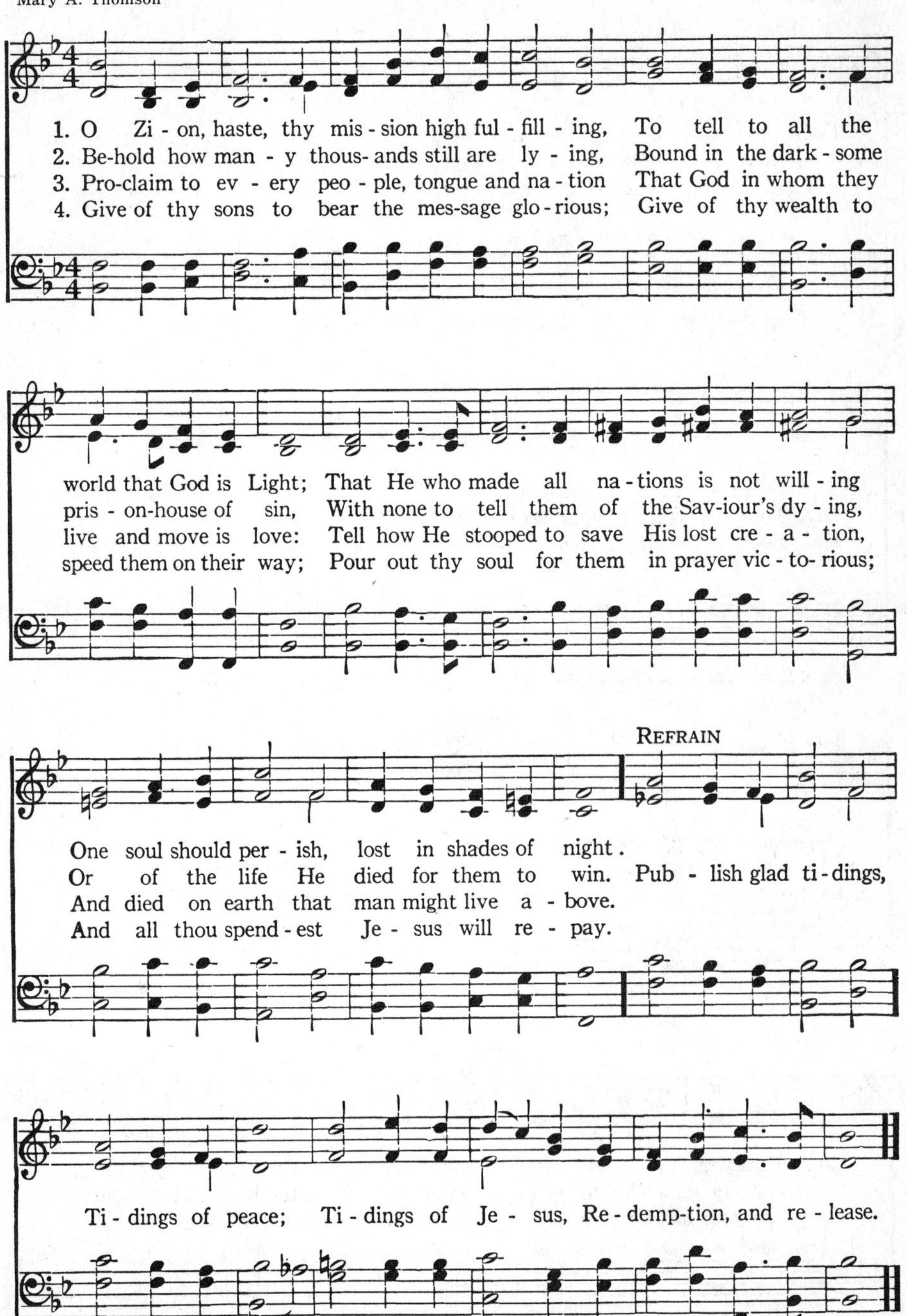
1. O Zi - on, haste, thy mis - sion high ful - fill - ing, To tell to all the
2. Be-hold how man - y thous- ands still are ly - ing, Bound in the dark - some
3. Pro-claim to ev - ery peo - ple, tongue and na - tion That God in whom they
4. Give of thy sons to bear the mes-sage glo - rious; Give of thy wealth to
world that God is Light; That He who made all na - tions is not will - ing
pris - on-house of sin, With none to tell them of the Sav-iour's dy - ing,
live and move is love: Tell how He stooped to save His lost cre - a - tion,
speed them on their way; Pour out thy soul for them in prayer vic - to- rious;
REFRAIN
One soul should per - ish, lost in shades of night.
Or of the life He died for them to win. Pub - lish glad ti - dings,
And died on earth that man might live a - bove.
And all thou spend - est Je - sus will re - pay.
Ti - dings of peace; Ti - dings of Je - sus, Re - demp-tion, and re - lease.

238 GIVE OF YOUR BEST TO THE MASTER

BARNARD. 8 7 8 7 D. Ref.

Howard B. Grose

Charlotte A. Barnard

1. Give of your best to the Mas - ter; Give of the strength of your youth;
2. Give of your best to the Mas - ter; Give Him first place in your heart;
3. Give of your best to the Mas - ter; Naught else is wor - thy His love;

REF.—*Give of your best to the Mas - ter; Give of the strength of your youth;*

FINE

Throw your soul's fresh, glowing ar - dor In - to the bat - tle for truth.
Give Him first place in your serv - ice, Con - se - crate ev - ery part.
He gave Him - self for your ran - som, Gave up His glo - ry a - bove:

Clad in sal - va - tion's full ar - mor, Join in the bat - tle for truth.

Je - sus has set the ex - am - ple; Daunt-less was He, young and brave;
Give, and to you shall be giv - en; God His be - lov - ed Son gave;
Laid down His life with-out mur - mur, You from sin's ru - in to save;

D. C.

Give Him your loy - al de - vo - tion, Give Him the best that you have.
Grate - ful - ly seek - ing to serve Him, Give Him the best that you have.
Give Him your heart's ad-o - ra - tion, Give Him the best that you have.

hymns of the christian hope

the physical objective of the historic crusades was the city of jerusalem at the heart of the holy land. the travelers hoped that the site of jesus' death and resurrection might be reclaimed from those who occupied it.

the goal of the modern crusader is the "new jerusalem" – the eternal dwelling place which christ has prepared for us. heaven is the eagerly-anticipated home of the christian, where we will enjoy endless spiritual growth and activity in the presence of the saviour whom we love.

this "blessed hope" has inspired many of our most joyful songs.

239 What if it were today?

SECOND COMING. Irregular. Ref.

Leila N. Morris — Leila N. Morris

1. Je - sus is com - ing to earth a - gain, What if it were to - day?
2. Sa - tan's do - min - ion will soon be o'er, Oh, that it were to - day!
3. Faith - ful and true would He find us here, If He should come to - day?
Com - ing in pow - er and love to reign, What if it were to - day?
Sor - row and sigh - ing shall be no more, Oh, that it were to - day!
Watch - ing in glad - ness and not in fear, If He should come to - day?
Com - ing to claim His cho - sen Bride, All the re - deemed and pu - ri - fied,
Then shall the dead in Christ a - rise, Caught up to meet Him in the skies,
Signs of His com - ing mul - ti - ply, Morning light breaks in east - ern sky,
rit. a tempo
O - ver this whole earth scat - tered wide, What if it were to - day?
When shall these glo - ries meet our eyes? What if it were to - day?
Watch, for that time is draw - ing nigh, What if it were to - day?
REFRAIN
Glo - ry, glo - ry! Joy to my heart 'twill bring;
Joy to my heart 'twill bring;

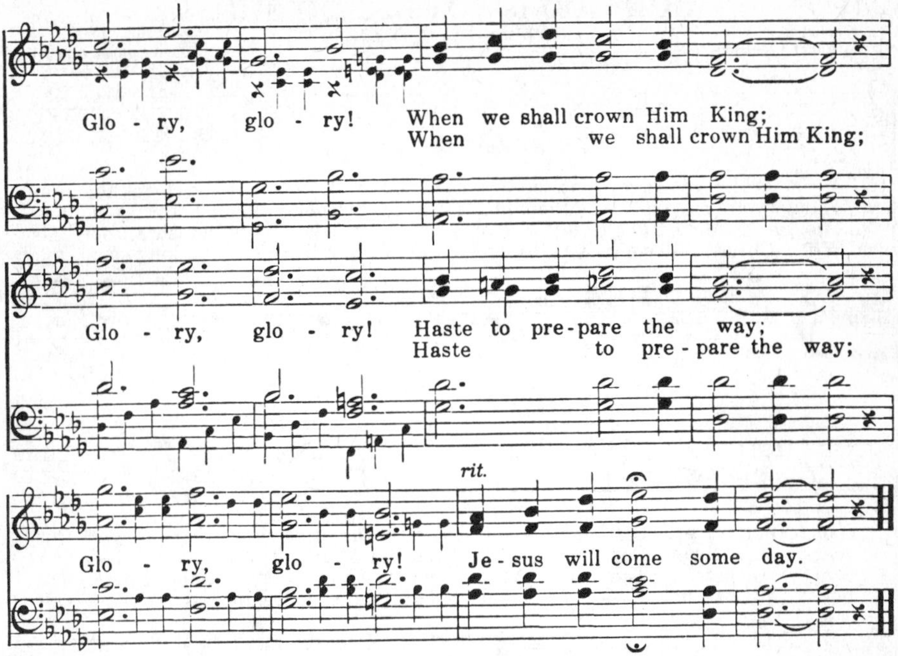

Glo - ry, glo - ry! When we shall crown Him King;
When we shall crown Him King;

Glo - ry, glo - ry! Haste to pre-pare the way;
Haste to pre-pare the way;

rit.

Glo - ry, glo - ry! Je-sus will come some day.

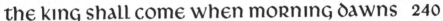

the king shall come when morning dawns 240

ST. STEPHEN. C.M.

Ancient Greek
Trans. by John Brownlie

William Jones

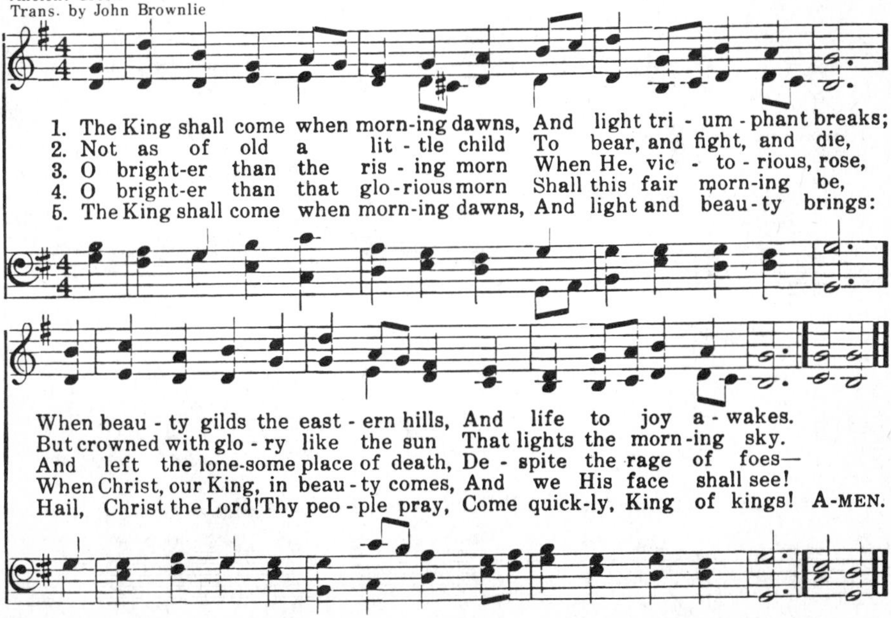

1. The King shall come when morn-ing dawns, And light tri - um - phant breaks;
2. Not as of old a lit - tle child To bear, and fight, and die,
3. O bright-er than the ris - ing morn When He, vic - to - rious, rose,
4. O bright-er than that glo-rious morn Shall this fair morn-ing be,
5. The King shall come when morn-ing dawns, And light and beau - ty brings:

When beau - ty gilds the east - ern hills, And life to joy a - wakes.
But crowned with glo - ry like the sun That lights the morn-ing sky.
And left the lone-some place of death, De - spite the rage of foes—
When Christ, our King, in beau - ty comes, And we His face shall see!
Hail, Christ the Lord! Thy peo - ple pray, Come quick-ly, King of kings! A-MEN.

241 OUR GOD IS SOVEREIGN STILL

SOVEREIGNTY. 9 9 9 6 Ref.

E. Margaret Clarkson E. Margaret Clarkson

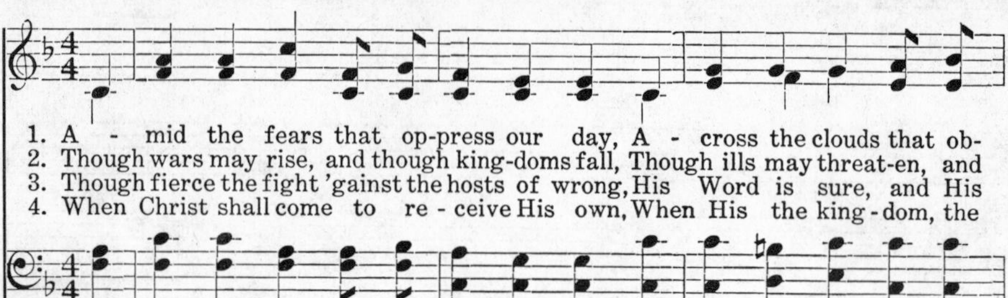

1. A - mid the fears that op-press our day, A - cross the clouds that ob-
2. Though wars may rise, and though king-doms fall, Though ills may threat-en, and
3. Though fierce the fight 'gainst the hosts of wrong, His Word is sure, and His
4. When Christ shall come to re - ceive His own, When His the king - dom, the

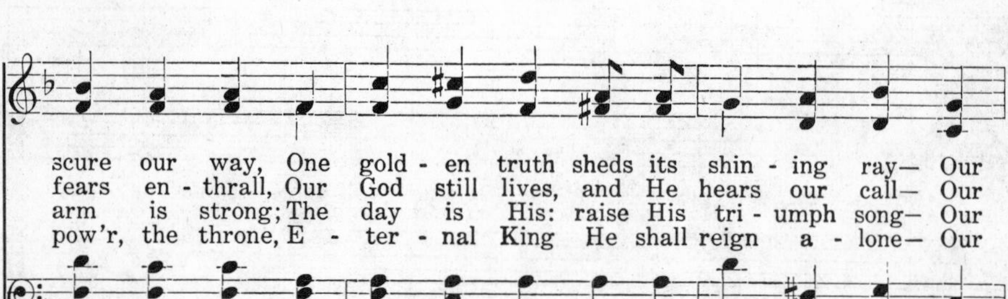

scure our way, One gold - en truth sheds its shin - ing ray— Our
fears en - thrall, Our God still lives, and He hears our call— Our
arm is strong; The day is His: raise His tri - umph song— Our
pow'r, the throne, E - ter - nal King He shall reign a - lone— Our

God is sov-ereign still.
God is sov-ereign still.
God is sov-ereign still.
God is sov-ereign still.

REFRAIN

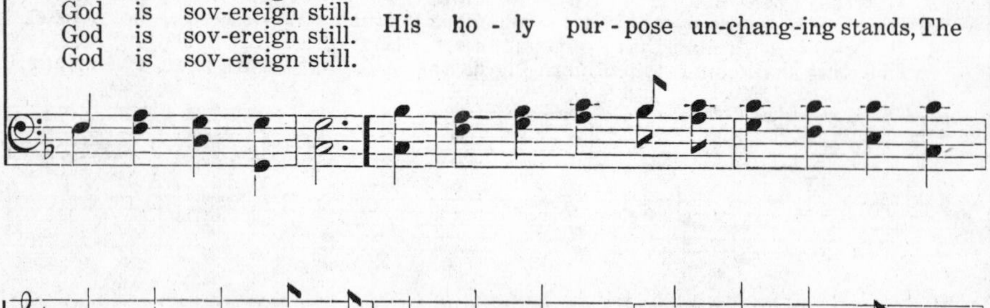

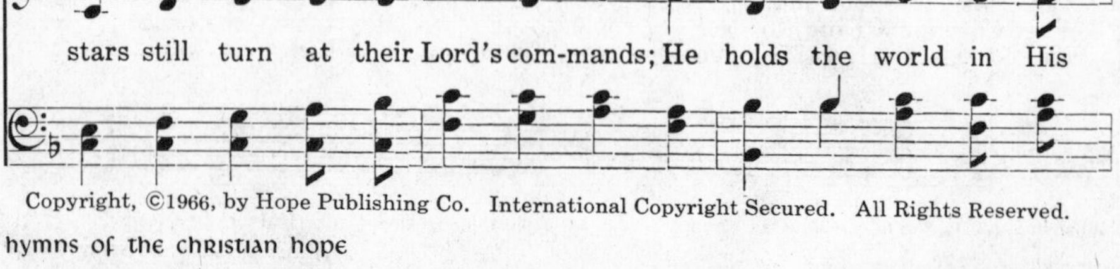

His ho - ly pur - pose un-chang-ing stands, The stars still turn at their Lord's com-mands; He holds the world in His

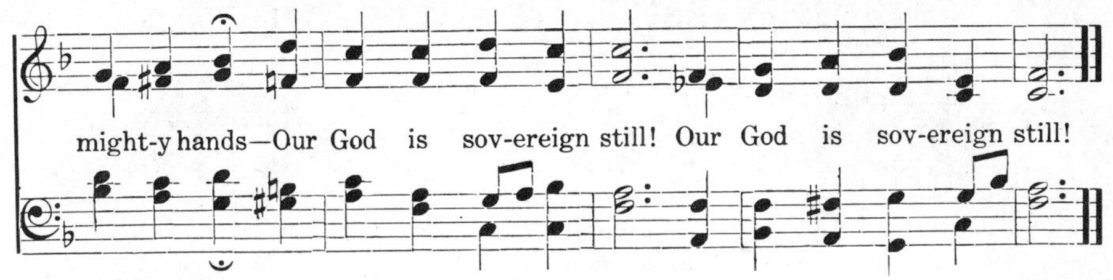
might-y hands—Our God is sov-ereign still! Our God is sov-ereign still!

when we all get to heaven 242

HEAVEN. 8 7 8 7 Ref.

Eliza E. Hewitt — Emily D. Wilson

1. Sing the won-drous love of Je-sus, Sing His mer-cy and His grace;
In the man-sions bright and bless-ed, He'll pre-pare for us a place.

2. While we walk the pil-grim pathway, Clouds will o-ver-spread the sky;
But when trav-'ling days are o-ver, Not a shad-ow, not a sigh.

3. Let us then be true and faith-ful, Trust-ing, serv-ing ev-ery day;
Just one glimpse of Him in glo-ry Will the toils of life re-pay.

4. On-ward to the prize be-fore us! Soon His beau-ty we'll be-hold;
Soon the pearl-y gates will o-pen, We shall tread the streets of gold.

REFRAIN

When we all get to heaven, What a day of re-joicing that will be!
When we all What a day of rejoicing that will be!
When we all see Je-sus, We'll sing and shout the victory.
When we all and shout the vic-to-ry.

243 Jesus, Jesus, We Are Waiting

TOCCOA. 8 7 8 7 D.

George Shaw, alt.

George Shaw
Arr. by Ruth E. Marsden

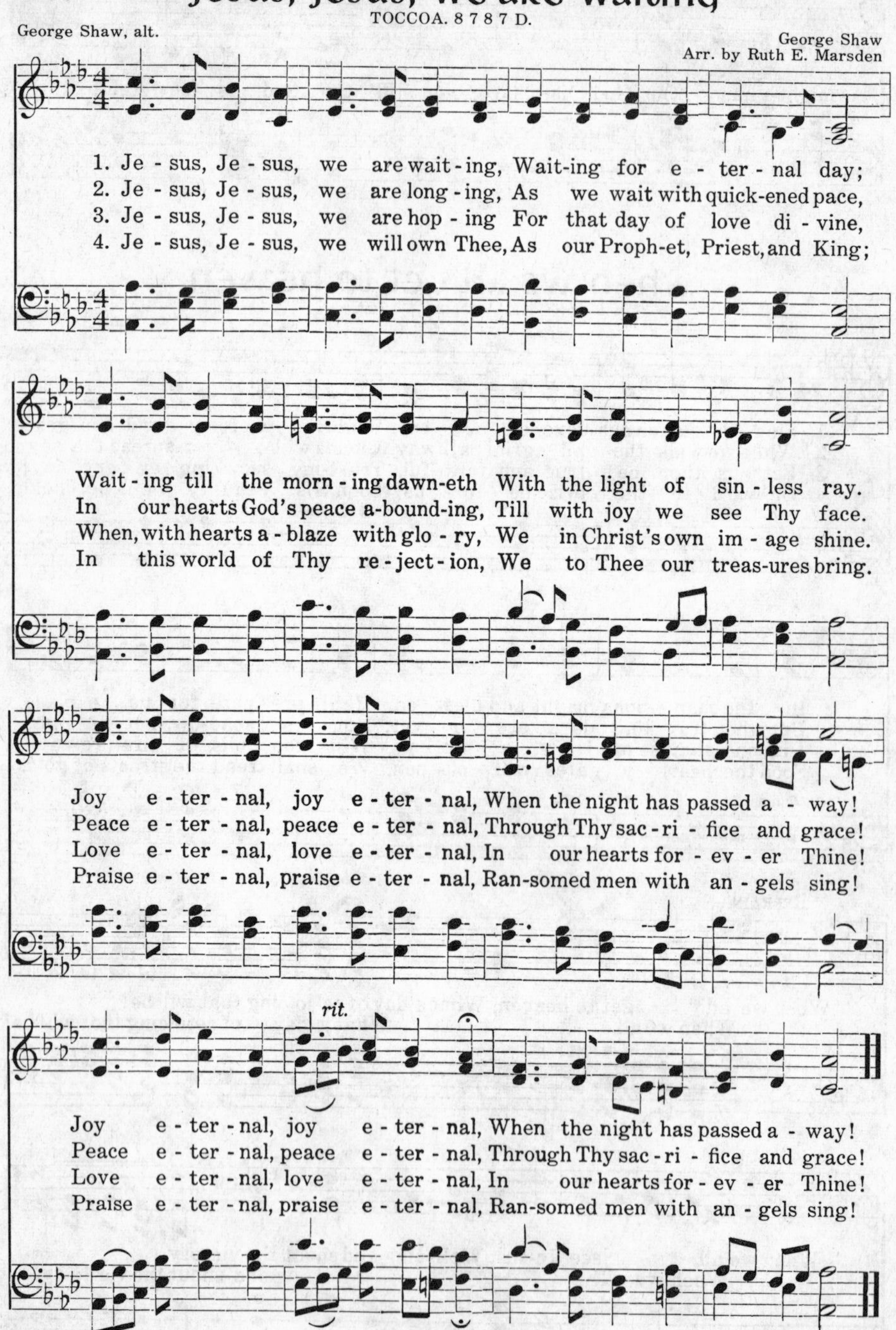

1. Je - sus, Je - sus, we are wait - ing, Wait-ing for e - ter - nal day;
2. Je - sus, Je - sus, we are long - ing, As we wait with quick-ened pace,
3. Je - sus, Je - sus, we are hop - ing For that day of love di - vine,
4. Je - sus, Je - sus, we will own Thee, As our Proph-et, Priest, and King;
Wait - ing till the morn - ing dawn-eth With the light of sin - less ray.
In our hearts God's peace a-bound-ing, Till with joy we see Thy face.
When, with hearts a - blaze with glo - ry, We in Christ's own im - age shine.
In this world of Thy re - ject - ion, We to Thee our treas-ures bring.
Joy e - ter - nal, joy e - ter - nal, When the night has passed a - way!
Peace e - ter - nal, peace e - ter - nal, Through Thy sac - ri - fice and grace!
Love e - ter - nal, love e - ter - nal, In our hearts for - ev - er Thine!
Praise e - ter - nal, praise e - ter - nal, Ran-somed men with an - gels sing!
rit.
Joy e - ter - nal, joy e - ter - nal, When the night has passed a - way!
Peace e - ter - nal, peace e - ter - nal, Through Thy sac - ri - fice and grace!
Love e - ter - nal, love e - ter - nal, In our hearts for - ev - er Thine!
Praise e - ter - nal, praise e - ter - nal, Ran-somed men with an - gels sing!

the sands of time are sinking

RUTHERFORD. 7 6 7 6 7 6 7 5

Anne Ross Cousin

Chrétien Urhan
Arr. by Edward F. Rimbault

1. The sands of time are sink - ing, The dawn of heav - en breaks;
2. O Christ, He is the foun - tain, The deep, sweet well of love!
3. With mer - cy and with judg - ment My web of time He wove,
The sum - mer morn I've sighed for, The fair, sweet morn, a - wakes;
The streams on earth I've tast - ed More deep I'll drink a - bove:
And aye the dews of sor - row Were lus - tered by His love.
Dark, dark hath been the mid - night, But day - spring is at hand,
There to an o - cean full - ness His mer - cy doth ex - pand,
I'll bless the hand that guid - ed, I'll bless the heart that planned,
And glo - ry, glo - ry dwell - eth In Im - man - uel's land.
And glo - ry, glo - ry dwell - eth In Im - man - uel's land.
When throned where glo - ry dwell - eth In Im - man - uel's land. A-MEN.

245 **For All the Saints**

SINE NOMINE. 10 10 10 Alleluias

William W. How — R. Vaughan Williams

1. For all the saints who from their la-bors rest, Who Thee by faith be-
2. Thou wast their rock, their fortress and their might; Thou, Lord, their cap-tain
6. But lo! there breaks a yet more glo-rious day; The saints tri-um-phant
7. From earth's wide bounds, from o-cean's far-thest coast, Thro' gates of pearl stream
fore the world con-fessed, Thy name, O Je-sus, be for-ev-er blest.
in the well-fought fight; Thou, in the dark-ness drear, their one true light.
rise in bright ar-ray; The King of Glo-ry pass-es on His way.
in the count-less host, Sing-ing to Fa-ther, Son, and Ho-ly Ghost.
(after stanza 7)
Al-le-lu-ia! Al-le-lu-ia! A-MEN.
HARMONY, stanzas 3, 4, 5
3. O blest com-mun-ion, fel-low-ship di-vine! We fee-bly strug-gle;
4. And when the strife is fierce, the war-fare long, Steals on the ear the
5. The gold-en eve-ning bright-ens in the west; Soon, soon to faith-ful
they in glo-ry shine. Yet all are one in Thee, for all are Thine.
dis-tant tri-umph song, And hearts are brave a-gain and arms are strong.
war-riors com-eth rest; And sweet the calm of Par-a-dise, the blest.

Music from "The English Hymnal." Used by permission of the Oxford University Press.

(Sop.) Al - le - lu - ia!
D. C. stanzas 6 and 7
Al - le - lu - ia! Al - le - lu - ia!
Face to Face
246
FACE TO FACE. 8 7 8 7 Ref.
Carrie E. Breck
Grant Colfax Tullar
1. Face to face with Christ my Sav - iour, Face to face—what will it be—
2. On - ly faint - ly now I see Him, With the dark - ling veil be - tween;
3. What re - joic - ing in His pres - ence, When are ban - ished grief and pain;
4. Face to face! O bliss - ful mo - ment! Face to face—to see and know;
When with rap - ture I be - hold Him, Je - sus Christ Who died for me?
But a bless - ed day is com - ing, When His glo - ry shall be seen.
When the crook - ed ways are straightened, And the dark things shall be plain.
Face to face with my Re - deem - er, Je - sus Christ Who loves me so.
Refrain
Face to face I shall be - hold Him, Far be - yond the star - ry sky;
Face to face in all His glo - ry, I shall see Him by and by!

247 When I Can Read My Title Clear

PISGAH. 8 6 8 6 6 6 8 6

Isaac Watts

Ascribed to J. C. Lowry

1. When I can read my ti - tle clear To man - sions in the skies,
2. Should earth a - gainst my soul en - gage, And fi - ery darts be hurled,
3. Let cares like a wild del - uge come, And storms of sor - row fall!
4. There shall I bathe my wea - ry soul In seas of heaven-ly rest,
I'll bid fare-well to ev - ery fear, And wipe my weep - ing eyes.
Then I can smile at Sa - tan's rage, And face a frown - ing world.
So I but safe - ly reach my home, My God, my heaven, my all.
And not a wave of troub - le roll A - cross my peace - ful breast.
And wipe my weep - ing eyes, And wipe my weep - ing eyes,
And face a frown - ing world, And face a frown - ing world,
My God, my heaven, my all, My God, my heaven, my all,
A - cross my peace - ful breast, A - cross my peace - ful breast,
I'll bid fare-well to ev - ery fear, And wipe my weep - ing eyes.
Then I can smile at Sa - tan's rage, And face a frown - ing world.
So I but safe - ly reach my home, My God, my heaven, my all.
And not a wave of troub - le roll A - cross my peace - ful breast. A-MEN.

My Saviour First of All

248

I SHALL KNOW HIM. 14 11 14 11 Ref.
Fanny J. Crosby
John R. Sweney
1. When my life-work is end-ed, and I cross the swell-ing tide, When the bright and glo-rious morn-ing I shall see; I shall know my Re-deem-er when I reach the oth-er side, And His smile will be the first to wel-come me.
2. Oh, the soul-thrill-ing rap-ture when I view His bless-ed face, And the lus-ter of His kind-ly beam-ing eye; How my full heart will praise Him for the mer-cy, love, and grace, That pre-pare for me a man-sion in the sky.
3. Oh, the dear ones in glo-ry, how they beck-on me to come, And our part-ing at the riv-er I re-call; To the sweet vales of E-den they will sing my wel-come home; But I long to meet my Sav-iour first of all.
4. Thro' the gates to the cit-y in a robe of spot-less white, He will lead me where no tears will ev-er fall; In the glad song of a-ges I shall min-gle with de-light; But I long to meet my Sav-iour first of all.
REFRAIN
I shall know Him, I shall know Him, And redeemed by His side I shall stand,
I shall know Him,
I shall know Him, I shall know Him By the print of the nails in His hand.
I shall know Him,

249 The King in His Beauty

NEW HAMPTON. 9 8 9 8 Ref.

Adoniram J. Gordon — Adoniram J. Gordon

1. I shall see the King in His beau-ty, In the land that is far a-way,
When the shad-ows at length have lift-ed, And the dark-ness has turned to day.
2. To be-hold the Chief of Ten Thousand, Ah! my soul, this were joy e-nough;
'Twill suf-fice for the bliss of hea-ven, That the Lamb is the light there-of.
3. Who can tell the rap-tur-ous meet-ing, When the Lord shall bring home His own?
With one sight all His saints are ravished, The Lamb in the midst of the throne.
4. Oh! to none will the King be a stranger Of the throngs who sur-round His seat;
For the hearts of the saved will know Him, By the prints of the nails in His feet.
5. I shall see Him, I shall be like Him, By one glance of His face transformed;
And this bod-y of sin and dark-ness To the im-age of Christ con-formed.
REFRAIN
I shall see Him in the glo-ry, The Lamb that once was slain;
How I'll then re-sound the sto-ry, With all the ran-somed train!
Hal-le-lu-jah, Hal-le-lu-jah! To the Lamb that once was slain;

Hal - le - lu - jah, Hal - le - lu - jah, Hal - le - lu - jah! A - men.

He the Pearly Gates Will Open 250

TRYGGARE KAN INGEN VARA. 8 7 8 7 Ref.

Fred Blom
Trans. by N. Carlson

Elsie Ahlwén

1. Love divine, so great and wondrous, Deep and mighty, pure, sublime;
Coming from the heart of Jesus—Just the same through tests of time.

2. Like a dove when hunted, frightened, As a wounded fawn was I;
Broken hearted, yet He healed me—He will heed the sinner's cry.

3. Love divine, so great and wondrous—All my sins He then forgave,
I will sing His praise forever, For His blood, His pow'r to save.

4. In life's eventide, at twilight, At His door I'll knock and wait;
By the precious love of Jesus, I shall enter heaven's gate.

Refrain

He the pearly gates will open, So that I may enter in;
For He purchased my redemption, And forgave me all my sin.

251 Christ Returneth

CHRIST RETURNETH. Irregular. Ref.

H. L. Turner — James McGranahan

1. It may be at morn, when the day is a - wak - ing, When
2. It may be at mid - day, it may be at twi - light, It
3. While its hosts cry Ho - san - na, from heav - en de - scend - ing, With
4. Oh, joy! oh, de - light! should we go with - out dy - ing, No
sun-light through darkness and shad - ow is break-ing, That Je - sus will
may be, per-chance, that the black-ness of mid-night Will burst in - to
glo - ri - fied saints and the an - gels at - tend - ing, With grace on His
sick-ness, no sad - ness, no dread and no cry - ing, Caught up through the
come in the full - ness of glo - ry, To re-ceive from the world "His own."
light in the blaze of His glo - ry, When Je - sus re - ceives "His own."
brow, like a ha - lo of glo - ry, Will Je - sus re - ceive "His own."
clouds with our Lord in - to glo - ry, When Je - sus re - ceives "His own."
Refrain
O Lord Je - sus, how long, how long Ere we shout the glad song, Christ re-
rit.
turn-eth! Hal-le - lu - jah! hal - le - lu - jah! A - men, Hal-le - lu - jah! A - men.

In Heaven Above

HAUGE. 8 6 8 6 8 8 6

Laurentius Laurentii Laurinus
Revised, Johan Astrom
Trans. by William Maccall

Norwegian Folk Melody

1. In heav'n a - bove, in heav'n a - bove, Where God our Fa - ther dwells,
2. In heav'n a - bove, in heav'n a - bove, What glo - ry deep and bright!
3. In heav'n a - bove, in heav'n a - bove, No tears of pain are shed;
4. In heav'n a - bove, in heav'n a - bove, God hath a joy pre - pared,

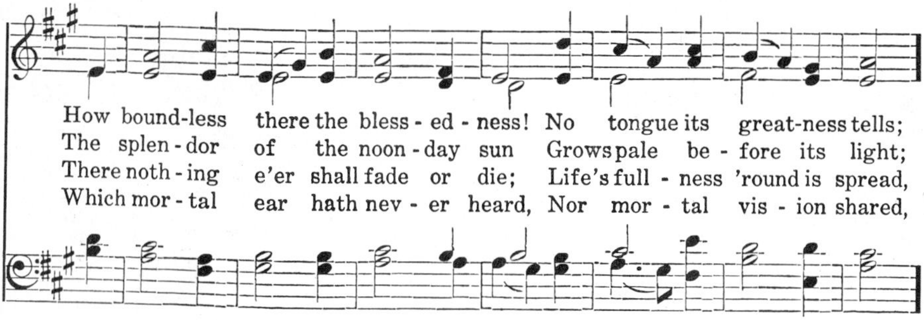

How bound-less there the bless - ed - ness! No tongue its great-ness tells;
The splen - dor of the noon - day sun Grows pale be - fore its light;
There noth - ing e'er shall fade or die; Life's full - ness 'round is spread,
Which mor - tal ear hath nev - er heard, Nor mor - tal vis - ion shared,

There face to face, and full and free, Ev - er and
That might - y Sun that ne'er goes down, Be - fore whose
And, like an o - cean, joy o'er - flows, And with im-
Which nev - er en - tered mor - tal breast, By mor - tal

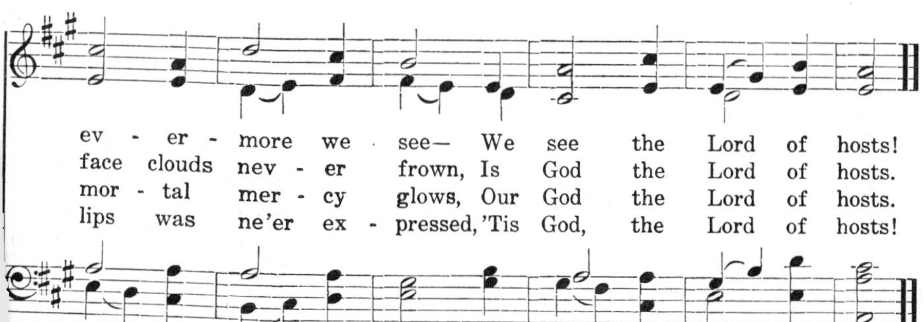

ev - er - more we see— We see the Lord of hosts!
face clouds nev - er frown, Is God the Lord of hosts.
mor - tal mer - cy glows, Our God the Lord of hosts.
lips was ne'er ex - pressed, 'Tis God, the Lord of hosts!

O That Will Be Glory

GLORY SONG. 10 10 10 10 Ref.

Charles H. Gabriel
Charles H. Gabriel
1. When all my la - bors and tri - als are o'er, And I am safe on that
2. When, by the gift of His in - fi - nite grace, I am ac - cord - ed in
3. Friends will be there I have loved long a - go; Joy like a riv - er a-
beau - ti - ful shore, Just to be near the dear Lord I a - dore,
heav - en a place, Just to be there and to look on His face,
round me will flow; Yet, just a smile from my Sav - iour, I know,
Will through the a - ges be glo - ry for me.
REFRAIN
O that will be
O that will
glo - ry for me, Glo - ry for me, glo - ry for me;
be glo - ry for me, Glo - ry for me, glo - ry for me;
When by His gra
I shall look on His face, That will be glo - ry, be glo - ry for m

hymns of all seasons

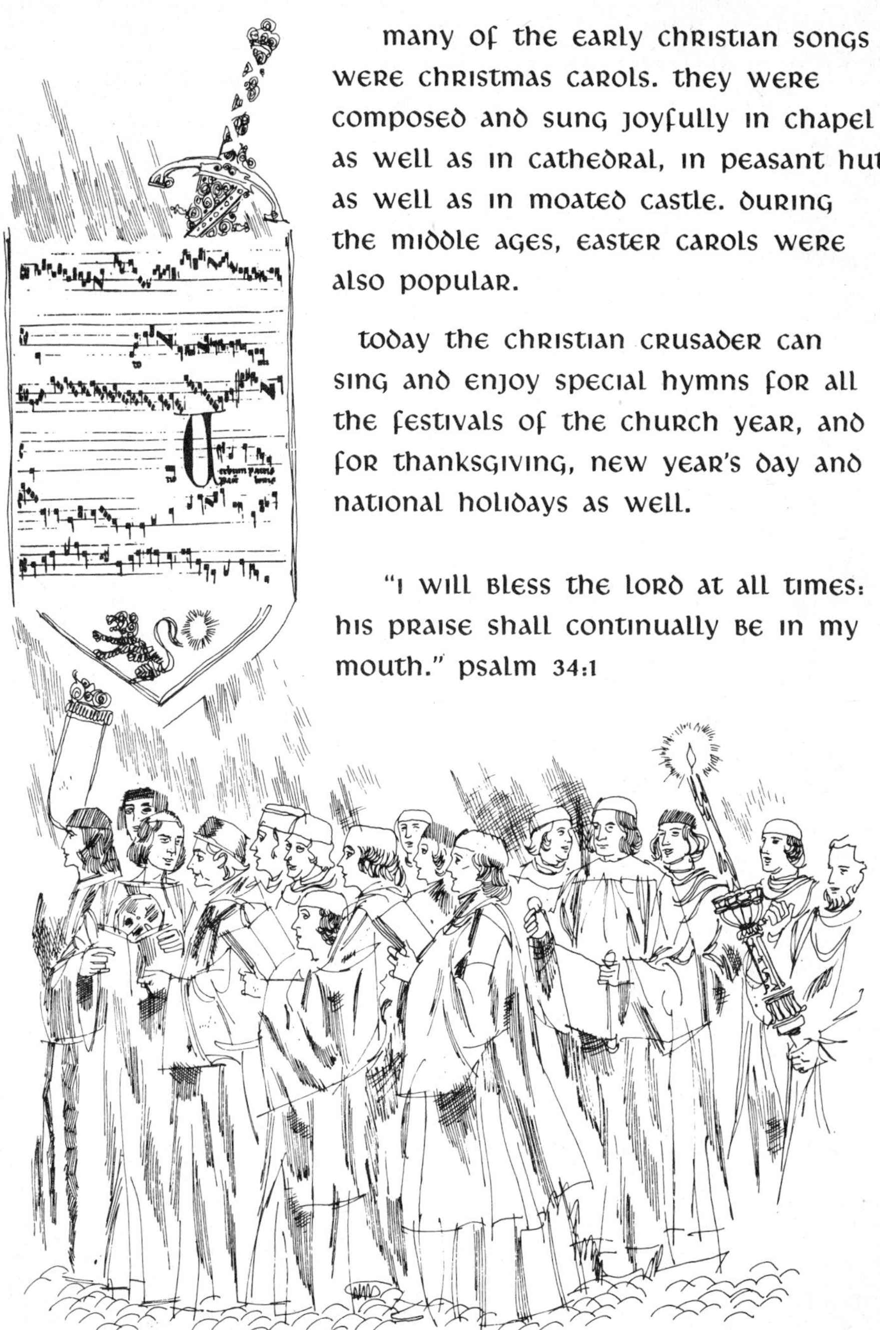

many of the early christian songs were christmas carols. they were composed and sung joyfully in chapel as well as in cathedral, in peasant hut as well as in moated castle. during the middle ages, easter carols were also popular.

today the christian crusader can sing and enjoy special hymns for all the festivals of the church year, and for thanksgiving, new year's day and national holidays as well.

"i will bless the lord at all times: his praise shall continually be in my mouth." psalm 34:1

254 WE GATHER TOGETHER

KREMSER. Irregular.

Source Unknown
Trans. by Theodore Baker

Netherlands Folk Song
Arr. by Edward Kremser

1. We gath - er to - geth - er to ask the Lord's bless - ing;
He chas - tens and has - tens His will to make known;
The wick - ed op - press - ing now cease from dis - tress - ing,
Sing prais - es to His Name: He for - gets not His own.

2. Be - side us to guide us, our God with us join - ing,
Or - dain - ing, main - tain - ing His king - dom di - vine;
So from the be - gin - ning the fight we were win - ning:
Thou, Lord, wast at our side, all glo - ry be Thine!

3. We all do ex - tol Thee, Thou Lead - er tri - um - phant,
And pray that Thou still our De - fend - er wilt be.
Let Thy con - gre - ga - tion es - cape trib - u - la - tion:
Thy Name be ev - er praised! O Lord, make us free!

A-MEN.

ALTERNATE ENDING (after third stanza)

Lord, make us free.

Come, ye thankful people, come

ST. GEORGE'S, WINDSOR. 7 7 7 7 D.

Henry Alford

George J. Elvey

1. Come, ye thank-ful peo-ple, come, Raise the song of har-vest-home:
2. All the world is God's own field, Fruit un-to His praise to yield;
3. For the Lord our God shall come, And shall take His har-vest home;
4. E-ven so, Lord, quick-ly come To Thy fi-nal har-vest-home;
All is safe-ly gath-ered in, Ere the win-ter storms be-gin;
Wheat and tares to-geth-er sown, Un-to joy or sor-row grown;
From His field shall in that day All of-fens-es purge a-way;
Gath-er Thou Thy peo-ple in, Free from sor-row, free from sin;
God, our Ma-ker, doth pro-vide For our wants to be sup-plied:
First the blade, and then the ear, Then the full corn shall ap-pear:
Give His an-gels charge at last In the fire the tares to cast;
There, for-ev-er pu-ri-fied, In Thy pres-ence to a-bide:
Come to God's own tem-ple, come, Raise the song of har-vest-home.
Lord of har-vest, grant that we Whole-some grain and pure may be.
But the fruit-ful ears to store In His gar-ner ev-er-more.
Come, with all Thine an-gels, come, Raise the glo-rious har-vest-home. A-MEN.

256 Now Thank We All Our God

NUN DANKET. 6 7 6 7 6 6 6 6

Martin Rinkart
Trans. by Catherine Winkworth

Johann Crüger
Harm. by Felix Mendelssohn

1. Now thank we all our God With heart and hands and voic - es,
2. O may this boun - teous God, Through all our life be near us,
3. All praise and thanks to God The Fa - ther now be giv - en,
Who won-drous things hath done, In whom His world re - joic - es;
With ev - er joy - ful hearts And bless-ed peace to cheer us;
The Son, and Him who reigns With them in high - est heav - en,
Who, from our moth - er's arms, Hath blessed us on our way
And keep us in His grace, And guide us when per - plexed,
The one e - ter - nal God, Whom earth and heaven a - dore;
With count-less gifts of love, And still is ours to - day.
And free us from all ills In this world and the next.
For thus it was, is now, And shall be ev - er - more. A-MEN.

Thanks to God for My Redeemer 257

TACK, O GUD. 8 7 8 7 D.

August Ludvig Storm
Trans. by Carl E. Backstrom

J. A. Hultman

1. Thanks to God for my Re-deem - er, Thanks for all Thou dost pro - vide!
2. Thanks for prayers that Thou hast answered, Thanks for what Thou dost de - ny!
3. Thanks for ros - es by the way-side, Thanks for thorns their stems con-tain!

Thanks for times now but a mem - 'ry, Thanks for Je - sus by my side!
Thanks for storms that I have weath-ered, Thanks for all Thou dost sup - ply!
Thanks for homes and thanks for fire - side, Thanks for hope, that sweet re - frain!

Thanks for pleas - ant, balm - y spring-time, Thanks for dark and drear - y fall!
Thanks for pain, and thanks for plea - sure, Thanks for com - fort in de - spair!
Thanks for joy and thanks for sor - row, Thanks for heav'n-ly peace with Thee!

Thanks for tears by now for - got - ten, Thanks for peace with - in my soul!
Thanks for grace that none can meas - ure, Thanks for love be - yond com-pare!
Thanks for hope in the to - mor - row, Thanks thro' all e - ter - ni - ty!

258 Hark, the Herald Angels Sing

Charles Wesley, alt. MENDELSSOHN. 7 7 7 7 D. Ref. Felix Mendelssohn
Arr. by William H. Cummings

1. Hark! the her - ald an - gels sing, "Glo - ry to the new-born King:
2. Christ, by high - est heaven a - dored; Christ, the Ev - er - last - ing Lord!
3. Hail the heaven-born Prince of Peace! Hail the Sun of Right-eous - ness!
Peace on earth, and mer - cy mild, God and sin - ners rec - on - ciled!"
Late in time be - hold Him come, Off - spring of the Vir - gin's womb:
Light and life to all He brings, Risen with heal - ing in His wings.
Joy - ful, all ye na - tions, rise, Join the tri - umph of the skies;
Veiled in flesh the God - head see; Hail th' In - car - nate De - i - ty,
Mild He lays His glo - ry by, Born that man no more may die,
With th' an - gel - ic host pro - claim, "Christ is born in Beth - le - hem!"
Pleased as man with men to dwell, Je - sus, our Em - man - u - el.
Born to raise the sons of earth, Born to give them sec - ond birth.
Hark! the her - ald an - gels sing, "Glo - ry to the new-born King." A-MEN.

Thou Didst Leave Thy Throne

MARGARET. Irregular. Ref.

Emily E. S. Elliott

Timothy R. Matthews

1. Thou didst leave Thy throne and Thy king-ly crown When Thou cam-est to earth for me; But in Beth-le-hem's home was there found no room For Thy ho-ly na-tiv-i-ty:
2. Heav-en's arch-es rang when the an-gels sang, Pro-claim-ing Thy roy-al de-gree; But in low-ly birth didst Thou come to earth, And in great hu-mil-i-ty:
3. Thou cam-est, O Lord, with the liv-ing Word That should set Thy peo-ple free; But with mock-ing scorn, and with crown of thorn, They bore Thee to Cal-va-ry:
4. When the heav-ens shall ring, and the an-gels sing, At Thy com-ing to vic-to-ry, Let Thy voice call me home, say-ing, "Yet there is room, There is room at My side for thee:"

Refrain

1–3. O come to my heart, Lord Je-sus! There is room in my heart for Thee.
4. My heart shall rejoice, Lord Je-sus! When Thou comest and call-est for me. A-men.

260 angels we have heard on high

GLORIA. 7 7 7 7 Ref.
Source Unknown
Old French Carol
1. An - gels we have heard on high, Sweet - ly sing - ing o'er the plains,
2. Shepherds, why this ju - bi - lee? Why your joy - ous strains pro - long?
3. Come to Beth - le - hem, and see Him whose birth the an - gels sing;
4. See with - in a man - ger laid Je - sus, Lord of heav'n and earth!
And the moun - tains in re - ply Ech - o back their joy - ous strains.
Say what may the ti - dings be, Which in - spire your heav'n - ly song?
Come, a - dore on bend - ed knee Christ the Lord, the new - born King.
Ma - ry, Jo - seph, lend your aid, With us sing our Sav - iour's birth.
Refrain
Glo - - - - - - - - - - - - - ri - a
in ex - cel - sis De - o, Glo - - - - - - - -
- - - - - - ri - a in ex - cel - sis De - o. A-MEN.

What Child is this, who, laid to Rest 261
CHRIST THE KING. 8 7 8 7 Ref.
Traditional
Arr. by William C. Dix
Old English Melody
1. What Child is this, who, laid to rest, On Ma - ry's lap is sleep-ing?
2. Why lies He in such mean es - tate Where ox and ass are feed - ing?
3. So bring Him in - cense, gold and myrrh, Come peas - ant, king to own Him;
Whom an - gels greet with an-thems sweet, While shep-herds watch are keep - ing?
Good Christian, fear; for sin - ners here The si - lent Word is plead - ing.
The King of kings sal - va - tion brings, Let lov - ing hearts en-throne Him.
Refrain
This, this is Christ the King, Whom shep - herds guard and an - gels sing:
This, this is Christ the King, The Babe, the Son of Ma - ry.

CHRISTMAS

262 O Come, O Come, Emmanuel

VENI EMMANUEL. 8 8 8 8 8 8

Latin Hymn
Trans. by John Mason Neale

Ancient Plainsong

1. O come, O come, Em - man - u - el, And ran - som cap - tive
2. O come, Thou Rod of Jes - se, free Thine own from Sa - tan's
3. O come, Thou Day-spring, come and cheer Our spir - its by Thine
4. O come, Thou Key of Da - vid, come, And o - pen wide our
Is - ra - el, That mourns in lone - ly ex - ile here
tyr - an - ny; From depths of hell Thy peo - ple save
ad - vent here; And drive a - way the shades of night,
heaven - ly home; Make safe the way that leads on high,
Un - til the Son of God ap - pear. Re - joice! re - joice! Em-
And give them vic - tory o'er the grave. Re - joice! re - joice! Em-
And pierce the clouds and bring us light! Re - joice! re - joice! Em-
And close the path to mis - er - y. Re - joice! re - joice! Em-
man - u - el Shall come to thee, O Is - ra - el!
man - u - el Shall come to thee, O Is - ra - el!
man - u - el Shall come to thee, O Is - ra - el!
man - u - el Shall come to thee, O Is - ra - el! A-MEN.

GOOD CHRISTIAN MEN, REJOICE

IN DULCI JUBILO. Irregular.

Medieval Latin Hymn
Trans. by John Mason Neale

German Melody, 14th Century

1. Good Chris - tian men, re - joice, With heart and soul and voice;
2. Good Chris - tian men, re - joice, With heart and soul and voice;
3. Good Chris - tian men, re - joice, With heart and soul and voice!
Give ye heed to what we say: Je - sus Christ is born to - day;
Now ye hear of end - less bliss; Je - sus Christ was born for this!
Now ye need not fear the grave; Je - sus Christ was born to save!
Ox and ass be - fore Him bow, And He is in the man - ger now.
He hath oped the heaven-ly door, And man is bless - ed ev - er - more.
Calls you one and calls you all To gain His ev - er - last - ing hall.
Christ is born to - day! Christ is born to - day!
Christ was born for this! Christ was born for this!
Christ was born to save! Christ was born to save!

264 THERE'S A SONG IN THE AIR

CHRISTMAS SONG. 6 6 6 6 12 12

Josiah G. Holland — Karl P. Harrington

3
4
1. There's a song in the air! There's a star in the sky!
2. There's a tu - mult of joy O'er the won - der - ful birth,
3. In the light of that star Lie the a - ges im - pearled,
4. We re - joice in the light, And we ech - o the song
There's a mo - ther's deep prayer, And a ba - by's low cry!
For the Vir - gin's sweet boy Is the Lord of the earth.
And that song from a - far Has swept o - ver the world.
That comes down through the night From the heav - en - ly throng.
And the star rains its fire while the beau - ti - ful sing,
Ay! the star rains its fire while the beau - ti - ful sing,
Ev - ery heart is a - flame, and the beau - ti - ful sing,
Ay! we shout to the love - ly e - van - gel they bring,
For the man - ger of Beth - le - hem cra - dles a King!
For the man - ger of Beth - le - hem cra - dles a King!
In the homes of the na - tions that Je - sus is King!
And we greet in His cra - dle our Sav - iour and King! A-MEN.

O Come, All Ye Faithful

ADESTE FIDELES. Irregular. Ref.

Latin Hymn, 18th Century
Trans. by Frederick Oakeley

John F. Wade's *Cantus Diversi*

1. O come, all ye faith - ful, Joy - ful - ly tri - um - phant,
O come ye, O come ye to Beth - le - hem!
Come and be - hold Him, Born the King of an - gels;

2. Sing, choirs of an - gels, Sing in ex - ul - ta - tion!
O sing, all ye bright hosts of heaven a - bove;
Glo - ry to God, all Glo - ry in the high - est;

3. Yea, Lord, we greet Thee, Born this hap - py morn - ing,
Je - sus, to Thee be all glo - ry given;
Word of the Fa - ther, Now in flesh ap - pear - ing;

REFRAIN

O come, let us a - dore Him, O come, let us a - dore Him,
O come, let us a - dore Him, Christ the Lord. A - MEN.

266 O Little Town of Bethlehem

ST. LOUIS. 7 6 8 6 D.

Phillips Brooks — Lewis H. Redner

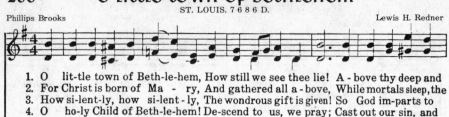

1. O lit-tle town of Beth-le-hem, How still we see thee lie! A - bove thy deep and
2. For Christ is born of Ma - ry, And gathered all a - bove, While mortals sleep, the
3. How si-lent-ly, how si-lent - ly, The wondrous gift is given! So God im-parts to
4. O ho-ly Child of Beth-le-hem! De-scend to us, we pray; Cast out our sin, and

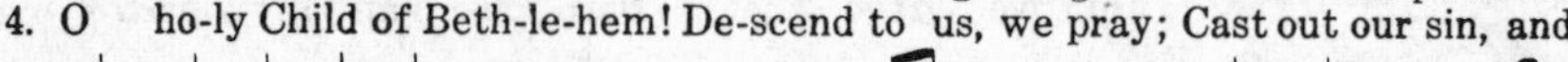

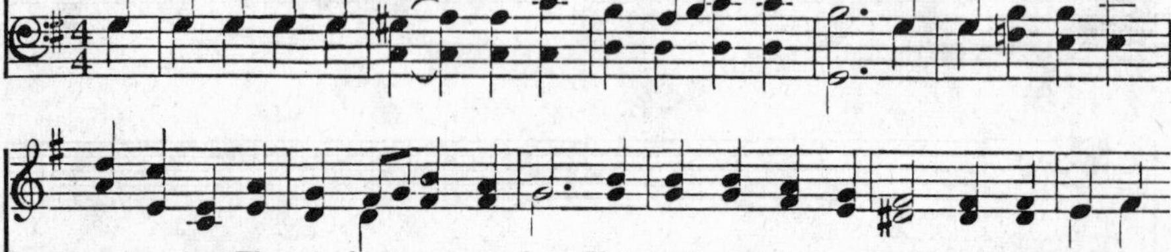

dreamless sleep The si - lent stars go by. Yet in thy dark streets shineth The ev - er-
an - gels keep Their watch of wondering love. O morn-ing stars, to-geth - er Proclaim the
human hearts The blessings of His heaven. No ear may hear His com-ing, But in this
en - ter in; Be born in us to - day. We hear the Christmas an-gels The great glad

last-ing Light; The hopes and fears of all the years Are met in thee to-night.
ho - ly birth! And prais-es sing to God the King, And peace to men on earth.
world of sin, Where meek souls will receive Him still, The dear Christ enters in.
ti - dings tell; O come to us, a - bide with us, Our Lord Em-man-u - el. A-MEN.

267 While Shepherds Watched Their Flocks

CHRISTMAS. C.M.

Nahum Tate — George F. Handel, arr.

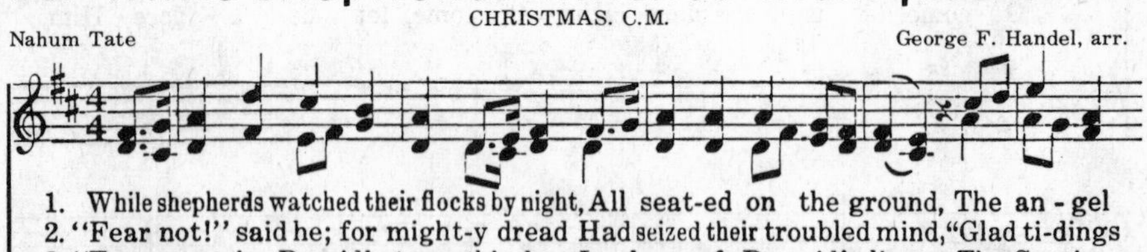

1. While shepherds watched their flocks by night, All seat-ed on the ground, The an - gel
2. "Fear not!" said he; for might-y dread Had seized their troubled mind, "Glad ti-dings
3. "To you, in Dav-id's town this day, Is born of Da - vid's line, The Sav-iour
4. "The heavenly Babe you there shall find To hu-man view dis-played, All mean-ly
5. "All glo - ry be to God on high, And to the earth be peace: Good will hence-

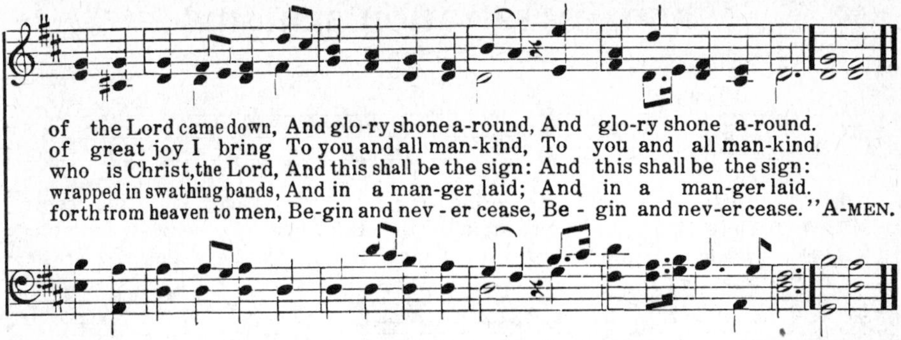

of the Lord came down, And glo-ry shone a-round, And glo-ry shone a-round.
of great joy I bring To you and all man-kind, To you and all man-kind.
who is Christ, the Lord, And this shall be the sign: And this shall be the sign:
wrapped in swathing bands, And in a man-ger laid; And in a man-ger laid.
forth from heaven to men, Be-gin and nev - er cease, Be - gin and nev-er cease." A-MEN.

SILENT NIGHT! HOLY NIGHT! 268

STILLE NACHT. Irregular.

Joseph Mohr — Franz Gruber

1. Si - lent night! ho - ly night! All is calm, all is bright
2. Si - lent night! ho - ly night! Shep-herds quake at the sight,
3. Si - lent night! ho - ly night! Son of God, Love's pure light,
4. Si - lent night! ho - ly night! All is dark save the light

'Round yon vir - gin mo-ther and Child, Ho - ly In - fant so ten-der and mild,
Glo - ries stream from heav-en a - far, Heavenly hosts sing Al - le - lu - ia;
Ra-diant beams from Thy ho-ly face, With the dawn of re - deem - ing grace,
Yon - der, where they sweet vi - gils keep O'er the Babe who in si - lent sleep

Sleep in heav - en - ly peace, Sleep in heav - en - ly peace.
Christ the Sav - iour is born, Christ the Sav - iour is born.
Je - sus, Lord, at Thy birth, Je - sus, Lord, at Thy birth.
Rests in heav - en - ly peace, Rests in heav - en - ly peace. A-MEN.

269 When, His Salvation Bringing

TOURS. 7 6 7 6 D.
John King
Berthold Tours
1. When, His sal - va - tion bring - ing, To Zi - on Je - sus came,
2. And since the Lord re - tain - eth His love for chil - dren still,
3. For should we fail pro - claim - ing Our great Re - deem - er's praise,
The chil - dren all stood sing - ing Ho - san - na to His name;
Though now as King He reign - eth On Zi - on's heaven - ly hill,
The stones, our si - lence sham - ing, Would their ho - san - nas raise.
Nor did their zeal of - fend Him, But, as He rode a - long,
We'll flock a - round His ban - ner Who sits up - on the throne,
But shall we on - ly ren - der The trib - ute of our words?
He bade them still at - tend Him, And smiled to hear their song.
And cry a - loud, "Ho - san - na To Da - vid's roy - al Son!"
No! while our hearts are ten - der, They, too, shall be the Lord's. A-MEN.

all glory, laud, and honor

ST. THEODULPH. 7 6 7 6 D. Ref.

Theodulph of Orleans
Trans. by John Mason Neale

Melchior Teschner

ASCRIPTION

All glo - ry, laud, and hon - or To Thee, Re - deem - er, King,
To whom the lips of chil - dren Make sweet ho - san - nas ring.

1. Thou art the King of Is - rael, Thou, Da - vid's roy - al Son,
2. The com - pa - ny of an - gels Are prais - ing Thee on high,
3. The peo - ple of the He - brews With palms be - fore Thee went;
4. To Thee, be - fore Thy pas - sion, They sang their hymns of praise;
5. Thou didst ac - cept their prais - es; Ac - cept the prayers we bring,

Who in the Lord's name com - est, The King and Bless - ed One.
And mor - tal men, and all things Cre - at - ed, make re - ply.
Our praise and prayer and an - thems Be - fore Thee we pre - sent.
To Thee, now high ex - alt - ed, Our mel - o - dy we raise.
Who in all good de - light - est, Thou good and gra - cious King.

REFRAIN

D. S.

All glo - ry, laud, and hon - or To Thee, Re-deem - er, King,
To whom the lips of chil - dren Make sweet ho-san - nas ring. A - MEN.

271

CHRIST AROSE

CHRIST AROSE. 6 5 6 4 Ref.

Robert Lowry

Robert Lowry

1. Low in the grave He lay— Je - sus my Sav - iour! Wait - ing the
2. Vain - ly they watch His bed— Je - sus my Sav - iour! Vain - ly they
3. Death can-not keep his prey— Je - sus my Sav - iour! He tore the
coming day— Je - sus my Lord!
seal the dead— Je - sus my Lord!
bars a - way— Je - sus my Lord!
REFRAIN
Up from the grave He a - rose,
He a - rose,
With a might - y tri-umph o'er His foes;
He a - rose!
He a - rose a
Vic - tor from the dark do-main, And He lives for - ev - er with His saints to reign.
He a - rose! He a - rose! Hal - le - lu - jah! Christ a-rose!
He a - rose! He a - rose!

Thine Is the Glory

JUDAS MACCABEUS. 10 11 11 11 Ref.

Edmond L. Budry
Trans. by R. Birch Hoyle

George F. Handel

1. Thine is the glo-ry, Ris-en, con-qu'ring Son; End-less is the vic-t'ry Thou o'er death hast won. An-gels in bright rai-ment Rolled the stone a-way, Kept the fold-ed grave-clothes Where Thy bod-y lay.
2. Lo! Je-sus meets thee, Ris-en, from the tomb; Lov-ing-ly He greets thee, Scat-ters fear and gloom; Let His church with glad-ness Hymns of tri-umph sing, For her Lord now liv-eth; Death hath lost its sting.
3. No more we doubt Thee, Glo-rious Prince of Life! Life is nought with-out Thee; Aid us in our strife; Make us more than con-qu'rors, Through Thy death-less love; Bring us safe through Jor-dan To Thy home a-bove.
REFRAIN
Thine is the glo-ry, Ris-en, con-qu'ring Son; End-less is the vic-t'ry Thou o'er death hast won. A-MEN.

This hymn is taken from "Cantate Domino" with the permission of the World Student Christian Federation, Geneva, Switzerland.

273 I know that my Redeemer liveth
HANNAH. 9 8 9 8 Ref.
Jessie B. Pounds
James H. Fillmore
1. I know that my Redeemer liv - eth, And on the earth a-gain shall stand;
2. I know His promise never fail - eth, The word He speaks, it can-not die;
3. I know my mansion He pre-par - eth, That where He is there I may be;
1. And on the earth again shall stand;
I know e - ter-nal life He giv - eth, That grace and pow'r are in His hand.
Tho'cru-el death my flesh as-sail - eth, Yet I shall see Him by and by.
O won-drous tho't, for me He careth, And He at last will come for me.
1. That grace and pow'r are in His hand.
Refrain
I know, I know that Je - sus liv - eth, And on the
I know, I know
earth a - gain shall stand; I know, I know
And on the earth
I know, I know
that life He giv - eth, That grace and pow'r are in His hand.
That grace and pow'r

Christ the Lord Is Risen Today

EASTER HYMN (WORGAN). 7 7 7 7 Alleluias.

Charles Wesley

Arr. from *Lyra Davidica*, 1708

1. Christ the Lord is risen to - day, Al - - - - - le - lu - ia!
2. Love's re - deem - ing work is done, Al - - - - - le - lu - ia!
3. Lives a - gain our glo - rious King; Al - - - - - le - lu - ia!
4. Soar we now where Christ has led, Al - - - - - le - le - ia!

Sons of men and an - gels say: Al - - - - - le - lu - ia!
Fought the fight, the bat - tle won; Al - - - - - le - lu - ia!
Where, O death, is now thy sting? Al - - - - - le - lu - ia!
Fol - lowing our ex - alt - ed Head; Al - - - - - le - lu - ia!

Raise your joys and tri - umphs high, Al - - - - - le - lu - ia!
Death in vain for - bids Him rise; Al - - - - - le - lu - ia!
Dy - ing once, He all doth save: Al - - - - - le - lu - ia!
Made like Him, like Him we rise; Al - - - - - le - lu - ia!

Sing, ye heavens, and earth re - ply, Al - - - - - le - lu - ia!
Christ has o - pened Par - a - dise. Al - - - - - le - lu - ia!
Where thy vic - to - ry, O grave? Al - - - - - le - lu - ia!
Ours the cross, the grave, the skies. Al - - - - - le - lu - ia! A-MEN.

275 THE STRIFE IS O'ER

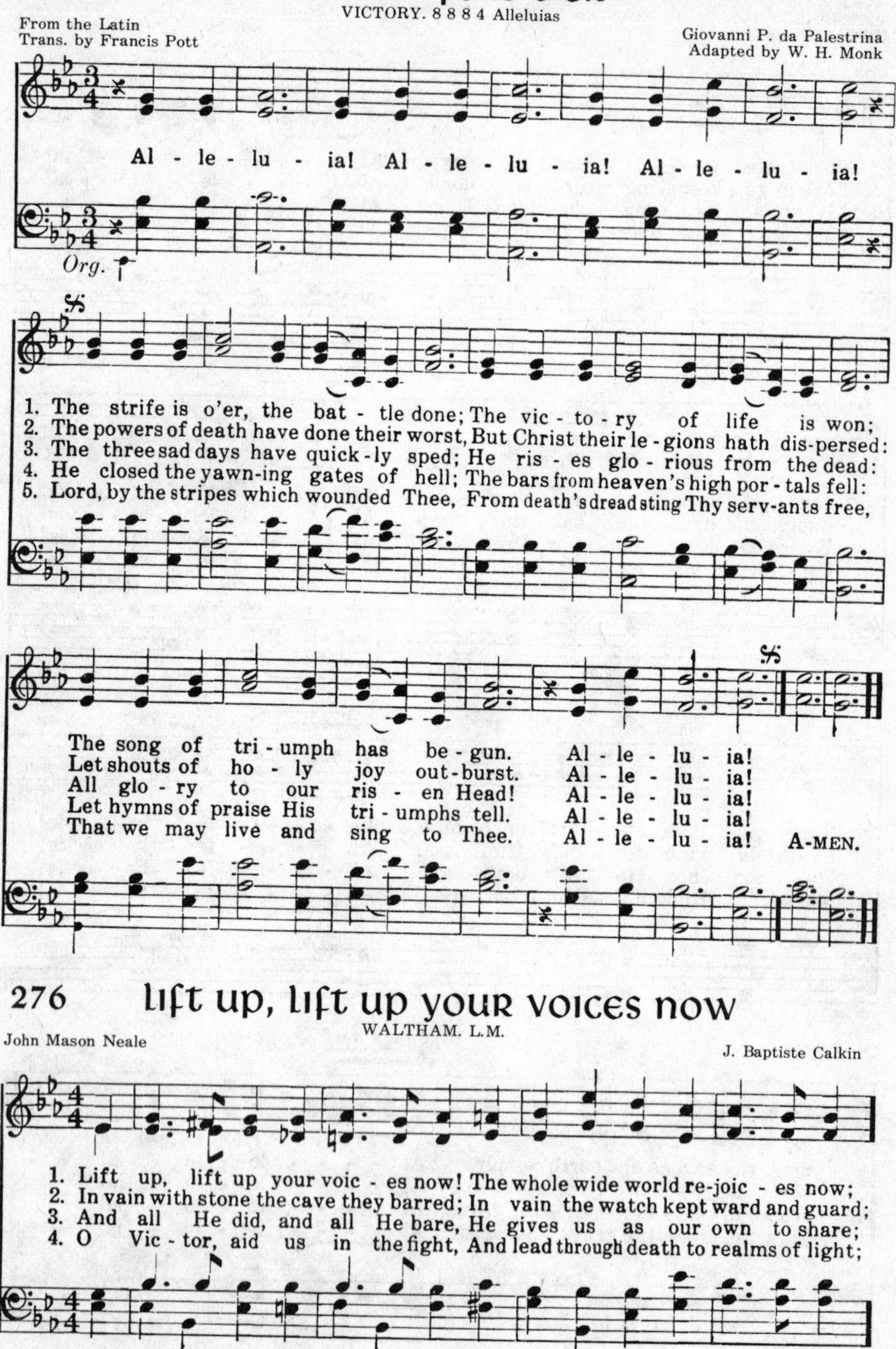
VICTORY. 8 8 8 4 Alleluias
From the Latin
Trans. by Francis Pott
Giovanni P. da Palestrina
Adapted by W. H. Monk
Al - le - lu - ia! Al - le - lu - ia! Al - le - lu - ia!
Org.
1. The strife is o'er, the bat - tle done; The vic - to - ry of life is won;
2. The powers of death have done their worst, But Christ their le - gions hath dis-persed:
3. The three sad days have quick - ly sped; He ris - es glo - rious from the dead:
4. He closed the yawn-ing gates of hell; The bars from heaven's high por - tals fell:
5. Lord, by the stripes which wounded Thee, From death's dread sting Thy serv-ants free,
The song of tri - umph has be - gun. Al - le - lu - ia!
Let shouts of ho - ly joy out-burst. Al - le - lu - ia!
All glo - ry to our ris - en Head! Al - le - lu - ia!
Let hymns of praise His tri - umphs tell. Al - le - lu - ia!
That we may live and sing to Thee. Al - le - lu - ia! A-MEN.
276 LIFT UP, LIFT UP YOUR VOICES NOW
WALTHAM. L.M.
John Mason Neale
J. Baptiste Calkin
1. Lift up, lift up your voic - es now! The whole wide world re-joic - es now;
2. In vain with stone the cave they barred; In vain the watch kept ward and guard;
3. And all He did, and all He bare, He gives us as our own to share;
4. O Vic - tor, aid us in the fight, And lead through death to realms of light;

I With Thee Would Begin

LAT MIG BORJA MED DIG. Irregular.

From the Swedish
Trans. by A. Samuel Wallgren

W. Theodor Söderberg

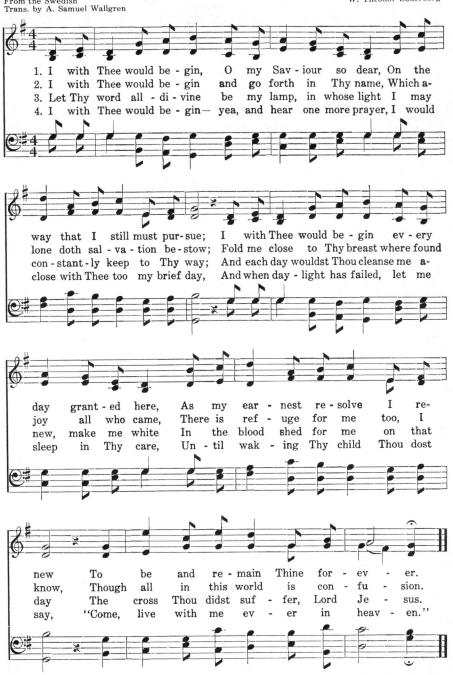

1. I with Thee would be - gin, O my Sav - iour so dear, On the
2. I with Thee would be - gin and go forth in Thy name, Which a-
3. Let Thy word all - di - vine be my lamp, in whose light I may
4. I with Thee would be - gin— yea, and hear one more prayer, I would

way that I still must pur- sue; I with Thee would be - gin ev - ery
lone doth sal - va - tion be - stow; Fold me close to Thy breast where found
con - stant - ly keep to Thy way; And each day wouldst Thou cleanse me a-
close with Thee too my brief day, And when day - light has failed, let me

day grant - ed here, As my ear - nest re - solve I re-
joy all who came, There is ref - uge for me too, I
new, make me white In the blood shed for me on that
sleep in Thy care, Un - til wak - ing Thy child Thou dost

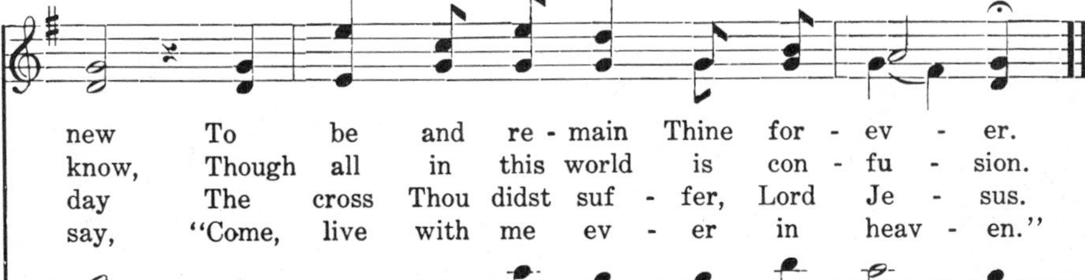

new To be and re - main Thine for - ev - er.
know, Though all in this world is con - fu - sion.
day The cross Thou didst suf - fer, Lord Je - sus.
say, "Come, live with me ev - er in heav - en."

280 God of our fathers, whose almighty hand

NATIONAL HYMN. 10 10 10 10

Daniel C. Roberts — George W. Warren

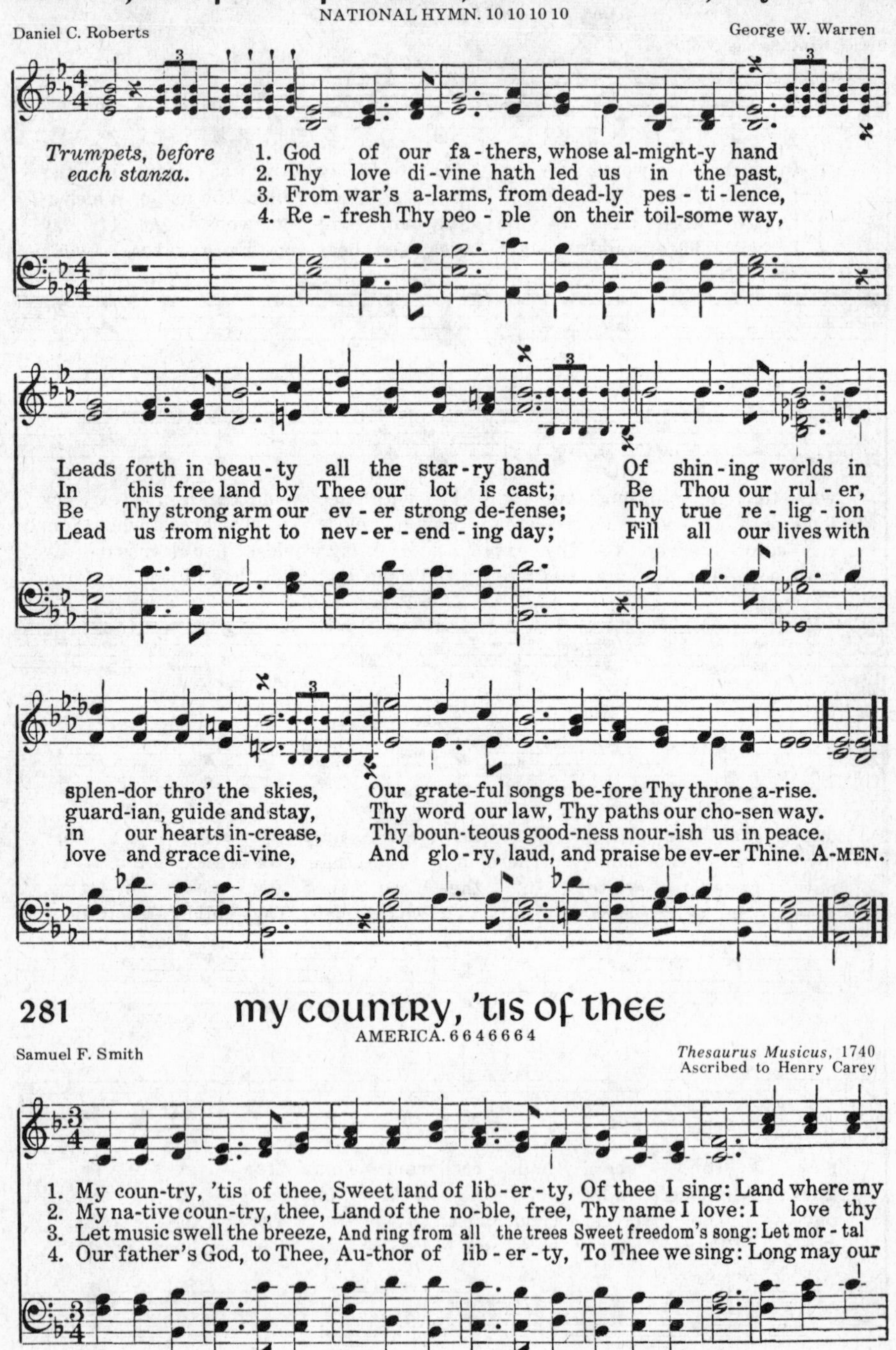

Trumpets, before each stanza.
1. God of our fa-thers, whose al-might-y hand Leads forth in beau-ty all the star-ry band Of shin-ing worlds in splen-dor thro' the skies, Our grate-ful songs be-fore Thy throne a-rise.
2. Thy love di-vine hath led us in the past, In this free land by Thee our lot is cast; Be Thou our rul-er, guard-ian, guide and stay, Thy word our law, Thy paths our cho-sen way.
3. From war's a-larms, from dead-ly pes-ti-lence, Be Thy strong arm our ev-er strong de-fense; Thy true re-lig-ion in our hearts in-crease, Thy boun-teous good-ness nour-ish us in peace.
4. Re-fresh Thy peo-ple on their toil-some way, Lead us from night to nev-er-end-ing day; Fill all our lives with love and grace di-vine, And glo-ry, laud, and praise be ev-er Thine. A-MEN.
281
my country, 'tis of thee
AMERICA. 6 6 4 6 6 6 4
Samuel F. Smith
Thesaurus Musicus, 1740
Ascribed to Henry Carey
1. My coun-try, 'tis of thee, Sweet land of lib-er-ty, Of thee I sing: Land where my
2. My na-tive coun-try, thee, Land of the no-ble, free, Thy name I love: I love thy
3. Let music swell the breeze, And ring from all the trees Sweet freedom's song: Let mor-tal
4. Our father's God, to Thee, Au-thor of lib-er-ty, To Thee we sing: Long may our

fa-thers died, Land of the pilgrim's pride, From ev - ery moun-tain side Let free-dom ring!
rocks and rills, Thy woods and templed hills; My heart with rapture thrills, Like that a - bove.
tongues awake; Let all that breathe partake; Let rocks their silence break, The sound prolong.
land be bright With freedom's ho-ly light; Pro-tect us by Thy might, Great God, our King! A-MEN.
GOD SAVE AMERICA!
282
RUSSIAN HYMN. 11 10 11 10
Henry F. Chorley; 1, 2
John Ellerton; 3, 4
Alexis F. Lvov
1. God save A - mer - i - ca! New world of glo - ry, New-born to
2. God save A - mer - i - ca! Here may all ra - ces Min - gle to -
3. God save A - mer - i - ca! Bear - ing the ol - ive, Hers be the
4. God save A - mer - i - ca! 'Mid all her splen - dors, Save her from
free - dom and knowl - edge and power, Lift - ing the towers of her
geth - er as chil - dren of God, Found - ing an em - pire on
bless - ing the peace - mak - ers prove, Call - ing the na - tions to
pride and from lux - u - ry; Throne in her heart the un-
light - ning-lit cit - ies Where the flood tides of hu-man - i - ty roar!
broth - er - ly kind-ness, E - qual in lib - er - ty, made of one blood!
glad fed - er - a - tion, Lead - ing the world in the tri - umph of love!
seen and e - ter - nal; Right be her might and the truth make her free! A-MEN.

283 O Beautiful for Spacious Skies

MATERNA. C.M.D.

Katharine Lee Bates — Samuel A. Ward

1. O beau - ti - ful for spa - cious skies, For am - ber waves of grain,
2. O beau - ti - ful for pil - grim feet, Whose stern, im - pas-sioned stress
3. O beau - ti - ful for he - roes proved In lib - er - at - ing strife,
4. O beau - ti - ful for pa - triot dream That sees be - yond the years
For pur - ple moun - tain maj - es - ties A - bove the fruit - ed plain!
A thor-ough - fare for free - dom beat A - cross the wil - der - ness!
Who more than self their coun - try loved, And mer - cy more than life!
Thine al - a - bas - ter cit - ies gleam, Un - dimmed by hu - man tears!
A - mer - i - ca! A - mer - i - ca! God shed His grace on thee,
A - mer - i - ca! A - mer - i - ca! God mend thine ev - ery flaw,
A - mer - i - ca! A - mer - i - ca! May God thy gold re - fine
A - mer - i - ca! A - mer - i - ca! God shed His grace on thee,
And crown thy good with broth - er-hood From sea to shin - ing sea!
Con - firm thy soul in self - con-trol, Thy lib - er - ty in law!
Till all suc - cess be no - ble-ness And ev - ery gain di - vine!
And crown thy good with broth - er-hood From sea to shin - ing sea! A-MEN.

Battle Hymn of the Republic

BATTLE HYMN. 15 15 15 6 Ref.

Julia Ward Howe

John William Steffe

1. Mine eyes have seen the glo-ry of the com-ing of the Lord; He is tram-pling out the vin-tage where the grapes of wrath are stored; He hath loosed the fate-ful light-ning of His ter-ri-ble swift sword; His truth is march-ing on.
2. I have seen Him in the watch-fires of a hun-dred cir-cling camps; They have build-ed Him an al-tar in the eve-ning dews and damps; I can read His right-eous sen-tence by the dim and flar-ing lamps; His day is march-ing on.
3. He has sound-ed forth the trum-pet that shall nev-er sound re-treat; He is sift-ing out the hearts of men be-fore His judg-ment seat. O be swift, my soul, to an-swer Him! be ju-bi-lant, my feet! Our God is march-ing on.
4. In the beau-ty of the lil-ies Christ was born a-cross the sea, With a glo-ry in His bos-om that trans-fig-ures you and me; As He died to make men ho-ly, let us die to make men free; While God is march-ing on.

REFRAIN

Glo-ry! glo-ry, hal-le-lu-jah! Glo-ry! glo-ry, hal-le-lu-jah!
Glo-ry! glo-ry, hal-le-lu-jah! Our God is march-ing on.

SCRIPTURE READINGS

The readings are in consecutive scriptural order with relation to the beginning passage of each reading. The text used is the King James Version, 1611, with a few exceptions, when the American Standard Version, 1901, is used for easier congregational participation.

The hymns listed at the bottom of each column are appropriate for singing in connection with that Scripture Reading.

285 GOD THE CREATOR

In the beginning God created the heaven and the earth.

And the earth was without form, and void; and darkness was upon the face of the deep.

And the Spirit of God moved upon the face of the waters. And God said, Let there be light: and there was light.

And God saw the light, that it was good: and God divided the light from the darkness.

And God called the light Day, and the darkness he called Night.

And the evening and the morning were the first day. — Genesis 1: 1-5.

By the word of the Lord were the heavens made; and all the host of them by the breath of his mouth.

He gathereth the waters of the sea together as an heap: he layeth up the depth in storehouses.

Let all the earth fear the Lord: let all the inhabitants of the world stand in awe of him.

For he spake, and it was done; he commanded, and it stood fast.

— Psalm 33: 6-9.

Let us come before his presence with thanksgiving, and make a joyful noise unto him with psalms.

For the Lord is a great God, and a great King above all gods.

In his hand are the deep places of the earth: the strength of the hills is his also.

The sea is his, and he made it: and his hands formed the dry land.

O come, let us worship and bow down: let us kneel before the Lord our maker.

For he is our God; and we are the people of his pasture, and the sheep of his hand. — Psalm 95: 2-7.

Hymns: 1, 5, 16, 18, 44, 48

286 GOD'S COMMANDMENTS

And the Lord came down upon Mount Sinai, on the top of the mount: and the Lord called Moses up to the top of the mount; and Moses went up. — Exodus 19:20.

And God spake all these words saying, I am the Lord thy God which have brought thee out of the land of Egypt, out of the house of bondage.

Thou shalt have no other Gods before me.

Thou shalt not make unto thee any graven image. Thou shalt not bow down thyself to them, nor serve them.

Thou shalt not take the name of the Lord thy God in vain.

Remember the sabbath day to keep it holy.

Honor thy father and thy mother.

Thou shalt not kill.

Thou shalt not commit adultery.

Thou shalt not steal.

Thou shalt not bear false witness against thy neighbor.

Thou shalt not covet.

— Exodus 20:1-7 (Abridged).

Then one of them, which was a lawyer, asked him a question, tempting him, and saying, Master, which is the great commandment in the law?

Jesus said unto him, Thou shalt love the Lord thy God with all thy heart, and with all thy soul, and with all thy mind. This is the first and great commandment.

And the second is like unto it. Thou shalt love thy neighbor as thyself.

On these two commandments hand all the law and the prophets.

— Matthew 22:35-40.

Hymns: 165, 181, 203, 207

287 THE WAY OF LIFE

Blessed is the man that walketh not in the counsel of the ungodly, nor standeth in the way of sinners, nor sitteth in the seat of the scornful.

But his delight is in the law of the Lord; and in his law doth he meditate day and night.

And he shall be like a tree planted by the rivers of water, that bringeth forth his fruit in his season; his leaf also shall not wither; and whatsoever he doeth shall prosper.

The ungodly are not so: but are like the chaff which the wind driveth away.

Therefore the ungodly shall not stand in the judgment, nor sinners in the congregation of the righteous.

For the Lord knoweth the way of the righteous: but the way of the ungodly shall perish. —Psalm 1.

Enter ye in at the strait gate: for wide is the gate, and broad is the way, that leadeth to destruction, and many there be which go in thereat:

Because strait is the gate, and narrow is the way, which leadeth unto life, and few there be that find it.

Hymns 55, 111, 117, 125 —Matthew 7: 13, 14.

288 THE SHEPHERD PSALM

The Lord is my shepherd; I shall not want.

He maketh me to lie down in green pastures: he leadeth me beside the still waters.

He restoreth my soul: he leadeth me in the paths of righteousness for his name's sake.

Yea, though I walk through the valley of the shadow of death, I will fear no evil:

For thou art with me; thy rod and thy staff they comfort me.

Thou preparest a table before me in the presence of mine enemies:

Thou anointest my head with oil; my cup runneth over.

Surely goodness and mercy shall follow me all the days of my life; and I will dwell in the house of the Lord for ever. —Psalm 23.

Hymns: 40, 133, 189, 198

289 DIVINE PROVIDENCE

I will bless the Lord at all times: his praise shall continually be in my mouth.

My soul shall make her boast in the Lord: the humble shall hear thereof, and be glad.

O magnify the Lord with me, and let us exalt his name together.

I sought the Lord, and he heard me, and delivered me from all my fears.

They looked unto him, and were lightened; and their faces were not ashamed.

This poor man cried, and the Lord heard him, and saved him out of all his troubles.

The angel of the Lord encampeth round about them that fear him, and delivereth them.

O taste and see that the Lord is good: blessed is the man that trusteth in him.

O fear the Lord, ye his saints; for there is no want to them that fear him.

The young lions do lack, and suffer hunger; but they that seek the Lord shall not want any good thing.

The eyes of the Lord are upon the righteous, and his ears are open unto their cry.

The face of the Lord is against them that do evil, to cut off the remembrance of them from the earth.

The righteous cry, and the Lord heareth, and delivereth them out of all their troubles.

The Lord is nigh unto them that are of a broken heart; and saveth such as be of a contrite spirit.

Many are the afflictions of the righteous: but the Lord delivereth him out of them all.

The Lord redeemeth the soul of his servants; and none of them that trust in him shall be desolate.

—Psalm 34: 1-10, 15-19, 22.

Hymns: 12, 19, 33, 182, 187

290 PRAYER OF PENITENCE

Have mercy upon me, O God, according to thy lovingkindness:

According unto the multitude of thy tender mercies blot out my transgressions.

Wash me thoroughly from mine iniquity, and cleanse me from my sin.

For I acknowledge my transgressions; and my sin is ever before me.

Against thee, thee only, have I sinned, and done this evil in thy sight; that thou mightest be justified when thou speakest, and be clear when thou judgest.

Purge me with hyssop, and I shall be clean: wash me, and I shall be whiter than snow.

Make me to hear joy and gladness; that the bones which thou hast broken may rejoice.

Hide thy face from my sins, and blot out all mine iniquities.

Create in me a clean heart, O God; and renew a right spirit within me.

Cast me not away from thy presence; and take not thy holy spirit from me.

Restore unto me the joy of thy salvation; and uphold me with thy free spirit.

Then will I teach transgressors thy ways; and sinners shall be converted unto thee.

Deliver me from bloodguiltiness, O God, thou God of my salvation; and my tongue shall sing aloud of thy righteousness.

O Lord, open thou my lips; and my mouth shall show forth thy praise.

For thou desirest not sacrifice; else would I give it: thou delightest not in burnt offering.

The sacrifices of God are a broken spirit: a broken and a contrite heart, O God, thou wilt not despise.

—From Psalm 51.

Hymns: 57, 71, 76, 84

291 OBEDIENCE TO GOD

Blessed are the undefiled in the way, who walk in the law of the Lord.

Blessed are they that keep his testimonies, and that seek him with the whole heart.

They also do no iniquity: they walk in his ways.

Thou hast commanded us to keep thy precepts diligently.

O that my ways were directed to keep thy statutes!

Then shall I not be ashamed, when I have respect unto all thy commandments.

I will praise thee with uprightness of heart, when I shall have learned thy righteous judgments.

I will keep thy statutes: O forsake me not utterly.

Wherewithal shall a young man cleanse his way? By taking heed thereto according to thy word.

With my whole heart have I sought thee: O let me not wander from thy commandments.

Thy word have I hid in mine heart, that I might not sin against thee.

Blessed art thou, O Lord: teach me thy statutes.

With my lips have I declared all the judgments of thy mouth.

I have rejoiced in the way of thy testimonies, as much as in all riches.

I will meditate in thy precepts, and have respect unto thy ways.

I will delight myself in thy statutes: I will not forget thy word.

Deal bountifully with thy servant, that I may live, and keep thy word.

Open thou mine eyes, that I may behold wondrous things out of thy law.

—Psalm 119: 1-18.

Hymns: 137, 146, 153, 165, 181

292 GOD'S OMNISCIENCE

O Lord, thou hast searched me, and known me.

Thou knowest my downsitting and mine uprising; thou understandest my thought afar off.

Thou compassest my path and my lying down, and art acquainted with all my ways.

For there is not a word in my tongue, but, lo, O Lord, thou knowest it altogether.

Thou has beset me behind and before, and laid thine hand upon me.

Such knowledge is too wonderful for me; it is high, I cannot attain unto it.

Whither shall I go from thy spirit? or whither shall I flee from thy presence?

If I ascend up into heaven, thou art there: if I make my bed in sheol, behold, thou art there.

If I take the wings of the morning, and dwell in the uttermost parts of the sea;

Even there shall thy hand lead me, and thy right hand shall hold me.

If I say, Surely the darkness shall cover me; even the night shall be light about me.

Yea, the darkness hideth not from thee; but the night shineth as the day: the darkness and the light are both alike to thee.

I will praise thee; for I am fearfully and wonderfully made:

Marvellous are thy works; and that my soul knoweth right well.

Search me, O God, and know my heart: try me, and know my thoughts;

And see if there be any wicked way in me, and lead me in the way everlasting.

— From Psalm 139.

Hymns: 9, 38, 43, 241

293 TRUE WISDOM

Happy is the man that findeth wisdom, and the man that getteth understanding.

For the merchandise of it is better than the merchandise of silver, and the gain thereof than fine gold.

She is more precious than rubies: and all the things thou canst desire are not to be compared unto her.

Length of days is in her right hand; and in her left hand riches and honour.

Her ways are ways of pleasantness, and all her paths are peace.

She is a tree of life to them that lay hold upon her: and happy is every one that retaineth her.

The Lord by wisdom hath founded the earth; by understanding hath he established the heavens.

By his knowledge the depths are broken up, and the clouds drop down the dew.

My son, let not them depart from thine eyes; keep sound wisdom and discretion:

So shall they be life unto thy soul, and grace to thy neck.

Then shalt thou walk in thy way safely, and thy foot shall not stumble.

When thou liest down thou shalt not be afraid: yea, thou shalt lie down, and thy sleep shall be sweet.

Be not afraid of sudden fear, neither of the desolation of the wicked, when it cometh.

For the Lord shall be thy confidence, and shall keep thy foot from being taken.

Trust in the Lord with all thine heart; and lean not unto thine own understanding.

In all thy ways acknowledge him, and he shall direct thy paths.

— Proverbs 3: 13-26, 5, 6.

Hymns: 48, 135, 144, 180, 198

294 ADORATION OF THE MAGI

Now when Jesus was born in Bethlehem of Judea in the days of Herod the king, behold, there came wise men from the east to Jerusalem, saying,

Where is he that is born King of the Jews? for we have seen his star in the east, and are come to worship him.

When Herod the king had heard these things, he was troubled, and all Jerusalem with him.

And when he had gathered all the chief priests and scribes of the people together, he demanded of them where Christ should be born.

And they said unto him, In Bethlehem of Judea: for thus it is written by the prophet,

And thou Bethlehem, in the land of Judah, art not the least among the princes of Judah: for out of thee shall come a governor, that shall rule my people Israel.

Then Herod, when he had privily called the wise men, enquired of them diligently what time the star appeared. And he sent them to Bethlehem, and said,

Go and search diligently for the young child; and when ye have found him, bring me word again, that I may come and worship him also.

When they had heard the king, they departed; and, lo, the star, which they saw in the east, went before them, till it came and stood over where the young child was.

When they saw the star, they rejoiced with exceeding great joy.

And when they were come into the house, they saw the young child with Mary his mother, and fell down, and worshipped him:

And when they had opened their treasures, they presented unto him gifts; gold, and frankincense, and myrrh.

—Matthew 2: 1-11.

Hymns: 258-268.

295 THE BEATITUDES

And seeing the multitudes, he went up into the mountain: and when he was set, his disciples came unto him:

And he opened his mouth, and taught them, saying,

Blessed are the poor in spirit: for theirs is the kingdom of heaven.

Blessed are they that mourn: for they shall be comforted.

Blessed are the meek: for they shall inherit the earth.

Blessed are they which do hunger and thirst after righteousness: for they shall be filled.

Blessed are the merciful: for they shall obtain mercy.

Blessed are the pure in heart: for they shall see God.

Blessed are the peacemakers: for they shall be called the children of God.

Blessed are they which are persecuted for righteousness' sake: for theirs is the kingdom of heaven.

Blessed are ye, when men shall revile you, and persecute you, and shall say all manner of evil against you falsely, for my sake.

Rejoice, and be exceeding glad: for great is your reward in heaven: for so persecuted they the prophets which were before you.

Ye are the salt of the earth: but if the salt have lost his savour, wherewith shall it be salted?

It is thenceforth good for nothing, but to be cast out, and to be trodden under foot of men.

Ye are the light of the world. A city that is set on an hill cannot be hid.

Let your light so shine before men, that they may see your good works, and glorify your Father which is in heaven.

—Matthew 5: 1-14, 16.

Hymns: 142, 145, 150, 157, 236

296 THE WHITENED HARVEST

And Jesus went about all the cities and villages, teaching in their synagogues, and preaching the gospel of the kingdom, and healing every sickness and every disease among the people.

But when he saw the multitudes, he was moved with compassion on them, because they fainted, and were scattered abroad, as sheep having no shepherd.

Then saith he unto his disciples, The harvest truly is plenteous, but the labourers are few;

Pray ye therefore the Lord of the harvest, that he will send forth labourers into his harvest.

— Matthew 9: 35-38.

For there is no difference between the Jew and the Greek: for the same Lord over all is rich unto all that call upon him.

For whosoever shall call upon the name of the Lord shall be saved.

How then shall they call on him in whom they have not believed? and how shall they believe in him of whom they have not heard? and how shall they hear without a preacher?

And how shall they preach, except they be sent? as it is written, How beautiful are the feet of them that preach the gospel of peace, and bring glad tidings of good things!

— Romans 10: 12-15.

Say not ye, There are yet four months, and then cometh harvest? behold, I say unto you, Lift up your eyes, and look on the fields; for they are white already to harvest.

— John 4: 35.

He that goeth forth and weepeth, bearing precious seed, shall doubtless come again with rejoicing, bringing his sheaves with him. — Psalm 126: 6.

Hymns: 215, 228, 230, 231, 237

297 THE LAST SUPPER

Now the first day of the feast of unleavened bread the disciples came to Jesus, saying unto him. Where wilt thou that we prepare for thee to eat the passover?

And he said, Go into the city to such a man, and say unto him, The Master saith, My time is at hand; I will keep the passover at thy house with my disciples.

And the disciples did as Jesus had appointed them; and they made ready the passover.

Now when the even was come, he sat down with the twelve.

And as they did eat, he said, Verily I say unto you, that one of you shall betray me.

And they were exceeding sorrowful, and began every one of them to say unto him, Lord, is it I?

And he answered and said, He that dippeth his hand with me in the dish, the same shall betray me.

The Son of man goeth as it is written of him: but woe unto that man by whom the Son of man is betrayed! it had been good for that man if he had not been born.

Then Judas, which betrayed him, answered and said, Master, is it I? He said unto him, Thou hast said.

And as they were eating, Jesus took bread, and blessed it, and brake it, and gave it to the disciples, and said, Take, eat; this is my body.

And he took the cup, and gave thanks, and gave it to them, saying, Drink ye all of it; For this is my blood of the new testament, which is shed for many for the remission of sins.

But I say unto you, I will not drink henceforth of this fruit of the vine, until that day when I drink it new with you in my Father's kingdom.

— Matthew 26: 17-29.

Hymns: 34, 70, 78, 88, 124

298 THE RISEN LORD

In the end of the sabbath, as it began to dawn toward the first day of the week, came Mary Magdalene and the other Mary to see the sepulchre.

And, behold, there was a great earthquake; for the angel of the Lord descended from heaven, and came and rolled back the stone from the door, and sat upon it.

His countenance was like lightning, and his raiment white as snow:

And for fear of him the keepers did shake, and became as dead men.

And the angel answered and said unto the women, Fear not ye: for I know that ye seek Jesus, which was crucified.

He is not here; for he is risen, as he said. Come, see the place where the Lord lay.

And go quickly, and tell his disciples that he is risen from the dead; and, behold, he goeth before you into Galilee; there shall ye see him: lo, I have told you.

And they departed quickly from the sepulchre with fear and great joy; and did run to bring his disciples word.

And as they went to tell his disciples, behold, Jesus met them, saying, All hail. And they came and held him by the feet, and worshipped him.

Then said Jesus unto them, Be not afraid: go tell my brethren that they go into Galilee, and there shall they see me. —Matthew 28: 1-10.

Then the same day at evening, being the first day of the week, when the doors were shut where the disciples were assembled for fear of the Jews, came Jesus and stood in the midst, and saith unto them, Peace be unto you.

And when he had so said, he shewed unto them his hands and his side. Then were the disciples glad, when they saw the Lord.

Hymns: 89, 126, 271-277 —John 20: 19, 20.

299 THE GREAT COMMISSION

Then the eleven disciples went away into Galilee, into a mountain where Jesus had appointed them.

And when they saw him, they worshipped him: but some doubted.

And Jesus came and spake unto them, saying, All power is given unto me in heaven and in earth.

Go ye therefore, and teach all nations, baptizing them in the name of the Father, and of the Son, and of the Holy Ghost:

Teaching them to observe all things whatsoever I have commanded you: and, lo, I am with you alway, even unto the end of the world.

Jesus said unto them, Thus it is written, and thus it behoved Christ to suffer, and to rise from the dead the third day:

And that repentance and remission of sins should be preached in his name among all nations, beginning at Jerusalem.

And ye are witnesses of these things.

And, behold, I send the promise of my Father upon you: but tarry ye in the city of Jerusalem, until ye be endued with power from on high.

—Luke 24: 46-49.

They asked of him, saying, Lord, wilt thou at this time restore again the kingdom to Israel?

And he said unto them, It is not for you to know the times or the seasons, which the Father hath put in his own power.

But ye shall receive power, after that the Holy Ghost is come upon you:

And ye shall be witnesses unto me both in Jerusalem, and in all Judaea, and in Samaria, and unto the uttermost part of the earth.

And when he had spoken these things, while they beheld, he was taken up; and a cloud received him out of their sight. —Acts 1: 6-9.

Hymns: 142, 155, 224, 226, 234

300 THE TRIUMPHAL ENTRY

And when they came nigh to Jerusalem, unto Bethphage and Bethany, at the mount of Olives, he sendeth forth two of his disciples, and saith unto them,

Go your way into the village over against you: and as soon as ye be entered into it, ye shall find a colt tied, whereon never man sat; loose him, and bring him.

And if any man say unto you, Why do ye this? say ye that the Lord hath need of him; and straightway he will send him hither.

And they went their way, and found the colt tied by the door without in a place where two ways met; and they loose him.

And certain of them that stood there said unto them, What do ye, loosing the colt?

And they said unto them even as Jesus had commanded: and they let them go.

And they brought the colt to Jesus, and cast their garments on him; and he sat upon him.

And many spread their garments in the way; and others cut down branches off the trees, and strawed them in the way.

And they that went before, and they that followed, cried, saying, Hosanna; Blessed is he that cometh in the name of the Lord:

Blessed be the kingdom of our father David, that cometh in the name of the Lord: Hosanna in the highest. And Jesus entered into Jerusalem, and into the temple.

—Mark 11: 1-11.

And when he was come into Jerusalem, all the city was moved, saying, Who is this?

And the multitude said, This is Jesus the prophet of Nazareth of Galilee. —Matthew 21: 10, 11.

Hymns: 28, 35, 269, 270

301 THE SAVIOUR'S ADVENT

And there were in the same country shepherds abiding in the field, keeping watch over their flock by night.

And, lo, the angel of the Lord came upon them, and the glory of the Lord shone round about them: and they were sore afraid.

And the angel said unto them, Fear not: for, behold, I bring you good tidings of great joy, which shall be to all people.

For unto you is born this day in the city of David a Saviour, which is Christ the Lord.

And this shall be a sign unto you; Ye shall find the babe wrapped in swaddling clothes, lying in a manger.

And suddenly there was with the angel a multitude of the heavenly host praising God, and saying,

Glory to God in the highest, and on earth peace, good will toward men.

And it came to pass, as the angels were gone away from them into heaven, the shepherds said one to another,

Let us now go even unto Bethlehem, and see this thing which is come to pass, which the Lord hath made known unto us.

And they came with haste, and found Mary, and Joseph, and the babe lying in a manger.

And when they had seen it, they made known abroad the saying which was told them concerning this child.

And all they that heard it wondered at those things which were told them by the shepherds.

But Mary kept all these things, and pondered them in her heart.

And the shepherds returned, glorifying and praising God for all the things that they had heard and seen, as it was told unto them. —Luke 2: 8-20.

Hymns: 258-268

302 CHRIST TEACHES PRAYER

And it came to pass, that, as he was praying in a certain place, when he ceased, one of his disciples said unto him, Lord, teach us to pray, as John also taught his disciples.

And he said unto them, When ye pray, say, Our Father which art in heaven, Hallowed be thy name. Thy kingdom come. Thy will be done, as in heaven, so in earth.

Give us day by day our daily bread.

And forgive us our sins; for we also forgive every one that is indebted to us.

And lead us not into temptation; but deliver us from evil.

And he said unto them, Which of you shall have a friend, and shall go unto him at midnight, and say unto him, Friend, lend me three loaves;

For a friend of mine in his journey is come to me, and I have nothing to set before him?

And he from within shall answer and say, Trouble me not: the door is now shut, and my children are with me in bed; I cannot rise and give thee.

I say unto you, Though he will not rise and give him because he is his friend, yet because of his importunity he will rise and give him as many as he needeth.

And I say unto you, Ask, and it shall be given you; seek, and ye shall find; knock, and it shall be opened unto you.

For every one that asketh receiveth; and he that seeketh findeth; and to him that knocketh it shall be opened.

If ye then, being evil, know how to give good gifts unto your children: how much more shall your heavenly Father give the Holy Spirit to them that ask him? —Luke 11: 1-10, 13.

Hymns: 164, 168, 175, 185, 186

303 THE INCARNATE CHRIST

In the beginning was the Word, and the Word was with God, and the Word was God.

The same was in the beginning with God.

All things were made by him; and without him was not anything made that was made.

In him was life; and the life was the light of men.

And th light shineth in darkness; and the darkness comprehended it not.

There was a man sent from God, whose name was John.

The same came for a witness, to bear witness of the Light, that all men through him might believe.

He was not that Light, but was sent to bear witness of that Light.

That was the true Light, which lighteth every man that cometh into the world.

He was in the world, and the world was made by him, and the world knew him not.

He came unto his own, and his own received him not.

But as many as received him, to them gave he power to become the sons of God, even to them that believe on his name:

Which were born, not of blood, nor of the will of the flesh, nor of the will of man, but of God.

And the Word was made flesh, and dwelt among us, and we beheld his glory, the glory as of the only begotten of the Father, full of grace and truth.

For God so loved the world, that he gave his only begotten Son, that whosoever believeth in him should not perish, but have everlasting life.

For God sent not his Son into the world to condemn the world; but that the world through him might be saved. —John 1: 1-14; 3: 16, 17.

Hymns: 4, 17, 42, 83, 262

304 THE HOLY SPIRIT

And it shall come to pass afterward, that I will pour out my spirit upon all flesh; and your sons and your daughters shall prophesy, your old men shall dream dreams, your young men shall see visions:

And also upon the servants and upon the handmaids in those days will I pour out my spirit. —Joel 2: 28, 29.

And I will pray the Father, and he shall give you another Comforter, that he may abide with you for ever;

Even the Spirit of truth; whom the world cannot receive, because it seeth him not, neither knoweth him: but ye know him; for he dwelleth with you, and shall be in you.

—John 14: 16, 17.

Nevertheless I tell you the truth: It is expedient for you that I go away: for if I go not away, the Comforter will not come unto you;

But if I depart, I will send him unto you. And when he is come, he will reprove the world of sin, and of righteousness, and of judgment.

—John 16: 7, 8.

But ye shall receive power, after that the Holy Ghost is come upon you:

And ye shall be witnesses unto me both in Jerusalem, and in all Judaea, and in Samaria, and unto the uttermost part of the earth.

—Acts 1: 8.

And when the day of Pentecost was fully come, they were all with one accord in one place.

And suddenly there came a sound from heaven as of a rushing mighty wind, and it filled all the house where they were sitting.

And there appeared unto them cloven tongues like as of fire, and it sat upon each of them.

And they were all filled with the Holy Ghost, and began to speak with other tongues, as the Spirit gave them utterance. —Acts 2: 1-4.

Hymns: 154, 155, 173, 175, 176

305 CHRISTIAN ASSURANCE

As many as are led by the Spirit of God, they are the sons of God.

For ye have not received the spirit of bondage again to fear; but ye have received the Spirit of adoption, whereby we cry, Abba, Father.

The Spirit itself beareth witness with our spirit, that we are the children of God:

And if children, then heirs; heirs of God, and joint-heirs with Christ; if so be that we suffer with him, that we may be also glorified together.

For I reckon that the sufferings of this present time are not worthy to be compared with the glory which shall be revealed in us.

And we know that all things work together for good to them that love God, to them who are the called according to his purpose.

What shall we then say to these things? If God be for us, who can be against us?

He that spared not his own Son, but delivered him up for us all, how shall he not with him also freely give us all things?

Who shall separate us from the love of Christ? shall tribulation, or distress, or persecution, or famine, or nakedness, or peril, or sword?

Nay, in all these things we are more than conquerors through him that loved us.

For I am persuaded, that neither death, nor life, nor angels, nor principalities, nor powers, nor things present, nor things to come.

Nor height, nor depth, nor any other creature, shall be able to separate us from the love of God, which is in Christ Jesus our Lord.

—Romans 8: 14-18, 28, 31, 32, 35, 37-39.

Hymns: 22, 123, 131, 179, 180

306 THE LOVE CHAPTER

Though I speak with the tongues of men and of angels, and have not love, I am become as sounding brass, or a tinkling cymbal.

And though I have the gift of prophecy, and understand all mysteries, and all knowledge; and though I have all faith, so that I could remove mountains, and have not love, I am nothing.

And though I bestow all my goods to feed the poor, and though I give my body to be burned, and have not love, it profiteth me nothing.

Love suffereth long, and is kind; love envieth not; love vaunteth not itself, is not puffed up.

Doth not behave itself unseemly, seeketh not her own, is not easily provoked, thinketh no evil;

Rejoiceth not in iniquity, but rejoiceth in the truth;

Beareth all things, believeth all things, hopeth all things, endureth all things.

Love never faileth: but whether there be prophecies, they shall fail; whether there be tongues, they shall cease; whether there be knowledge, it shall vanish away.

For we know in part, and we prophesy in part.

But when that which is perfect is come, then that which is in part shall be done away.

When I was a child, I spake as a child, I understood as a child, I thought as a child: but when I became a man, I put away childish things.

For now we see through a glass, darkly; but then face to face:

Now I know in part; but then shall I know even as also I am known.

And now abideth faith, hope, love, these three; but the greatest of these is love. — I Corinthians 13.

Hymns: 52, 74, 150, 170

307 SPIRITUAL WARFARE

Finally, my brethren, be strong in the Lord, and in the power of his might.

Put on the whole armour of God, that ye may be able to stand against the wiles of the devil.

For we wrestle not against flesh and blood, but against principalities, against powers, against the rulers of the darkness of this world, against spiritual wickedness in high places.

Wherefore take unto you the whole armour of God, that ye may be able to withstand in the evil day, and having done all, to stand.

Stand therefore, having your loins girt about with truth, and having on the breastplate of righteousness; and your feet shod with the preparation of the gospel of peace;

Above all, taking the shield of faith, wherewith ye shall be able to quench all the fiery darts of the wicked.

And take the helmet of salvation, and the sword of the Spirit, which is the word of God:

Praying always with all prayer and supplication in the Spirit, and watching thereunto with all perseverance and supplication for all saints. — Ephesians 6: 10-18.

Thou therefore endure hardness as a good soldier of Jesus Christ.

No man that warreth entangleth himself with the affairs of this life; that he may please him who hath chosen him to be a soldier.

— II Timothy 2: 3, 4.

I have fought a good fight, I have finished my course, I have kept the faith:

Henceforth there is laid up for me a crown of righteousness, which the Lord, the righteous judge, shall give me at that day: and not to me only, but unto all them also that love his appearing. — II Timothy 4: 7, 8.

Hymns: 216, 218, 219, 223, 225

308 THE RETURN OF CHRIST

But I would not have you to be ignorant, brethren, concerning them which are asleep, that ye sorrow not, even as others which have no hope.

For if we believe that Jesus died and rose again, even so them also which sleep in Jesus will God bring with him.

For this we say unto you by the word of the Lord, that we which are alive and remain unto the coming of the Lord shall not precede them which are asleep.

For the Lord himself shall descend from heaven with a shout, with the voice of the archangel, and with the trump of God: and the dead in Christ shall rise first.

Then we which are alive and remain shall be caught up together with them in the clouds, to meet the Lord in the air: and so shall we ever be with the Lord.

Wherefore comfort one another with these words.

But of the times and the seasons, brethren, ye have no need that I write unto you.

For yourselves know perfectly that the day of the Lord so cometh as a thief in the night.

But ye, brethren, are not in darkness, that that day should overtake you as a thief. Ye are all the children of the day: we are not of the night, nor of darkness.

Therefore let us not sleep, as do others; but let us watch and be sober.

For God hath not appointed us to wrath, but to obtain salvation by our Lord Jesus Christ,

Who died for us, that, whether we wake or sleep, we should live together with him.

— I Thessalonians 4: 13-18; 5: 1, 2, 4-6, 9, 10.

Hymns: 239, 240, 241, 243, 251

309 THE HOLY SCRIPTURES

Knowing this first, that no prophecy of the scripture is of any private interpretation.

For the prophecy came not in old time by the will of man: but holy men of God spake as they were moved by the Holy Ghost.

— II Peter 1: 20, 21.

All scripture is given by inspiration of God, and is profitable for doctrine, for reproof, for correction, for instruction in righteousness:

That the man of God may be perfect, thoroughly furnished unto all good works. — II Timothy 3: 16, 17.

Study to show thyself approved unto God, a workman that needeth not to be ashamed, rightly dividing the word of truth. — II Timothy 2: 15.

For the word of God is quick, and powerful, and sharper than any two-edged sword, piercing even to the dividing asunder of soul and spirit, and of the joints and marrow, and is a discerner of the thoughts and intents of the heart. — Hebrews 4: 12.

But these are written, that ye might believe that Jesus is the Christ, the Son of God; and that believing ye might have life through his name. — John 20: 31.

For whatsoever things were written aforetime were written for our learning, that we through patience and comfort of the scriptures might have hope. — Romans 15: 4.

Teach me, O Lord, the way of thy statutes; and I shall keep it unto the end.

Give me understanding, and I shall keep thy law; yea, I shall observe it with my whole heart.

The entrance of thy words giveth light; it giveth understanding unto the simple.

Great peace have they which love thy law: and nothing shall offend them. — Psalm 119: 33, 34, 130, 165.

Hymns: 101, 153, 202-206

310 BLESSINGS FROM GOD

Bless the Lord, O my soul; and all that is within me, bless his holy name.

Bless the Lord, O my soul, and forget not all his benefits:

Who forgiveth all thine iniquities; who healeth all thy diseases;

Who redeemeth thy life from destruction; who crowneth thee with lovingkindness and tender mercies;

Who satisfieth thy mouth with good things; so that thy youth is renewed like the eagle's.

The Lord executeth righteousness and judgment for all that are oppressed.

He made known his ways unto Moses, his acts unto the children of Israel.

The Lord is merciful and gracious, slow to anger, and plenteous in mercy.

He will not always chide; neither will he keep his anger for ever.

He hath not dealt with us after our sins, nor rewarded us according to our iniquities.

For as the heaven is high above the earth, so great is his mercy toward them that fear him.

As far as the east is from the west, so far hath he removed our transgressions from us.

Like as a father pitieth his children, so the Lord pitieth them that fear him.

For he knoweth our frame; he remembereth that we are dust.

As for man, his days are as grass; as a flower of the field, so he flourisheth.

For the wind passeth over it, and it is gone; and the place thereof shall know it no more.

But the mercy of the Lord is from everlasting to everlasting upon them that fear him, and his righteousness unto children's children;

Bless the Lord, all his works, in all places of his dominion: bless the Lord, O my soul. From Psalm 103.

Hymns: 1, 13, 22, 32, 52

311 COMFORT FROM CHRIST

Let not your heart be troubled: ye believe in God, believe also in me.

In my Father's house are many mansions: if it were not so, I would have told you. I go to prepare a place for you.

And if I go and prepare a place for you, I will come again, and receive you unto myself; that where I am, there ye may be also.

And whither I go ye know, and the way ye know.

Thomas saith unto him, Lord, we know not whither thou goest; and how can we know the way?

Jesus saith unto him, I am the way, the truth, and the life: no man cometh unto the Father, but by me.

If ye had known me, ye should have known my Father also: and from henceforth ye know him, and have seen him.

Philip saith unto him, Lord, show us the Father, and it sufficeth us.

Jesus saith unto him, Have I been so long time with you, and yet hast thou not known me, Philip? he that hath seen me hath seen the Father; and how sayest thou then, Show us the Father?

Believest thou not that I am in the Father, and the Father in me? the words that I speak unto you I speak not of myself: but the Father that dwelleth in me, he doeth the works.

Verily, verily, I say unto you, He that believeth on me, the works that I do shall he do also; and greater works than these shall he do; because I go unto my Father.

Peace I leave with you, my peace I give unto you: not as the world giveth, give I unto you. Let not your heart be troubled, neither let it be afraid. —John 14: 1-12, 27.

Hymns: 188, 192, 245, 252, 253

index of authors, composers, and sources

A

Ackley, Alfred Henry (1887-1960); 89.
Ackley, Bentley DeForest (1872-1958); 145.
Ahlwén, Elsie (b. 1905) ; 250.
Alexander, James Waddell (1804-1859); 34.
Alford, Henry (1810-1871); 255.
Allen, Chester G. (1838-1878); 29.
American Melody, Anonymous; 81, 108, 180.
Arne, Thomas Augustus (1710-1778); 219.
Astrom, Johan (1767-1844); 253.
Atkinson, Frederick Cook (1841-1897); 175.

B

Babcock, Maltbie Davenport (1858-1901); 44.
Bach, Johann Sebastian (1685-1750); 34.
Backstrom, Carl Ernest (b. 1901); 257.
Baker, Henry (1835-1910); 7.
Baker, Henry Williams (1821-1877); 63.
Baker, Theodore (1851-1934); 254.
Barham-Gould, A. Cyril (1891-1953); 135.
Baring-Gould, Sabine (1834-1924); 47, 217.
Barnard, Charlotte Alington (1830-1869); 238.
Barnby, Joseph (1838-1896); 41, 66, 125.
Barraclough, Henry (b. 1891); 86.
Barthélémon, Francois Hippolyte (1741-1808); 50.
Bateman, Christian Henry (1813-1889); 30.
Bates, Katharine Lee (1859-1929); 283.
Bennard, George (1873-1958); 77.
Berg, Carolina V. (Sandell) (1832-1903); 189.
Bernard of Clairvaux (1091-1153); 7, 25, 34.
Bevan, Emma Frances (1827-1909); 55.
"Bible Class Magazine", 1860; 130.
Bickersteth, Edward Henry (1825-1906); 192.
Bilhorn, Peter Philip (1865-1936); 94.
Bittikofer, Talmadge John (b. 1892); 114.
Black, James Milton (1856-1938); 62.
Bliss, Philip Paul (1838-1876); 73, 93, 101, 119, 200, 233, 235.
Blom, Fred (20th Century); 250.
Boberg, Carl (1859-1940); 1.
Bode, John Ernest (1816-1874); 172.
Bohemian Brethren's "Kirchengesänge," 1566 ; 9.
Bonar, Horatius (1808-1889); 45, 56, 125, 133.
Borthwick, Jane Laurie (1813-1897); 197.
Bortniansky, Dimitri Stepanovich (1752-1825); 140, 229.
Bourgeois, Louis (1510-1561); 51.
Bowring, John (1792-1872); 72.
Bradbury, William Batchelder (1816-1868); 21, 57, 92, 198, 206.
Breck, Carrie E. (1855-1934); 246.
Bridges, Matthew (1800-1894); 31.
Brooks, Phillips (1835-1893); 266.
Brownlie, John (1859-1925); 240.
Budry, Edmond Louis (1854-1932); 272.
Bullinger, Ethelbert William (1837-1913); 102.
Bunyan, John (1628-1688); 212.
Burton, John (1773-1822); 206.
Byrne, Mary Elizabeth (1880-1931); 147.

C

Caldbeck, George Thomas (1852-1912); 192.
Calkin, John Baptiste (1827-1905); 276.
Campbell, John Douglas Sutherland (1845-1914); 187.
Campbell, Thomas (1777-1844); 74.
Carey, Henry (1690-1743); 281.
Carlson, Nathaniel (1879-1957); 250.
Carter, Russell Kelso (1849-1926); 202.
Caswall, Edward (1814-1878); 25, 41.
Chapman, J. Wilbur (1859-1918); 4, 116.
Chisholm, Thomas Obediah (1866-1960); 33, 146, 152.
Chorley, Henry Fothergill (1808-1872); 282.
Christiansen, Avis Burgeson (b. 1895); 20, 60, 178.
Clarke, Harry D. (1888-1957); 60.
Clarkson, E. Margaret (b. 1915); 52, 224, 241.
Clayton, Norman J. (b. 1903); 103, 129.
Clayton, William (19th Century); 178.
Clemm, J. B. O. (19th Century); 231.
Clephane, Elizabeth Cecilia (1830-1869); 151.
Conkey, Ithamar (1815-1867); 72.
Converse, Charles Crozat (1832-1918); 185.
Cousin, Anne Ross (1824-1906); 244.
Cowper, William (1731-1800); 81.
Cox, Frances Elizabeth (1812-1897); 9.
Croft, William (1678-1727); 12.
Croly, George (1780-1860); 175.
Crosby, Fanny Jane (1820-1915); 3, 29, 91, 97, 99, 127, 160, 179, 227, 248.
Crüger, Johann (1598-1662) ; 256, 277.
Cummings, William Hayman (1831-1915); 258.
Cushing, William Orcutt (1823-1902); 195.
Cutler, Henry Stephen (1824-1902); 223.

D

Darwall, John (1731-1789); 6, 17.
Davis, Frank M. (1839-1896); 69
Dix, William Chatterton (1837-1898); 261.
Doane, William Howard (1832-1915); 3, 96, 127, 150, 160, 227.
Doddridge, Philip (1702-1751); 75, 128.
Douglas, Charles Winfred (1867-1944); 212.
Draper, William Henry (1885-1933); 16.
Dunbar, C. R. (19th Century); 143.
Duffield, George (1818-1888); 225.
Dykes, John Bacchus (1823-1876); 8, 25, 56.

E

Edmunds, Lidie H. (19th Century); 111.
Ellerton, John (1826-1893); 282.
Elliott, Charlotte (1789-1871); 57, 199.
Elliott, Emily Elizabeth Steele (1836-1897); 259.
Elvey, George Job (1816-1893); 31, 201, 216, 255.
Ely, Effie Smith (b. 1879); 22.
English Melody, Anonymous; 261.
Evans, David (1874-1948); 30, 147.
Excell, Edwin Othello (1851-1921); 108.

F

Faber, Frederick William (1814-1863); 47, 207.
Featherstone, William Ralph (1846-1873); 163.
Fillmore, James Henry (1849-1936); 273.
Fink, Gottfried Wilhelm (1783-1846); 204.
Fischer, William Gustavus (1835-1912); 95.
Flemming, Friedrich Ferdinald (1778-1813); 46.
Foulkes, William H. (1877-1962); 144.
Francis, Samuel Trevor (1834-1925); 85.
Fraser, M. (19th Century); 131.
French Carol, Anonymous; 260.

G

Gabriel, Charles Hutchison (1856-1932); 98, 112, 120, 157, 252.
Geibel, Adam (1885-1933); 225.
"Geistliche Kirchengesänge," 1623; 16.
Gellert, Christian Fürchtegott (1715-1769) ; 277.
"Genevan Psalter", 1551; 51.
Gerhardt, Paul (1607-1676); 34, 201.
German Melody, Anonymous; 23, 221, 263.
German Text, Anonymous; 11, 39, 41.
"Gesangbuch der Herzogl," Württemberg, 1784 ; 5.
Giardini, Felice de (1716-1796); 28.
Gibbs, Ada Rose (20th Century); 169.
Gibbs, Alfred P. (b. 1890); 78.
Gilmore, Joseph Henry (1834-1918); 198.
Gladden, Washington (1836-1918); 211.
Gläser, Carl Gotthelf (1784-1829) ; 24.
Gordon, Adoniram Judson (1836-1895); 121, 163, 249.
Goss, John (1800-1880); 10, 221.
Gottschalk, Louis Moreau (1829-1869); 173.
Grant, David (1833-1893); 40.
Grant, Robert (1779-1838); 48.
Gray, James Martin (1851-1935); 114.
Greek Text, Anonymous; 63, 240.
Green, Harold (1871-1931); 168.
Greenwell, Dora (1821-1882); 83.
Gregorian Melody, Anonymous; 71, 128.
Grimes, E. May (1868-1927); 168.

index of authors, composers, and sources

Grimes, Katherine A. (b. 1877); 137.
Grose, Howard Benjamin (1851-1939); 238.
Gruber, Franz Xaver (1787-1863); 268.

h

Hanby, Benjamin Russell (1833-1867); 15.
Handel, George Frederick (1685-1759); 267, 272.
Hankey, Arabella Catherine (1834-1911); 95, 96.
Harkness, Robert (1880-1961); 4.
Harrington, Karl Pomeroy (1861-1953); 264.
Harrison, Ralph (1748-1810); 13.
Hart, Joseph (1712-1768); 53.
Hassler, Hans Leo (1564-1612); 34.
Hastings, Thomas (1784-1872); 191.
Hatch, Edwin (1835-1889); 155, 176.
Hatton, John (1710-1793); 232.
Havergal, Frances Ridley (1836-1879); 102, 140, 142, 162, 188, 221, 222, 235, 278.
Hawks, Annie Sherwood (1836-1918); 149.
Haydn, Franz Joseph (1732-1809); 208.
Haydn, Johann Michael (1737-1806); 48, 278.
Hayford, Jack W. (b. 1934); 14.
Hearn, Marianne (1834-1909); 66.
Heber, Reginald (1783-1826); 8, 223.
Hebrew Melody, Anonymous; 38, 224.
Hedge, Frederick Henry (1805-1890); 32.
Hemy, Henri Frederick (1818-1888); 207.
Herbert, George (1593-1632); 36.
Hewitt, Eliza Edmunds (1851-1920); 61, 242.
Hickman, Roger M. (b. 1888); 110.
Hine, Stuart K. (b. 1899); 1.
Hodder, Edwin (1837-1904); 204.
Hoffman, Elisha Albright (1839-1929); 42, 159, 190.
Holden, Oliver (1765-1844); 35.
Holland, Josiah Gilbert (1819-1881); 264.
How, William Walsham (1823-1897); 65, 245.
Howe, Julia Ward (1819-1910); 284.
Hoyle, Richard Birch (1875-1939); 272.
Hudson, Ralph E. (1843-1901); 88, 107, 143.
Hughes, John (1873-1932); 213
Hull, Eleanor Henrietta (1860-1935); 147.
Hultman, John Alfred (1861-1942); 257.
Husband, Edward (1843-1908); 65.
Husband, John Jenkins (1760-1825); 156.
Hussey, Jennie Evelyn (1874-1958); 67.
Hustad, Donald Paul (b. 1918); 20, 22, 86, 98, 115, 141, 148, 177.

i

Ingall's "Christian Harmony", 1805; 37.
Irish Text, Anonymous; 147.
Irish Melody, Anonymous; 147.
Irvine, Jessie Seymour (1836-1887); 40.

j

Jackson, H. G. (19th Century); 62.
Jackson, Robert (1842-1914); 155.
John F. Wade's "Cantus Diversi", 1751; 265.
Johnston, Julia Harriette (1849-1919); 76.
Jones, William (1726-1800); 240.
Judah, Daniel ben (14th Century); 38.

k

K. in Rippon's "A Selection of Hymns", 1787; 180.
"Katholisches Gesangbuch", 1774; 11.
Kelly, Thomas (1769-1855); 23.
Ken, Thomas (1637-1711); 50.
Ketchum, Albert Allen (20th Century); 118.
Kethe, William (d. ca. 1593); 51.
Kidder, Mary Ann (1820-1905); 69.
King, John (1789-1858); 269.
Kirkpatrick, William James (1838-1921); 61, 67, 83, 87, 99, 109, 111, 146, 179.
Knapp, Phoebe Palmer (1839-1908); 97.
Knecht, Justin Heinrich (1752-1817); 65.
Kocher, Conrad (1786-1872); 18.
Kremser, Edward (1838-1869); 254.

l

Langran, James (1835-1909); 45.
Lathbury, Mary Artemisia (1841-1913); 205.
Latin Text, Anonymous; 262, 263, 265, 275.
Laufer, Calvin Weiss (1874-1938); 144.
Laurinus, Laurentius Laurentii (1573-1655); 253.
Lester, John Henry (19th Century); 138.
Lillenas, Haldor (1885-1959); 106.
Loes, Harry Dixon (1892-1965); 113.
Longstaff, William Dunn (1822-1894); 136.
Loveless, Wendell P. (b. 1892); 234.
Lowden, Carl Harold (b. 1883); 152.
Lowry, Joseph C. (19th Century); 247.
Lowry, Robert (1826-1899); 149, 161, 271.
Luther, Martin (1483-1546); 32.
Lvov, Alexis F. (ca. 1799-1870); 282.
Lyne, J. L. (19th Century); 138.
Lyon, Meyer (1751-1799); 38, 224.

m

McAfee, Cleland Boyd (1866-1944); 193.
McCutchan, Robert Guy (1877-1958); 36.
McDaniel, Rufus Henry (1850-1940); 120.
McGranahan, James (1840-1907); 55, 123, 126, 251.
McKinney, Baylus Benjamin (1866-1952); 176, 215.
Macaulay, Joseph C. (b. 1900); 174, 234.
Maccall, William (1812-1888); 253.
Mackay, William Paton (1839-1885); 156.
Main, Hubert Platt (1839-1925); 214, 228.
Maker, Frederick Charles (1844-1927); 59, 151.
Malan, Henri Abraham César (1787-1864); 162, 186.
Mann, Arthur Henry (1850-1929); 172.
Maori Melody (Traditional); 148.
March, Daniel (1816-1909); 228.
Marsden, Ruth E. (20th Century); 243.
Marsh, Charles Howard (1886-1956); 116.
Marsh, Simeon Butler (1798-1875); 78.
Martin, Civilla Durfee (1866-1948); 182.
Martin, Walter Stillman (1862-1935); 182.
Mason, Lowell (1792-1872); 24, 49, 71, 81, 128, 165, 167.
Matheson, George (1842-1906); 139, 141.
Matthews, Timothy Richard (1826-1910); 259.
Maxwell, Mary E. (20th Century); 169.
Medley, Samuel (1738-1799); 49.
Mendelssohn, Felix (1809-1847); 256, 258.
Merrill, William Pierson (1867-1954); 210.
Messiter, Arthur Henry (1834-1916); 26.
Miles, C. Austin (1868-1946); 196.
Miller, Edward (1731-1807); 70.
Mohr, Joseph (1792-1848); 268.
Monk, William Henry (1823-1889); 275.
Monsell, John Samuel Bewley (1811-1875); 222.
Moody, May Whittle (1870-1963); 184.
Moore, Thomas (1779-1852); 191.
Morris, Leila Naylor (1862-1929); 166, 239.
Mote, Edward (1797-1874); 92.
Mountain, James (1844-1933); 104, 188, 194.
Mozart, Wolfgang Amadeus (1756-1791); 49, 214, 228.
Murray, Robert (1832-1910); 171.

n

Neale, John Mason (1818-1866); 63, 262, 263, 270, 276.
Neander, Joachim (1650-1680); 19.
Netherlands Melody, Anonymous; 254.
Neumeister, Erdmann (1671-1756); 55.
Newell, William Reed (1868-1956); 117.
Newton, John (1725-1807); 108, 186, 208.
Nichol, Henry Ernest (1862-1928); 230.
North, Frank Mason (1850-1935); 220, 229.
Norwegian Melody, Anonymous; 111, 253.

o

Oakeley, Frederick (1802-1880); 265.
Olivers, Thomas (1725-1799); 38.
Orr, J. Edwin (b. 1912); 148.
Ovens, W. G. (19th Century); 124.

Owen, William (1814-1893); 53.
Owens, Priscilla Jane (1829-1907); 87.

P

Palestrina, Giovanni Pierluigi da (1525-1594); 275.
Palmer, Ray (1808-1887); 7, 167.
Parker, Edwin Pond (1836-1925); 173.
Parry, Joseph (1841-1903); 79.
Peace, Albert Lister (1844-1912); 139.
Perronet, Edward (1726-1792); 35.
Phelps, Sylvanus Dryden (1816-1895); 161.
Pierpoint, Folliott Sanford (1835-1917); 18.
Pigott, Jean Sophia (19th Century); 194.
Plainsong Melody, Anonymous; 262.
Plumptre, Edward Hayes (1821-1891); 26.
Pollard, Adelaide Addison (1862-1934); 154.
Pott, Francis (1832-1909); 275.
Pounds, Jessie Brown (1861-1921); 273.
Prentiss, Elizabeth Payson (1818-1878); 150.
Prichard, Rowland Hugh (1811-1887); 4, 93.
Psalm 23 (40), 46 (197), 51 (71), 72 (232), 90 (12), 100 (51), 104 (48), 119 (203), 121 (187), 136 (13).
Purday, Charles H. (1799-1885); 187.

R

Redner, Lewis Henry (1830-1908); 266.
Reed, Andrew (1787-1862); 173.
Rees, John P. (1828-1900); 108.
Rimbault, Edward Francis (1816-1876); 244.
Rinkart, Martin (1586-1649); 256.
Rippon, John (1751-1836); 35.
Roberts, Daniel Crane (1841-1907); 280.
Roberts, Gladys Watkin (19th Century); 124.
Robinson, George Wade (1838-1877); 104.
Robinson, Robert (1735-1790); 2.
Roth, Elton Menno (1891-1951); 105.
Rowe, James (1865-1933); 145.
Rowlands, William Penfro (1860-1937); 170.
Rowley, Francis Harold (1854-1952); 94.
Runyan, William Marion (1870-1957); 33, 137, 164.

S

St. Francis of Assisi (1182-1226); 16.
Sammis, John H. (1846-1919); 181.
Sankey, Ira David (1840-1908); 75, 183, 195.
Schaff, Philip (1819-1893); 277.
Schlegel, Katharina Amalia von (1697-?); 197.
"Schlesische Volkslieder", 1842; 39.
Schuler, George S. (b. 1882); 236.
Schultz, Audrey B. (b. 1940); 80.
Schumann, Robert (1810-1856); 142.
Schütz, Johann Jakob (1640-1690) ; 9.
Scott, Clara H. (1841-1897); 153.
"Scottish Psalter", 1650; 40.
Scriven, Joseph Medlicott (1819-1886); 185.
Sea, M. A. (19th Century); 131.
Seiss, Joseph Augustus (1823-1904); 39.
Sellers, Ernest Orlando (1869-1952); 203.
Shaw, George (1870-1949); 243.
Sheppard, Franklin Lawrence (1852-1930); 44.
Sherwin, William Fiske (1826-1888); 205.
Showalter, Anthony Johnson (1858-1924); 190.
Shrubsole, William (1760-1806); 35.
Shurtleff, Ernest Warburton (1862-1917); 218.
Sibelius, Jean (1865-1959); 197.
Sleeper, William True (1819-1904); 54, 68.
Small, James Grindlay (1817-1888); 122.
Smart, Henry Thomas (1813-1879); 218.
Smith, Henry Percy (1825-1898); 211.
Smith, Oswald J. (b. 1890); 110, 132.
Smith, Samuel Francis (1808-1895); 226, 281.
Smith, Walter Chalmers (1824-1908); 43.
Snead, Alfred C. (1884-1961); 134.
Söderberg, Wilhelm Theodor (1845-1922) ; 279.
Source Unknown (Text); 21, 28, 37, 46, 64, 78, 158, 254, 260, 261.
Source Unknown (Melody); 30, 70, 84, 90.
Spafford, Horatio Gates (1828-1888); 200.
Stead, Louisa M. R. (1850-1917); 109.
Stebbins, George Coles (1846-1945); 54, 68, 122, 134, 136, 154, 158.
Steffe, John William (b. ca. 1852); 284.
Stites, Edgar Page (1836-1921); 183.
Stockton, John Hart (1813-1877); 58.
Stone, Samuel John (1839-1900); 209.
Storm, August Ludvig (1862-1914); 257.
"Stralsund Gesangbuch", 1665; 19.
Sullivan, Arthur Seymour (1842-1900); 199, 217.
Swedish Text, Anonymous; 279.
Swedish Melody, Anonymous; 1, 189
Sweney, John R. (1827-1899); 91, 248.

T

Tate, Nahum (1652-1715); 267.
Teschner, Melchior (1584-1635); 270.
"The Hymnal", 1933; 197.
"The Sacred Harp", 1844; 178.
Theodulph of Orleans (760-821); 270.
"Thesaurus Musicus", 1740; 281.
Thompson, John O. (1782-1818); 231.
Thompson, Will Lamartine (1847-1909); 100
Thomson, Mary Ann (1834-1923); 237.
Thring, Godfrey (1823-1903); 31.
Toplady, Augustus Montague (1740-1778); 75.
Tours, Berthold (1838-1897); 269.
Towner, Daniel Brink (1850-1919); 76, 117, 132, 181.
Tullar, Grant Colfax (1869-1950); 115, 246.
Turner, H. L. (19th Century); 251.

U

Urhan, Chretien (1790-1845); 244.

V

Van DeVenter, Judson W. (1855-1939); 177.
Vincent, Charles John (1852-1934); 192.

W

Walch, James (1837-1901); 237.
Walker, Mary Jane (1816-1878); 130.
Wallgren, A. Samuel (1885-1940); 279.
Walter, William Henry (1825-1893); 210.
Walton, James George (1821-1905); 207.
Walton, W. Spencer (1850-1906); 121.
Walworth, Clarence (1820-1900); 11.
Ward, Samuel Augustus (1847-1903); 283.
Warren, George William (1828-1902); 280.
Watts, Isaac (1674-1748); 5, 12, 13, 17, 27, 70, 71, 88, 219, 232, 247.
Webb, George James (1803-1887); 226.
Webbe, Samuel (1786-1826); 191.
Weeden, Winfield Scott (1847-1908); 177.
Welsh Text, Anonymous; 213.
Welsh Hymn Melody, Anonymous; 43.
Wesley, Charles (1707-1788); 6, 24, 74, 79, 165, 170, 216, 258, 274.
Wesley, John (1703-1791); 82, 201.
Wesley, Samuel Sebastian (1810-1876); 209.
White, J. T. (19th Century); 178.
Whitfield, Frederick (1829-1904); 84, 90.
Whittle, Daniel Webster (1840-1901); 64, 123, 126, 184.
Wigner, John Murch (1844-1911); 59.
Wilkinson, Kate Barclay (1859-1928); 135.
William Gardiner's "Sacred Melodies", 1815; 82, 220.
Williams, Aaron (1731-1776); 27.
Williams, C. C. (19th Century); 64.
Williams, Clara Tear (1858-1937); 107.
Williams, Peter (1722-1796); 213.
Williams, Ralph Vaughan (1872-1958); 245.
Williams, Thomas John (1869-1944); 85.
Williams, William (1717-1791); 213.
Willis, Richard Storrs (1819-1900); 39.
Wilson, Emily Divine (1865-1942); 242.
Wilson, Ira Bishop (1880-1950); 236.
Winkworth, Catherine (1827-1878); 19, 256.
Wolfe, Aaron Robarts (1821-1902); 114.
Wyeth, John (1770-1858); 2.

Y

"Yigdal, The"; 38.

Z

Zinzendorf, Nicolaus Ludwig von (1700-1760); 82.
Zundel, John (1815-1882); 133, 171.

index of tunes

a

Aberystwyth, 79
Acclaim, 23
Ackley, 89
Adelaide, 154
Adeste Fideles, 265
Aletta, 206
All Is Well, 178
All Saints, New, 223
All the World, 36
Amazing Grace, 108
America, 281
Angel's Story, 172
Any Room, 64
Ariel, 49
Arlington, 219
Armageddon, 221
Assurance, 97
Augustana, 189
Aurelia, 209
Austrian Hymn, 208
Azmon, 24

B

Barnard, 238
Battle Hymn, 284
Bauhofer, 80
Beecher, 171
Believe, 60
Benton Harbor, 42
Blaenwern, 170
Born Again, 54
Boylston, 165
Bread of Life, 205
Brink, 132
Bullinger, 102
Bryn Calfaria, 53

C

Calvary, 117
Canonbury, 142
Caritas, 163
Channels, 169
Chapman, 116
Christ Arose, 271
Christ Liveth, 126
Christ Returneth, 251
Christ the King, 261
Christmas, 267
Christmas Song, 264
Clarendon, 121
Cleansing Fountain, 81
Clemm, 231
Consolation (Webbe), 191
Converse, 185
Coronation, 35
Crimond, 40
Crusaders' Hymn, 39
Cwm Rhondda, 213

D

Darwall, 6, 17
Dedication, 131
Diademata, 31, 201, 216
Dix, 18
Duke Street, 232
Dunbar, 143
Duncannon, 67

E

Easter Hymn (Worgan), 274
Ein' Feste Burg, 32
Elizabeth, 100
Ellacombe, 5
Ellesdie, 214, 228
Ellsworth, 103
El Nathan, 123
Eola, 203
Eudoxia, 47
Everlasting Love, 104

F

Face to Face, 246
Faithfulness, 33
Falls Creek, 215
Festal Song, 210
Finlandia, 197
Flemming, 46
For Me, 124
Foundation, 180
Foursquare, 14
Friend, 122

G

Garden, 196
Geibel, 225
Germany, 82, 220
Gloria, 260
Glory Song, 252
God Cares, 182
Goshen, 130
Grace, 75
Greenwell, 83

H

Hall, 144
Harvey, 20
Hanby, 15
Hanford, 199
Hankey, 95
Hannah, 273
Hamburg, 71, 128
Hauge, 253
Heart Melody, 105
Heaven, 242
He Leadeth Me, 198
Hendon, 162, 186
Hermas, 222
Highlands, 115
Hingham, 195
Hoffman, 159
Homer, 98
Hudson, 88
Hutchison, 157
Hyfrydol, 4, 93

I

I Am Thine, 160
I Love Thee, 37
I Shall Know Him, 248
In Dulci Jubilo, 263
Infinity, 52
Invitation, 59

J

Jesus, I Come, 68
Jesus Saves, 87
Joanna, 43
Joyful Song, 29
Judas Maccabeus, 272
Just As I Am, 66

K

Kenosis, 235
Ketchum, 118
Kidder, 69
Kirkpatrick, 179
Kremser, 254

L

Lancashire, 218
Landas, 111
Langran, 45
Lasst Uns Erfreuen, 16
Låt Mig Börja Med Dig, 279
Lauda Anima, 10
Laudes Domini, 41
Lebanon, 133
Leoni, 38, 224
Living, 152
Llanthony Abbey, 138
Lobe Den Herren, 19
Longstaff, 136
Lower Lights, 233
Lyons, 48

m

Madrid, 30
Man of Sorrows, 73
Maori, 148
Margaret, 259
Marion, 26
Martyn, 78
Maryton, 211
Materna, 283
McAfee, 193
McDaniel, 120
Mercy, 173
Mendelssohn, 258
Message, 230
Miles Lane, 35
Minerva, 58
Mit Freuden Zart, 9
Montreat, 86
Moody, 76
Morecambe, 175
More Love To Thee, 150
Morning Hymn, 50
Morris, 166
Moscow (Italian Hymn), 28
My Saviour's Love, 112

n

National Hymn, 280
Near the Cross, 127
Need, 149
Nettleton, 2
Neumeister, 55
New Hampton, 249
Nicaea, 8
Nun Danket, 256

o

O Store Gud, 1
Oh, How I Love Jesus, 90
Okmulgee, 113
Old Hundredth, 51
Old, Old Story, 96
Old Rugged Cross, 77
Olivet, 167
Once for All, 119
Orleans, 158

p

Paradoxy, 141
Passion Chorale, 34
Pax Tecum, 192
Peoples Church, 110
Pine Street, 62
Pisgah, 247
Plagal, 22
Promises, 202

q

Quebec (Hesperus), 7
Quietude, 168

r

Rathbun, 72
Redeemed, 99
Rescue, 227
Revive Us Again, 156
Rockingham Old, 70
Rondinella, 146
Russian Hymn, 282
Rutherford, 244

s

Sagina, 74
St. Agnes, 25
St. Andrew, 125
St. Anne, 12
St. Catherine, 207
St. Christopher, 151
St. Dunstan's, 212
St. George's, Windsor, 255
St. Gertrude, 217
St. Hilda, 65
St. Leonards, 135
St. Louis, 266
St. Margaret, 139
St. Petersburg, 140, 229
St. Stephen, 240
St. Theodulph, 270
St. Thomas, 27
Salvatori, 278
Sanctuary, 164
Sandon, 187
Satisfied, 107
Schuler, 236
Scott, 153
Second Coming, 239
Seraph (Bethlehem), 204
Showalter, 190
Sine Nomine, 245
Slane, 147
Snead, 134
Solid Rock, 92
Something for Thee, 161
Sovereignty, 241
Stephanos, 63
Stille Nacht, 268
Story of Jesus, 91
Surrender, 177

t

Tack, O Gud, 257
Talmadge, 114
Teach Me, 137
Te Deum, 11
Terra Beata, 44
The Sweetest Name, 21
Tidings, 237
Toccoa, 243
To God Be the Glory, 3
Ton-Y-Botel, 85
Tours, 269
Tranquillity, 194
Trentham, 155
Trust and Obey, 181
Trust in Jesus, 109
Trusting Jesus, 183
Truett, 176
Tryggare Kan Ingen Vara, 250

v

Veni Emmanuel, 262
Victory, 275
Ville Du Havre, 200
Voluntas Dei, 174
Vox Dilecti, 56

w

Wakefield, 129
Waltham, 276
Warrington, 13
Webb, 226
Whitfield, 84
Whittle, 184
Wimby, 234
Winona Lake, 145
Wonderful Grace, 106
Wondrous Story, 94
Woodworth, 57
Words of Life, 101
Wye Valley, 188

z

Zeruiah, 61
Zuversicht, 277

topical index

ADORATION
All People That on Earth, 51
Be Thou My Vision, 147
Come, Thou Almighty King, 28
Crown Him With Many, 31
Fairest Lord Jesus, 39
Hallelujah, What a Saviour, 73
Here, O My Lord, 45
I Love Thee, 37
Jesus, Gentlest Saviour, 47
Jesus, My Saviour, Look, 199
Jesus, the Very Thought, 25
Jesus, Thou Joy of Loving, 7
Join All the Glorious Names, 17
My God and King, 36
My Jesus, I Love Thee, 163
O Sacred Head, Now Wounded, 34
O the Deep, Deep Love, 85
Praise Ye the Lord, the, 19
Rejoice, My Soul, 20
Rejoice, Ye Pure in Heart, 26
The Sands of Time, 244
(See Praise; Worship)

ASPIRATION
A Charge to Keep I Have, 165
Beneath the Cross of Jesus, 151
Christ Liveth in Me, 126
I Would Be Like Jesus, 145
Jesus, Master, Whose I Am, 140
Jesus Only, Let Me See, 132
May the Mind of Christ, 135
More Like the Master, 157
More Love to Thee, 150
My Faith Looks Up to Thee, 167
Nearer, Still Nearer, 166
O Jesus, I Have Promised, 172
O Love That Wilt Not Let, 139
O Master, Let Me Walk, 211
Oh, to Be Like Thee, 146
Open My Eyes, That I, 153
Revive Us Again, 156
Saviour, Thy Dying Love, 161
Spirit of God, Descend Upon, 175
Teach Me Thy Will, O Lord, 137
(See Consecration; Holiness of Life)

ASSURANCE
All Is Well!, 178
All Things in Jesus, 113
Be Still, My Soul, 197
Blessed Assurance, 97
Children of the Heavenly, 189
Great Is Thy Faithfulness, 33
He Hideth My Soul, 179
He Leadeth Me, 198
I Know That My Redeemer, 273
I Know Whom I Have, 123
It Is Well With My Soul, 200
Jesus, Thy Blood, 82
Moment by Moment, 184
On Our Way Rejoicing, 222
Standing on the Promises, 202
The Solid Rock, 92
Unto the Hills, 187
(See Trust)

BROTHERHOOD
O Master, Let Me Walk, 211
Rise Up, O Men of God, 210
(See Peace: Temporal)

CHALLENGE
A Charge to Keep I Have, 165
Awake, My Soul, 50
Faith of Our Fathers, 207
Give of Your Best, 238
O Master of the Waking, 229
Rise Up, O Men of God, 210
Trust and Obey, 181
Who Is on the Lord's Side?, 221
(See Warfare, Christian)

CHOIR
A Mighty Fortress Is Our God, 32
All Creatures of Our God, 16
Guide Me, O Thou Great, 213
Hallelujah, What a Saviour!, 73
Jesus, Lover of My Soul, 79
Living for Jesus, 152
Now I Belong to Jesus, 103
We Gather Together, 254
Wonderful Grace of Jesus, 106

CHORUSES
Refrains of the Following:
Believe on the Lord Jesus, 60
Blessed Assurance, 97
He Lives, 89
I Need Thee Every Hour, 149
In My Heart There Rings, 105
Moment by Moment, 184
My Saviour's Love, 112
Now I Belong to Jesus, 103
O That Will Be Glory, 252
Oh, How I Love Jesus, 90
One Day, 116
Since Jesus Came Into, 120
Thy Word Have I Hid, 203
When We All Get to Heaven, 242
Ye Must Be Born Again, 54

CHRIST
Advent:
O Come, O Come, Emmanuel, 262
Thou Didst Leave Thy Throne, 259
Ascension:
Crown Him with Many Crowns, 31
Rejoice, the Lord is King!, 6
Beauty of:
Fairest Lord Jesus, 39
O Could I Speak, 49
Why Do I Sing about Jesus, 118
Birth of:
Angels We Have Heard, 260
Good Christian Men, Rejoice, 263
Hark, the Herald Angels Sing, 258
O Come, All Ye Faithful, 265
O Little Town of Bethlehem, 266
Silent Night! Holy Night!, 268
There's a Song in the Air, 264
Thou Didst Leave Thy Throne, 259
What Child Is This?, 261
While Shepherds Watched, 267
Call of:
Believe on the Lord Jesus, 60
I Heard the Voice of Jesus Say, 56
I've Heard the King, 115
Just as I Am, 57
Lead Me to Calvary, 67
O Jesus, Thou Art Standing, 65
Only Trust Him, 58
There Is a Fountain, 81
Ye Must Be Born Again, 54
(See Invitation)
Ever-living:
Be Thou My Vision, 147
Christ Liveth in Me, 126
He Lives, 89
I Know That My Redeemer, 273
Jesus Lives, and So Shall I, 277
Wounded for Me, 124
Example:
I Would Be Like Jesus, 145
Jesus Only, Let Me See, 132
More Like the Master, 157
Oh, to Be Like Thee, 146
King:
All Hail the Power, 35
Crown Him with Many Crowns, 31
Jesus Shall Reign, 232
Lead On, O King Eternal, 218
Lift Up, Lift Up Your Voices, 276
Nailed Upon Golgotha's Tree, 78
Rejoice, My Soul, 20
The King Shall Come, 240
Life and Earthly Ministry:
Fairest Lord Jesus, 39
O For a Thousand Tongues, 24
One Day, 116
Tell Me the Story of Jesus, 91
Who Is He in Yonder Stall?, 15
(See Christ: Ministry)
Love of:
He the Pearly Gates Will Open, 250
Love Divine, 170
My Saviour's Love, 112
O Love That Wilt Not Let, 139
O the Deep, Deep Love, 85
Ministry (Present):
Art Thou Weary, 63
Children of the Heavenly, 189
Come, Christians, Join to Sing, 30
He Hideth My Soul, 179
He Leadeth Me, 198
How Firm a Foundation, 180
I Was a Wandering Sheep, 133
I've Found a Friend, 122
Jesus Is All the World to Me, 100
Jesus, Lover of My Soul, 79
Jesus, Thy Blood, 82
My Hope Is in the Lord, 129
Saviour, Thy Dying Love, 161
Teach Me Thy Will, O Lord, 137
The Lord's My Shepherd, 40
What a Friend We Have, 185
Name of:
All Glory, Laud, and Honor, 270
All Hail the Power, 35
I Heard the Voice of Jesus Say, 56
Jesus, the Very Thought, 25
Join All the Glorious Names, 17
O Come, O Come, Emmanuel, 262
Oh, How I Love Jesus, 90
There Is No Name so Sweet, 21
Passion:
At the Cross, 88
Hallelujah, What a Saviour!, 73
I Gave My Life for Thee, 235
In the Cross of Christ, 72
Ivory Palaces, 86
Lead Me to Calvary, 67
Nailed upon Golgotha's Tree, 78
O Sacred Head, Now Wounded, 34
Oh, It is Wonderful!, 98
The Old Rugged Cross, 77
Thy Will, Not Mine, 174
When I Survey the Wondrous, 70
Wounded for Me, 124
Resurrection:
Christ Arose, 271
Christ the Lord Is Risen Today, 274
He Lives, 89
In the Garden, 196
Lift Up, Lift Up Your Voices, 276
The Strife Is O'er, 275
Thine Is the Glory, 272
(See Christ: Ever-living)
Saviour:
All My Life Long, 107
And Can It Be That I Should, 74
I Am Not Skilled to Understand, 83
I Will Sing of My Redeemer, 93
I Will Sing the Wondrous Story, 94
In Tenderness He Sought Me, 121
Jesus, My Saviour, Look, 199
Our Great Saviour, 4
Praise Him! Praise Him!, 29
We Lift Our Voice Rejoicing, 14
What a Wonderful Saviour, 42
Second Coming:
Christ Returneth, 251
Come, Ye Thankful People, 255
How Great Thou Art, 1
Jesus, Jesus, We Are Waiting, 243
O Come, O Come, Emmanuel, 262

Our God Is Sovereign Still, 241
The King Shall Come, 240
What if It Were Today?, 239
Wounded for Me, 124

Triumphal Entry:
All Glory, Laud, and Honor, 270
When, His Salvation Bringing, 269

CHURCH

Her Faith:
Faith of Our Fathers, 207
I Know Whom I Have, 123
One Day, 116
The Church's One Foundation, 209

Her Fellowship and Unity:
Glorious Things of Thee Are, 208
Onward, Christian Soldiers, 217

Militant and Triumphant:
Onward, Christian Soldiers, 217
(See Warfare, Christian)

COMFORT

All Things in Jesus, 113
Come, Ye Disconsolate, 191
Give to the Winds Thy Fears, 201
God Will Take Care of You, 182
Jesus, My Saviour, Look, 199
What a Friend We Have, 185

COMMUNION

(See Fellowship; Lord's Supper)

CONFESSION OF SIN

Beneath the Cross of Jesus, 151
Grace Greater than Our Sin, 76
I Saw the Cross of Jesus, 84
Is My Name Written There?, 69
Jesus, Lover of My Soul, 79
Just as I Am, Without One Plea, 57
O Thou That Hear'st, 71

CONSECRATION

Blessed Assurance, 97
Breathe on Me, Breath of God, 155
Channels Only, 169
Draw Me Nearer, 160
Fully Surrendered, 134
Have Thine Own Way, Lord, 154
Holy Ghost, with Light, 173
I Gave My Life for Thee, 235
I Surrender All, 177
I'll Live for Him, 143
Is Your All on the Altar?, 159
Jesus, I My Cross Have Taken, 214
Jesus, Master, Whose I Am, 140
Just as I Am, Thine Own to Be, 66
Let Me Come Closer to Thee, 138
Living for Jesus, 152
Make Me a Blessing, 236
Make Me a Captive, Lord, 141
My Jesus, I Love Thee, 163
Near to the Heart of God, 193
Nearer, Still Nearer, 166
O Love that Wilt Not Let Me, 139
Saviour, My Heart Is Thine, 158
Search Me, O God, 148
Speak, Lord, in the Stillness, 168
Take My Life, and Let It Be, 162
Take Time to Be Holy, 136
Thy Will, not Mine, Be Done, 174
When I Survey the Wondrous, 70
Wherever He Leads I'll Go, 215
(See Aspiration; Invitation)

CONTENTMENT

All Things in Jesus, 113
Be Still, My Soul, 197
He Leadeth Me, 198
I Am His, and He Is Mine, 104
Jesus, I am Resting, 194
Like a River Glorious, 188
Lord, I Have Shut the Door, 164
Moment by Moment, 184
Near to the Heart of God, 193
(See Peace)

CROSS

Of Christ:
At Calvary, 117
At the Cross, 88
Beneath the Cross, 151
I Saw the Cross of Jesus, 84
In the Cross of Christ, 72
Lead Me to Calvary, 67
Nailed Upon Golgotha's Tree, 78
Near the Cross, 127
The Old Rugged Cross, 77
When I Survey the Wondrous, 70

Of the Believer:
Jesus, I My Cross Have Taken, 214
O Love that Wilt Not Let Me, 139
Wherever He Leads I'll Go, 215

DEVOTIONAL

Jesus, I am Resting, Resting, 194
Jesus, the Very Thought, 25
Lord, I Have Shut the Door, 164
More Love to Thee, 150
My Faith Looks Up to Thee, 167
Near the Cross, 127
Near to the Heart of God, 193
O Love That Wilt Not Let Me, 139
The Old Rugged Cross, 77
(See Aspiration; Adoration)

DISCIPLESHIP

Art Thou Weary, 63
I With Thee Would Begin, 279
(See Christ: Ministry; God: His Care and Guidance; Pilgrimage)

EASTER

(See Christ: Resurrection)

EDUCATION

May the Mind of Christ, 135
Spirit of God, 175
Take Thou Our Minds, 144
Teach Me Thy Will, O Lord, 137

ETERNAL LIFE

Be Still, My Soul, 197
He the Pearly Gates Will Open, 250
Jesus Lives, and So Shall I, 277
My Saviour First of All, 248
O That Will Be Glory, 252
(See Heaven)

EVANGELISM

(See Missions; Soul Winning; Testimony)

FAITH

Faith of Our Fathers, 207
My Faith Looks Up to Thee, 167
(See Assurance; Trust)

FAITHFULNESS

Of God:
(See God: His Care and Guidance)

Of the Believer:
A Charge to Keep I Have, 165
Living for Jesus, 152
O Jesus, I Have Promised, 172
(See Aspiration; Warfare)

FELLOWSHIP

With God:
I Am His, and He Is Mine, 104
I Need Thee Every Hour, 149
In the Garden, 196
Let Me Come Closer to Thee, 138
Nearer, Still Nearer, 166
O Love That Wilt Not Let Me, 139
O Master, Let Me Walk, 211
Trust and Obey, 181
(See Pilgrimage, Christian)

With Men:
(See Church: Fellowship and Unity; Brotherhood)

GOD

His Attributes and Character:
A Mighty Fortress Is Our God, 32
Forever, 22
Give to Our God Immortal, 13
Great Is Thy Faithfulness, 33
Holy, Holy, Holy, 8
How Great Thy Loving, 52
Immortal, Invisible, God Only, 43
Join All the Glorious Names, 17
Moment by Moment, 184
O God, Our Help in Ages Past, 12
O Worship the King, 48
Our God Is Sovereign Still, 241
Praise Ye the Lord, The, 19
Sing Praise to God Who Reigns, 9
The God of Abraham Praise, 38
This Is My Father's World, 44

His Care and Guidance:
Be Still, My Soul, 197
Children of the Heavenly, 189
Give to the Winds Thy Fears, 201
God Will Take Care of You, 182
Great Is Thy Faithfulness, 33
Guide Me, O Thou Great, 213
He Leadeth Me, 198
O God, Our Help in Ages Past, 12
Praise, My Soul, the King, 10
Praise Ye the Lord, the, 19
Sing Praise to God Who Reigns, 9
Thanks to God, 257
The Lord's My Shepherd, 40
Unto the Hills, 187

In Nature:
All Creatures of Our God, 16
For the Beauty of the Earth, 18
Give to Our God Immortal, 13
How Great Thou Art, 1
I Sing the Mighty Power of God, 5
O Worship the King, 48
This is My Father's World, 44

GRACE

Amazing Grace!, 108
Grace Greater Than Our Sin, 76
Grace! 'Tis a Charming Sound, 75
Wonderful Grace of Jesus, 106
(See Salvation)

GUIDANCE

(See God: His Care and Guidance; Pilgrimage)

HEAVEN

Be Still, My Soul, 197
Face to Face, 246
For All the Saints, 245
How Great Thy Loving, 52
In Heaven Above, 253
Is My Name Written There?, 69
O That Will Be Glory, 252
The King in His Beauty, 249
When I Can Read My Title, 247
When We All Get to Heaven, 242
(See Eternal Life)

HOLINESS OF LIFE

Breathe On Me, Breath of God, 155
Love Divine, 170
More Like the Master, 157
Oh, to Be Like Thee, 146
Take Time to Be Holy, 136
Thy Word Have I Hid, 203
(See Sanctification; Aspiration)

HOLY SPIRIT

Break Thou the Bread of Life, 205
Breathe on Me, Breath of God, 155
Have Thine Own Way, Lord, 154
Holy Ghost, with Light, 173
Holy Spirit, Breathe on Me, 176
I Surrender All, 177
Open My Eyes, That I May, 153
Search Me, O God, 148
Spirit of God, 175

topical index

HOME

For the Beauty of the Earth, 18

INVITATION

To Consecration:
Give Me Thy Heart, 61
I Gave My Life for Thee, 235
Is Your All On the Altar, 159
Just as I Am, Thine Own to Be, 66

To Salvation:
Art Thou Weary, 63
Christ Receiveth Sinful Men, 55
Come to the Saviour Now, 59
Come, Ye Sinners, 53
Give Me Thy Heart, 61
Have You Any Room for Jesus?, 64
Jesus, I Come, 68
Just As I Am, 57
Look to the Lamb of God, 62
O Jesus, Thou Art Standing, 65
Only Trust Him, 58
(See Christ: Call of)

JOY

Come, We That Love the Lord, 27
I Am His and He Is Mine, 104
I Love Thee, 37
In the Garden, 196
My God and King!, 36
O Happy Day, 128
O That Will Be Glory, 252
On Our Way Rejoicing, 222
Redeemed, 99
Rejoice, the Lord Is King, 6
Rejoice, Ye Pure in Heart, 26
Since Jesus Came Into My, 120
Why Do I Sing About Jesus, 118
(See Testimony)

KINGDOM

All Hail the Power, 35
Jesus Shall Reign, 232
The Morning Light Is, 226
We've a Story to Tell, 230
(See Christ: King)

LORD'S SUPPER

At the Cross, 88
Here, O My Lord, 45
In the Cross of Christ, 72
Jesus, the Very Thought, 25
Jesus, Thou Joy of Loving, 7
My Jesus, I Love Thee, 163
Near the Cross, 127
There Is a Fountain, 81
When I Survey the Wondrous, 70

LOVE

God's Love:
And Can It Be That I Should, 74
How Great Thy Loving, 52
Ivory Palaces, 86
O Love That Wilt Not Let Me, 139
(See Christ: Love of)

Our Love:
More Love to Thee, 150
My Jesus, I Love Thee, 163
Oh, How I Love Jesus, 90

MEMORIAL OCCASIONS

Faith of Our Fathers, 207
For All the Saints, 245
The Son of God Goes Forth, 223
(See Church)

MISSIONS

Jesus Saves, 87
Jesus Shall Reign, 232
My God and King!, 36
O Master of the Waking World, 229
O Zion, Haste, 237
The Battle Is the Lord's, 224
The Morning Light Is, 226
To All the World, 234
We've a Story to Tell, 230
Where Cross the Crowded, 220
(See Service; Soul Winning)

NATION

God of Our Fathers, 280
God Save America!, 282
My Country, 'Tis of Thee, 281
O Beautiful for Spacious Skies, 283
O Master of the Waking World, 229
We Gather Together, 254
Where Cross the Crowded, 220

NEW YEAR

Another Year Is Dawning, 278
I With Thee Would Begin, 279
O God, Our Help in Ages Past, 12

PALM SUNDAY

(See Christ: Triumphal Entry)

PEACE

Spiritual:
Leaning On the Everlasting, 190
Like a River Glorious, 188
Peace, Perfect Peace, 192

Temporal:
God of Our Fathers, 280
God Save America!, 282

PILGRIMAGE, CHRISTIAN

All Is Well!, 178
Children of the Heavenly, 189
Guide Me, O Thou Great, 213
He Who Would Valiant Be, 212
Jesus, I My Cross Have Taken, 214
On Our Way Rejoicing, 222
(See God: His Care and Guidance)

PRAISE

All Creatures of Our God, 16
Blessed Assurance, 97
Come, Christians, Join to Sing, 30
Come, Thou Almighty King, 28
Come, Thou Fount, 2
Come, We That Love the Lord, 27
How Great Thou Art, 1
I've Found a Friend, 122
I Will Sing of My Redeemer, 93
In Tenderness He Sought Me, 121
Jesus Is All the World to Me, 100
My Saviour's Love, 112
O Could I Speak, 49
O for a Thousand Tongues, 24
Oh, It Is Wonderful!, 98
Our Great Saviour, 4
Praise Him! Praise Him!, 29
Praise the Saviour, 23
Praise Ye the Triune God!, 46
Revive Us Again, 156
Sing Praise to God Who Reigns, 9
The Lord's My Shepherd, 40
There Is No Name So Sweet, 21
Thine Is the Glory, 272
To God Be the Glory, 3
What a Wonderful Saviour, 42
When Morning Gilds the Skies, 41
(See Adoration; Worship; Testimony)

PRAYER

Come, My Soul, Thy Suit, 186
Come, Ye Disconsolate, 191
Lord, I Have Shut the Door, 164
Speak, Lord, in the Stillness, 168
What a Friend We Have, 185

PSALMS

All People That On Earth (100), 51
Jesus Shall Reign (72), 232
O God, Our Help in Ages (90), 12
O Thou That Hear'st (51), 71
Praise, My Soul, the King (103), 10
The Lord's My Shepherd (23), 40
Thy Word Have I Hid (119), 203
Unto the Hills (121), 187

PURITY

(See Holiness of Life; Sanctification)

SALVATION

Amazing Grace!, 108
And Can It Be That I Should, 74
At Calvary, 177
Believe on the Lord Jesus, 60
Christ Liveth in Me, 126
Christ Receiveth Sinful Men, 55
Complete in Thee, 114
Grace! 'Tis a Charming Sound, 75
I Am Not Skilled to Understand, 83
I Am Trusting Thee, Lord, 102
I Love to Tell the Story, 95
Is My Name Written There?, 69
Jesus Saves, 87
My Hope Is in the Lord, 129
No Other Plea, 111
Not What These Hands Have, 125
Now I Belong to Jesus, 103
O for a Thousand Tongues, 24
Once for All, 119
Saved, 110
There Is a Fountain, 81
To God Be the Glory, 3
Wonderful Words of Life, 101
Ye Must Be Born Again, 54
(See Christ: Saviour; Testimony)

SANCTIFICATION

Channels Only, 169
Complete in Thee, 114
Grace Greater Than Our Sin, 76
Holy Spirit, Breathe on Me, 176
Love Divine, 170
Search Me, O God, 148
There Is a Fountain, 81
(See Consecration; Holiness of Life)

SATAN

A Mighty Fortress Is Our God, 32
(See Warfare)

SCRIPTURES

Break Thou the Bread of Life, 205
Holy Bible, Book Divine, 206
How Firm a Foundation, 180
Open My Eyes, 153
Standing on the Promises, 202
Thy Word Have I Hid, 203
Thy Word Is Like a Garden, 204
'Tis So Sweet to Trust, 109
Wonderful Words of Life, 101

SECOND COMING

(See Christ: Second Coming)

SECURITY

Forever, 22
He Hideth My Soul, 179
How Firm a Foundation, 180
I Belong to Jesus, 131
I Know Whom I Have, 123
Jesus Lives, and So Shall I, 277
Praise the Saviour, 23
Under His Wings, 195
(See Assurance)

SERVICE

A Charge to Keep I Have, 165
Am I a Soldier of the Cross?, 219
Lord, Speak to Me, 142
Make Me a Blessing, 236
More Love to Thee, 150
Stand Up, Stand Up for Jesus, 225
Where Cross the Crowded, 220
Wherever He Leads I'll Go, 215
Who Is on the Lord's Side, 221
(See Missions; Soul Winning; Stewardship of Life)

topical index

SOLOS
I Heard the Voice of Jesus Say, 56
I With Thee Would Begin, 279
I've Heard the King, 115
Lord, I Have Shut the Door, 164
Now I Belong to Jesus, 103

SOUL WINNING
Christ Receiveth Sinful Men, 55
Hark, the Voice of Jesus, 228
Let the Lower Lights, 233
Make Me a Blessing, 236
Rescue the Perishing, 227
The Call for Reapers, 231
(See Missions; Stewardship)

STEWARDSHIP
Of Life and Talents:
At the Cross, 88
Give of Your Best, 238
Hark, the Voice of Jesus, 228
I'll Live for Him, 143
Make Me a Blessing, 236
Saviour, Thy Dying Love, 161
Take My Life, and Let It Be, 162
Take Thou Our Minds, Dear, 144
Of Substance:
Fully Surrendered, 134
I Gave My Life for Thee, 235
Lord, Thou Lov'st the, 171
Take My Life, and Let It Be, 162

TEMPTATION
I Need Thee Every Hour, 149
O Jesus, I Have Promised, 172
Spirit of God, Descend, 175

TESTIMONY
All My Life Long, 107
All Things in Jesus, 113
Amazing Grace, 108
And Can It Be That I Should, 74
At Calvary, 117
Christ Liveth in Me, 126
Come, Thou Fount, 2
Grace! 'Tis a Charming Sound, 75
He Lives, 89
I Belong to Jesus, 131
I Heard the Voice of Jesus Say, 56
I Know Whom I Have, 123
I Love to Tell the Story, 95
I Was a Wandering Sheep, 133
I Will Sing the Wondrous Story, 94
I've Heard the King, 115
In My Heart There Rings, 105
It Is Well with My Soul, 200
No Other Plea, 111
Now I Belong to Jesus, 103
O Happy Day, 128
Oh, How I Love Jesus, 90
One Day, 116
Redeemed, 99
Saved, 110
Since Jesus Came Into, 120
Trusting Jesus, 183
Wonderful Grace of Jesus, 106
(See Praise; Salvation)

THANKSGIVING
Come, Ye Thankful People, 255
I Sing the Mighty Power of God, 5
Lord, Thou Lov'st the, 171
Now Thank We All Our God, 256
Thanks to God, 257
We Gather Together, 254
(See Praise)

TRINITY
Come, Thou Almighty King, 28
Holy God, We Praise Thy Name, 11
Holy, Holy, Holy, 8
Praise Ye the Triune God, 46
The Church's One Foundation, 209

TRUST
He Leadeth Me, 198
How Firm a Foundation, 180
I Am Trusting Thee, 102
In the Garden, 196
Jesus, I Am Resting, 194
Jesus, Lover of My Soul, 79
Leaning on the Everlasting, 190
Only Trust Him, 58
'Tis So Sweet to Trust, 109
Trust and Obey, 181
Trusting Jesus, 183
Under His Wings, 195
(See Assurance)

UNITY, CHRISTIAN
Onward, Christian Soldiers, 217
The Church's One Foundation, 209
(See Church)

WARFARE, CHRISTIAN
A Mighty Fortress Is Our God, 32
Am I a Soldier of the Cross?, 219
He Who Would Valiant Be, 212
Lead On, O King Eternal, 218
Our God Is Sovereign Still, 241
Soldiers of Christ, Arise, 216
Stand Up, Stand Up for Jesus, 225
The Battle Is the Lord's, 224
The Son of God Goes Forth, 223
Who Is on the Lord's Side?, 221
(See Challenge)

WITNESSING
Lord, Speak to Me, 142
Tell Me the Old, Old Story, 96
Tell Me the Story of Jesus, 91
There Is a Fountain, 81
Wonderful Words of Life, 101
(See Missions; Soul Winning; Testimony)

WORSHIP
All Hail the Power, 35
Give to Our God Immortal, 13
Holy God, We Praise Thy Name, 11
How Great Thy Loving, 52
Immortal, Invisible, God, 43
O God, Our Help in Ages Past, 12
O Worship the King, 48
Praise, My Soul, the King, 10
Rejoice, the Lord Is King, 6
The God of Abraham Praise, 38
When Morning Gilds the Skies, 41
(See Adoration; Praise)

alphabetical index of scripture readings

Adoration of the Magi, 294
Blessings from God, 310
Christ Teaches Prayer, 302
Christian Assurance, 305
Comfort from Christ, 311
Divine Providence, 289
God the Creator, 285
God's Commandments, 286
God's Omniscience, 292
Obedience to God, 291
Prayer of Penitence, 290
Spiritual Warfare, 307
The Beatitudes, 295
The Great Commission, 299
The Holy Scriptures, 309
The Holy Spirit, 304
The Incarnate Christ, 303
The Last Supper, 297
The Love Chapter, 306
The Return of Christ, 308
The Risen Lord, 298
The Saviour's Advent, 301
The Shepherd Psalm, 288
The Triumphal Entry, 300
The Way of Life, 287
The Whitened Harvest, 296
True Wisdom, 293

General Index

Titles are in small CAPS; first lines in lower case type

A

165 **A CHARGE TO KEEP I HAVE**—reminds the Christian of his obligation to live victoriously and to serve God faithfully.

32 **A MIGHTY FORTRESS IS OUR GOD**—the Battle Hymn of the Reformation, is Martin Luther's free adaptation of Psalm 46.

54 **A ruler once came to Jesus by night** (see YE MUST BE BORN AGAIN)

179 **A wonderful Saviour is Jesus my Lord** (see HE HIDETH MY SOUL)

88 **Alas, and did my Saviour bleed?** (see AT THE CROSS)

16 **ALL CREATURES OF OUR GOD AND KING**—says that all creation praises the Creator; written by Francis of Assisi, "the patron saint of animals."

270 **ALL GLORY, LAUD, AND HONOR**—Tradition says the singing of this Palm Sunday hymn won its 8th century author, Theodulph of Orleans, freedom from prison.

35 **ALL HAIL THE POWER**—calls all ransomed men of earth and all angels, to crown Jesus Christ "Lord of all."

178 **ALL IS WELL!**—is an adaptation of an early American text and tune, and breathes utter confidence in the providence of God.

107 **ALL MY LIFE LONG**—speaks of the soul's thirst, hunger and poverty, and of Jesus Christ who is a "well of water," "bread of life" and "untold wealth."

51 **ALL PEOPLE THAT ON EARTH DO DWELL**—is a poetic version of Psalm 100, one of the oldest hymns in the English language.

113 **ALL THINGS IN JESUS**—is a testimony that man's deepest longings and needs are satisfied only by Christ.

177 **All to Jesus I surrender** (see I SURRENDER ALL)

219 **AM I A SOLDIER OF THE CROSS?**—calls us to "endure hardness as a good soldier of Jesus Christ." (II Timothy 2:3)

108 **AMAZING GRACE! HOW SWEET THE SOUND**—is the testimony of John Newton, by the grace of God, a slave trader who became a clergyman.

241 **Amid the fears that oppress our day** (see OUR GOD IS SOVEREIGN STILL)

74 **AND CAN IT BE THAT I SHOULD GAIN?**—expresses abject wonder and humble confidence in the salvation bought and wrought by our Lord.

260 **ANGELS WE HAVE HEARD ON HIGH**—is in both words and music a traditional French carol based on the song of the angels in Luke 2:14.

278 **ANOTHER YEAR IS DAWNING**—is a prayer that in the year ahead we may "grow in grace and knowledge" and serve God faithfully. (II Peter 3:18)

63 **ART THOU WEARY, HEAVY LADEN?**—is an ancient Greek "question and answer hymn" based on Matthew 11:28; it may be sung antiphonally.

117 **AT CALVARY**—is a testimony of the love, grace and mercy shown in Jesus' death; words and music were written by men associated with Moody Bible Institute, Chicago.

88 **AT THE CROSS**—Isaac Watts' verses speak our sorrow and wonder as we contemplate the cross; Ralph Hudson's refrain expresses the joy of our salvation.

50 **AWAKE, MY SOUL, AND WITH THE SUN**—is a morning hymn of praise, which commits the day to God; it was written by an Anglican bishop of Winchester, Thomas Ken.

B

284 **BATTLE HYMN OF THE REPUBLIC**—a purely American hymn written during the Civil War, was sung at the funeral of England's Sir Winston Churchill.

182 **Be not dismayed whate'er betide** (see GOD WILL TAKE CARE OF YOU)

197 **BE STILL, MY SOUL**—says that in the middle of life's problems, our strength comes from "quietness and confidence" in God. (Isaiah 30:15)

147 **BE THOU MY VISION**—is an ancient Irish poem dating probably from the 8th century; the tune is a traditional Irish melody.

60 **BELIEVE ON THE LORD JESUS CHRIST**—is the answer to the question "What must I do to be saved?", and is based on Paul's experience in the jail at Philippi. (Acts 16:24-34)

151 **BENEATH THE CROSS OF JESUS**—expresses all that the believer feels as he thinks about the cross of Jesus Christ.

97 **BLESSED ASSURANCE**—a theme song of a Billy Graham Crusade, tells of the unending joy of the person who knows God accepts him.

205 **BREAK THOU THE BREAD OF LIFE**—is a prayer that God's Spirit will help us understand the Bible; it is based on Jesus' feeding the multitude. (John 6:1-14)

155 **BREATHE ON ME, BREATH OF GOD**—based on John 20:22, speaks of the Holy Spirit's work in salvation, in making us holy, and in our full consecration.

233 **Brightly beams our Father's mercy** (see LET THE LOWER LIGHTS BE BURNING)

80 **BY FAITH IN CHRIST WE LIVE**—is a new hymn submitted in a 1961 contest conducted by the National Church Music Fellowship.

General Index

C

169 **CHANNELS ONLY**—is a prayer that we may be used of God to bring His message and His blessings to others.

189 **CHILDREN OF THE HEAVENLY FATHER**—written by Lina Sandell ("The Fanny Crosby of Sweden"), tells of God's loving care of us, His children.

271 **CHRIST AROSE**—was written by Robert Lowry, Baptist minister and professor, in 1874; note the dramatic contrast between the stanzas and the refrain.

42 **Christ has for sin atonement made** (see WHAT A WONDERFUL SAVIOUR!)

126 **CHRIST LIVETH IN ME**—explains what we mean when we say, "A Christian is a person in whom Christ lives."

55 **CHRIST RECEIVETH SINFUL MEN**—An old German hymn has been translated and given a gospel song melody; it is based on I Timothy 1:15.

251 **CHRIST RETURNETH**—a favorite hymn on Christ's second coming, was written by James McGranahan, a songleader in evangelism from 1876 to 1887.

274 **CHRIST THE LORD IS RISEN TODAY**—refers to many scripture passages which teach us what the resurrection means.

30 **COME, CHRISTIANS, JOIN TO SING**—urges us to sing praise, because God demands it and because He is worthy of it.

178 **Come, come, ye saints** (see ALL IS WELL!)

58 **Come, every soul by sin oppressed** (see ONLY TRUST HIM)

186 **COME, MY SOUL, THY SUIT PREPARE**—compares our praying to the case or "suit" that a lawyer presents in court.

28 **COME, THOU ALMIGHTY KING**—is a prayer to each member of the Trinity in turn—Father, Son, and Holy Spirit—and finally to the "One in Three."

2 **COME, THOU FOUNT**—sings praise to God, from whom every blessing flows, as streams from a fountain.

59 **COME TO THE SAVIOUR NOW**—is a gentle call to the sinner, the "backslider" and the burdened Christian to "come to the Saviour."

27 **COME, WE THAT LOVE THE LORD**—explains why no true Christian can refuse to sing about His experience with God.

191 **COME, YE DISCONSOLATE**—a hymn of comfort written by the Irish poet Thomas Moore, has been altered by Thomas Hastings, an American church musician.

53 **COME, YE SINNERS, POOR AND WRETCHED**—a historic, theological hymn of invitation, was penned by Joseph Hart, a contemporary of the Wesleys.

255 **COME, YE THANKFUL PEOPLE, COME**—by Henry Alford, Dean of Canterbury, is a harvest hymn which also teaches the second coming and God's final judgment.

114 **COMPLETE IN THEE**—is based on Col. 2:10, "and ye are complete in Him;" the refrain outlines our total salvation, in this world and in the next.

31 **CROWN HIM WITH MANY CROWNS**—is a hymn about Christ the King; the text was contributed by two 19th century Anglican rectors, Matthew Bridges and Godfrey Thring.

D

118 **Deep in my heart there's a gladness** (see WHY DO I SING ABOUT JESUS?)

160 **DRAW ME NEARER**—was written by Fanny Crosby after a conversation (with musician W. H. Doane) about the nearness of God.

184 **Dying with Jesus, by death reckoned mine** (see MOMENT BY MOMENT)

E

145 **Earthly pleasures vainly call me** (see I WOULD BE LIKE JESUS)

F

246 **FACE TO FACE**—an "Eternal Life" hymn, is based on I Cor. 13:12. "For now we see through a glass, darkly; but then face to face . . . . "

39 **FAIREST LORD JESUS**—despite the title "Crusader's Hymn," first appeared in a German hymnal in 1677. This tune was first published in the 19th century.

207 **FAITH OF OUR FATHERS!**—originally Roman Catholic in emphasis, has been altered to speak of our common and historic faith in Christ.

231 **Far and near the fields are teeming** (see THE CALL FOR REAPERS)

245 **FOR ALL THE SAINTS**—a memorial hymn of saints now departed, is set to a famous tune by the English composer, Vaughan Williams.

132 **For salvation full and free** (see JESUS ONLY, LET ME SEE)

18 **FOR THE BEAUTY OF THE EARTH**—speaks our gratitude for the common things of life, as well as for the fellowship of the Church.

22 **FOREVER**—reminds us that, in the midst of life's uncertainties, God's love and peace and help are eternal.

General Index

119 **Free from the law, O happy condition** (see ONCE FOR ALL)

113 **Friends all around us are trying to find** (see ALL THINGS IN JESUS)

134 **FULLY SURRENDERED** – expresses the Christian's desire for a total consecration of himself to God.

G

61 **GIVE ME THY HEART** – is the work of two Philadelphians: words by Eliza Hewitt, public school teacher, and music by W. J. Kirkpatrick, music publisher.

238 **GIVE OF YOUR BEST TO THE MASTER** – is a hymn of challenge, for youth. This tune was originally written for a secular English ballad.

13 **GIVE TO OUR GOD IMMORTAL PRAISE** – Isaac Watts paraphrases Psalm 136, and adds the New Testament truth of God's gift of His Son.

201 **GIVE TO THE WINDS THY FEARS** – reflecting complete optimism about God's providence, was written by Paul Gerhardt in one of Germany's darkest hours.

208 **GLORIOUS THINGS OF THEE ARE SPOKEN** – "Zion" represents "the Church;" phrases are quoted from Revelation 21:12; 22:1 and Exodus 13:21.

280 **GOD OF OUR FATHERS, WHOSE ALMIGHTY HAND** – a prayer for our nation, was written in 1876, for a centennial celebration of the Declaration of Independence.

282 **GOD SAVE AMERICA!** – a modern hymn, asks that our country may lead in social and political righteousness.

182 **GOD WILL TAKE CARE OF YOU** – was written on a Sunday afternoon in 1904 by Civilla D. Martin and her evangelist-husband, W. Stillman Martin.

263 **GOOD CHRISTIAN MEN, REJOICE** – like most of our hymns of Latin and Greek origin, was translated by the English clergyman John Mason Neale (1818-1866).

76 **GRACE GREATER THAN OUR SIN** – is based on Romans 5:20b. Composer D. B. Towner was a leading gospel song writer at the turn of the century.

75 **GRACE! 'TIS A CHARMING SOUND** – "Grace is the undeserved favor of God;" an 18th century poem with late 19th century music.

33 **GREAT IS THY FAITHFULNESS** – a beloved 20th century hymn about the constancy of God, is based on Lam. 3:23.

213 **GUIDE ME, O THOU GREAT JEHOVAH** – translated from Welsh, uses figures from Israel's ancient wandering in the wilderness to tell how God guides us.

H

73 **HALLELUJAH, WHAT A SAVIOUR!** – based on Isaiah 53:3, tells of the passion and final victory of Jesus Christ, "man of sorrows."

258 **HARK, THE HERALD ANGELS SING** – is perhaps the strongest doctrinal statement of the incarnation found in a hymn.

228 **HARK, THE VOICE OF JESUS CALLING** – gives a call to witness on the mission field or here at home; it was inspired by Isaiah 6:8.

154 **HAVE THINE OWN WAY, LORD!** – was written by Adelaide Pollard as a personal expression of submission to the will of God.

64 **HAVE YOU ANY ROOM FOR JESUS?** – reiterates the call of Christ, "Behold, I stand at the door and knock." (Rev. 3:20)

179 **HE HIDETH MY SOUL** – The wonder of fellowship with God is expressed in imaginative phrases, possibly derived from Exodus 33:22.

198 **HE LEADETH ME** – was written during the Civil War by Joseph H. Gilmore, after delivering a sermon on Psalm 23:2 in First Baptist Church, Philadelphia.

89 **HE LIVES** – was the reply of author A. H. Ackley when someone asked him "Why should I worship a dead Jew?"

250 **HE THE PEARLY GATES WILL OPEN** – a favorite Swedish hymn, tells of the love of Christ, which we will know fully only after we get to heaven.

212 **HE WHO WOULD VALIANT BE** – recalls many of the scenes in the volume **Pilgrim's Progress,** which, like the hymn, was written by John Bunyan.

45 **HERE, O MY LORD** – was specifically written for a Communion service in 1855 by the Scottish Free Church minister, Horatius Bonar.

206 **HOLY BIBLE, BOOK DIVINE** – tells the many riches in the Word of God; it was written for youth (ca. 1805) by John Burton, a Baptist Sunday School teacher.

173 **HOLY GHOST, WITH LIGHT DIVINE** – is a prayer that the Holy Spirit may flood the heart with the light, power and joy of God.

11 **HOLY GOD, WE PRAISE THY NAME** – is a translation of a German hymn that was based on the 4th century Latin hymn of praise, **Te Deum.**

8 **HOLY, HOLY, HOLY** – is a hymn that abounds in trinities, recalling the **Tersanctus,** the song of the angels in Isaiah's vision (Isa. 6:3).

176 **HOLY SPIRIT, BREATHE ON ME** – is a paraphrase of Edwin Hatch's hymn (No. 155), by the Southern Baptist musician, B. B. McKinney.

General Index

180 **HOW FIRM A FOUNDATION** – mentions (vs. 2, 3, 4) three promises in Scripture in which we trust; the tune is an early American folk melody.

1 **HOW GREAT THOU ART** – First written in Sweden in 1886, this hymn of praise became popular around the world through Billy Graham Crusades.

52 **HOW GREAT THY LOVING KINDNESS IS** – This new hymn uses an Old Testament phrase "loving kindness" to recount God's providence in life and in eternity.

169 **How I praise Thee, precious Saviour** (see CHANNELS ONLY)

I

104 **I AM HIS, AND HE IS MINE** – is an exquisite expression of the joy of the believer who has not left his first love – Jesus Christ.

83 **I AM NOT SKILLED TO UNDERSTAND** – is a folk-like hymn which echoes repeatedly our wonder at the work of "Christ – my Saviour."

160 **I am Thine, O Lord** (see DRAW ME NEARER)

102 **I AM TRUSTING THEE, LORD JESUS** – is an intimate expression of trust in Christ, by Frances Ridley Havergal, one of Britain's leading women hymnists.

131 **I BELONG TO JESUS** – Like many other children's hymns, this simple expression of commitment will be enjoyed by older persons as well.

196 **I come to the garden alone** (see IN THE GARDEN)

235 **I GAVE MY LIFE FOR THEE** – is the author's response to a motto under a picture of the crucified Christ: "I did this for thee; what hast thou done for me?"

105 **I have a song that Jesus gave me** (see IN MY HEART THERE RINGS A MELODY)

56 **I HEARD THE VOICE OF JESUS SAY** – is based on John 1:16; each stanza gives first a call of Christ, and then the believer's response.

123 **I know not why God's wondrous grace** (see I KNOW WHOM I HAVE BELIEVED)

273 **I KNOW THAT MY REDEEMER LIVETH** – quotes and expounds the words of Job 19:25, 26 and John 14:2, 3 pertaining to our hope of eternal life.

123 **I KNOW WHOM I HAVE BELIEVED** – The stanzas list many things about God which are a mystery; the refrain counters with the positive note of II Timothy 1:12.

37 **I LOVE THEE** – is a simple expression of praise whose author and composer are unknown; the pentatonic melody signifies a true "folk hymn."

95 **I LOVE TO TELL THE STORY** – taken from a long poem on the life of Christ, expresses the universal appeal of the oft-repeated gospel story.

149 **I NEED THEE EVERY HOUR** – a confession of dependence on God written about 1870 by Annie S. Hawks; the refrain and melody are by Robert Lowry, her pastor.

84 **I SAW THE CROSS OF JESUS** – a meditation on the cross by Anglican rector Frederick Whitfield; the tune is adapted from an ancient Greek melody.

89 **I serve a risen Saviour** (see HE LIVES)

249 **I shall see the King in His beauty** (see THE KING IN HIS BEAUTY)

5 **I SING THE MIGHTY POWER OF GOD** – expresses the glory of God in creation, His universal presence and His perfect providence.

98 **I stand all amazed at the love** (see OH, IT IS WONDERFUL!)

112 **I stand amazed in the presence** (see MY SAVIOUR'S LOVE)

177 **I SURRENDER ALL** – written by J. W. Van DeVenter about 1895, tells of his long struggle against a call to Christian service, and his final surrender.

133 **I WAS A WANDERING SHEEP** – identifies the author and the singer with the lost sheep, for which the Shepherd sought, at great sacrifice. (Luke 15:4-7)

93 **I WILL SING OF MY REDEEMER** – was found in the effects of P. P. Bliss after he died in a train wreck in 1876. Try it with this Welsh tune.

94 **I WILL SING THE WONDROUS STORY** – A narrative testimony written by Rev. Francis Rowley in 1886, when conducting a mission in his church at Fall River, Mass.

279 **I WITH THEE WOULD BEGIN** – A Swedish hymn of "beginnings" – for each new day, or for each new experience of commitment to Christ.

145 **I WOULD BE LIKE JESUS** – is a personal expression of a desire to "be conformed to the image of Jesus Christ." (Rom. 8:29)

143 **I'LL LIVE FOR HIM** – one of our simplest hymns of commitment was written about 1880, by Ralph E. Hudson, Methodist lay preacher, music teacher and publisher.

122 **I'VE FOUND A FRIEND** – recounts the attributes and ministries of Jesus Christ, "a friend who sticketh closer than a brother." (Prov. 18:24)

115 **I'VE HEARD THE KING** – written during World War II, was inspired by a broadcast of England's King George VI, heard in this country.

62 **If you from sin are longing to be free** (see LOOK TO THE LAMB OF GOD)

43 **IMMORTAL, INVISIBLE, GOD ONLY WISE** – speaks of God in terms of transcendent "light," which reveals all things but obscures itself.

253 **IN HEAVEN ABOVE** – is a Scandinavian hymn, both words and music, telling of blessedness "where God the Father dwells."

105 **IN MY HEART THERE RINGS A MELODY** – is based on Eph. 5:19 ("making melody in your heart to the Lord.") It is the heart's song that God hears!

General Index

121 **IN TENDERNESS HE SOUGHT ME** – a song of Christian witness, recalls the stories of the lost sheep (Luke 15:4-7), and the good Samaritan (Luke 10:30-37).

72 **IN THE CROSS OF CHRIST I GLORY** – is based on Paul's words: "God forbid that I should glory, save in the cross of our Lord Jesus Christ." (Gal. 6:14)

196 **IN THE GARDEN** – allows the singer to share the experience of Mary Magdalene, as she met Jesus outside the tomb on Easter morning. (John 20:11-18)

69 **IS MY NAME WRITTEN THERE?** – The Bible suggests that all who know Jesus Christ as personal Saviour are recorded in "The Book of Life." (Rev. 20:12, 15)

159 **IS YOUR ALL ON THE ALTAR?** – Using Old Testament imagery, the author likens a full consecration of self to a sacrifice on God's altar. (Rom. 12:1, 2)

200 **IT IS WELL WITH MY SOUL** – an expression of faith in God's inscrutable providence, was written after the author H. G. Spafford had lost four daughters at sea.

251 **It may be at morn** (see CHRIST RETURNETH)

86 **IVORY PALACES** – was written by a Presbyterian layman (Henry Barraclough) at Montreat, North Carolina, after hearing J. Wilbur Chapman preach on Psalm 45:8.

J

47 **JESUS, GENTLEST SAVIOUR** – A children's hymn, suitable also for adults, tells of the transcendence and the immanence of our Lord.

194 **JESUS, I AM RESTING, RESTING** – is a devotional hymn expressing the joy of intimate fellowship between the Christian and his Saviour.

68 **JESUS, I COME** – suggests the many needs of those who come to Christ; verse one alone lists "freedom," "gladness," "light," "health" and "wealth."

214 **JESUS, I MY CROSS HAVE TAKEN** – is the answer of a true disciple (Mark 10:28) to Jesus' challenge – to take up our cross and follow Him. (Luke 9:23)

130 **JESUS, I WILL TRUST THEE** – says that to trust in Christ is the only rational decision we can make; the final stanza translates the decision into action.

100 **JESUS IS ALL THE WORLD TO ME** – was written (ca. 1900) by Will Thompson, renowned composer and publisher in East Liverpool, Ohio and Chicago, Illinois.

239 **Jesus is coming to earth again** (see WHAT IF IT WERE TODAY?)

243 **JESUS, JESUS, WE ARE WAITING** – was written by a former teacher of Bible at Toccoa Falls Institute (Georgia), and was harmonized by a music teacher there.

127 **Jesus, keep me near the cross** (see NEAR THE CROSS)

277 **JESUS LIVES, AND SO SHALL I** – by a German Reformed pastor, Christian Gellert, is based on Jesus' words, "Because I live, ye shall live also." (John 14:19)

79 **JESUS, LOVER OF MY SOUL** – called by hymnologist Louis F. Benson "the best-loved hymn in the language," was written soon after Charles Wesley's conversion.

140 **JESUS, MASTER, WHOSE I AM** – set to a brilliant Russian melody by Dimitri Bortniansky, is a prayer to "Jesus, Master" – "King of my life."

103 **Jesus my Lord will love me forever** (see NOW I BELONG TO JESUS)

199 **JESUS, MY SAVIOUR, LOOK ON ME** – may be based on the story in Matt. 9:36. Note the climax phrase of each stanza.

132 **JESUS ONLY, LET ME SEE** – was written by Oswald J. Smith, the famous pastor and missionary statesman of Toronto, Canada.

87 **JESUS SAVES** – a missions poem, was first written for a Sunday School missions anniversary, and first sung to Meyerbeer's "Vive le Roi!"

232 **JESUS SHALL REIGN** – looks forward to the day when "every knee shall bow and every tongue confess that Jesus Christ is Lord." (Phil. 2:10, 11)

25 **JESUS, THE VERY THOUGHT OF THEE** – is taken from **Jesu, dulcis memoria**, a long Latin poem of devotion written in the twelfth century.

7 **JESUS, THOU JOY OF LOVING HEARTS** – from the same Latin source as the previous hymn, is attributed by some scholars to Bernard of Clairvaux.

82 **JESUS, THY BLOOD AND RIGHTEOUSNESS** – written by the Moravian leader Count Zinzendorf, reveals the source of our confidence before a holy God.

4 **Jesus! what a Friend for sinners** (see OUR GREAT SAVIOUR)

17 **JOIN ALL THE GLORIOUS NAMES** – insists that all the names given to Christ are inadequate to express His true character.

66 **JUST AS I AM, THINE OWN TO BE** – A "youth" version of the earlier invitation hymn (listed next), by Marianne Hearn, a leading Sunday School writer of Britain.

57 **JUST AS I AM, WITHOUT ONE PLEA** – perhaps the most famous and most biblical of invitation hymns, is used often in Billy Graham Crusades.

K

67 **King of my life, I crown Thee now** (see LEAD ME TO CALVARY)

GENERAL INDEX

L

67 **LEAD ME TO CALVARY** — teaches that true devotion to Christ results from a contemplation of His passion, death and resurrection.

218 **LEAD ON, O KING ETERNAL** — first written for a seminary graduation, is a challenge to follow Christ in His struggle with sin and evil.

190 **LEANING ON THE EVERLASTING ARMS** — was written as a hymn of comfort for two bereaved families; it is based on Deut. 33:27.

36 **Let all the world in every corner sing** (see MY GOD AND KING!)

138 **LET ME COME CLOSER TO THEE, JESUS** — is a very personal and intimate expression of love and devotion to our Lord Jesus Christ.

233 **LET THE LOWER LIGHTS BE BURNING** — was inspired by the story of a boat lost on the rocks, because the "lower" shore lights were not burning.

276 **LIFT UP, LIFT UP YOUR VOICES NOW** — tells the story of Christ's resurrection, and relates it to the Christian's own victory over sin and death.

188 **LIKE A RIVER GLORIOUS** — suggests that a remedy for today's personality conflicts is a heart "stayed upon Jehovah."

152 **LIVING FOR JESUS** — is a favorite youth hymn of consecration. The words were written by an insurance agent, Thomas Chisholm; the tune by music editor C. Harold Lowden.

62 **LOOK TO THE LAMB OF GOD** — An invitation hymn, inspired by John the Baptist's words: "Behold the Lamb of God, which taketh away the sin of the world." (Jn. 1:29)

69 **Lord, I care not for riches** (see IS MY NAME WRITTEN THERE?)

164 **LORD, I HAVE SHUT THE DOOR** — is based on Jesus' suggestion for effective privacy in prayer. (Matt. 6:6)

142 **LORD, SPEAK TO ME** — shows the progression of discipleship. God speaks; we are taught by Him and filled with His Spirit; then we are ready to serve as He directs.

171 **LORD THOU LOV'ST THE CHEERFUL GIVER** — is a call to full stewardship which begins with the pocketbook.

170 **LOVE DIVINE, ALL LOVES EXCELLING** — sets forth Charles Wesley's teaching of sanctification; this tune is a favorite in Great Britain.

250 **Love divine, so great and wondrous** (see HE THE PEARLY GATES WILL OPEN)

104 **Loved with everlasting love** (see I AM HIS, AND HE IS MINE)

271 **Low in the grave He lay** (see CHRIST AROSE)

M

236 **MAKE ME A BLESSING** — dedicated to the choir of the famed Moody Memorial Church, says that each believer is an ambassador of Jesus Christ.

141 **MAKE ME A CAPTIVE, LORD** — as indicated by the tune name, sets forth the seeming paradoxes of a life which is given wholly to God.

73 **"Man of Sorrows," what a name** (see HALLELUJAH, WHAT A SAVIOUR!)

76 **Marvelous grace of our loving Lord** (see GRACE GREATER THAN OUR SIN)

135 **MAY THE MIND OF CHRIST, MY SAVIOUR** — is a prayer growing out of the admonition in Phil. 2:5, "Let this mind be in you, which was also in Christ Jesus . . . . "

284 **Mine eyes have seen the glory** (see BATTLE HYMN OF THE REPUBLIC)

184 **MOMENT BY MOMENT** — a poem by the evangelist D. W. Whittle, is set to music by his daughter May, who married Will R. Moody, son of D. L. Moody.

157 **MORE LIKE THE MASTER** — says that Jesus was a perfect example of what we should be, and that His death makes it possible for us to be like Him.

150 **MORE LOVE TO THEE** — as suggested in the third stanza, was written at a time when its author Elizabeth Prentiss was experiencing both physical and mental anguish.

281 **MY COUNTRY, 'TIS OF THEE** — written by Baptist seminary student Samuel F. Smith, was first sung in Park Street Church, Boston, at a 4th of July celebration in 1831.

111 **My faith has found a resting place** (see NO OTHER PLEA)

167 **MY FAITH LOOKS UP TO THEE** — was written when Ray Palmer its author was only 22 years old, and has been called the greatest American hymn.

36 **MY GOD AND KING!** — a poem by one of the earliest English hymnwriters, is set to music by the late Robert McCutchan, a leading Methodist hymnologist.

92 **My hope is built on nothing less** (see THE SOLID ROCK)

129 **MY HOPE IS IN THE LORD** — one of the best new congregational hymns of salvation, was written by Norman Clayton, a brick layer turned musician!

163 **MY JESUS, I LOVE THEE** — though written when Wm. Featherstone was still a teenager, is the sort of hymn no adult Christian dare sing carelessly!

143 **My life, my love I give to Thee** (see I'LL LIVE FOR HIM)

86 **My Lord has garments so wondrous fine** (see IVORY PALACES)

248 **MY SAVIOUR FIRST OF ALL** — is blind Fanny Crosby's attempt to say that in heaven our joy will center in our Lord, not in harps or golden streets!

112 **MY SAVIOUR'S LOVE** — was written by Charles H. Gabriel (1856-1932), one of the most prolific gospel song composers, who excelled in both lyrics and music.

GENERAL INDEX

N

78 **NAILED UPON GOLGOTHA'S TREE** – a hymn of Christ's passion and final victory over death, is a favorite of the fellowship called "Plymouth Brethren."

127 **NEAR THE CROSS** – was first a tune written by the manufacturer-musician Wm. Howard Doane, for which his friend Fanny Crosby wrote these words.

193 **NEAR TO THE HEART OF GOD** – was written in 1901 by a pastor of Chicago's First Presbyterian Church, to express his faith in spite of personal tragedy.

166 **NEARER, STILL NEARER** – can be said to be a companion hymn to "Nearer, My God, to Thee," because it breathes the same prayer of intense devotion.

111 **NO OTHER PLEA** – emphasizes that the basis of our eternal salvation is nothing more nor less than the atoning death of Jesus Christ.

125 **NOT WHAT THESE HANDS HAVE DONE** – says that good works and even suffering can not bring peace with God; it comes only through His love and grace.

103 **NOW I BELONG TO JESUS** – is a testimony which follows the truth, "ye are not your own; for ye are bought with a price." (I Cor. 6:19, 20)

256 **NOW THANK WE ALL OUR GOD** – a chorus of praise for God's blessings, was written during the Thirty Years War (1618-1648), one of Europe's darkest hours.

O

283 **O BEAUTIFUL FOR SPACIOUS SKIES** – was written by Katherine Lee Bates in 1893, after a visit to the summit of Pike's Peak in Colorado.

265 **O COME, ALL YE FAITHFUL** – latest research says, was written by John Francis Wade, a Catholic layman who sold music in the 18th century at Douai, France.

262 **O COME, O COME, EMMANUEL** – derived from 12th century Latin antiphons, anticipates the coming of Jesus Christ. See Isa. 7:14; Luke 1:78; Isa. 22:22.

49 **O COULD I SPEAK THE MATCHLESS WORTH** – suggests that human words and melodies are inadequate to express the glory of our Lord Jesus Christ.

24 **O FOR A THOUSAND TONGUES TO SING** – was inspired by these words spoken to Charles Wesley, "Had I a thousand tongues, I would praise Him with them all."

12 **O GOD, OUR HELP IN AGES PAST** – is Isaac Watts' poetic version of Psalm 90:1, 2, 4; it was first sung in 1719.

128 **O HAPPY DAY THAT FIXED MY CHOICE** – describes conversion as "a choice," "a bond," "a great transaction," and "rest for my long-divided heart."

172 **O JESUS, I HAVE PROMISED** – originally written for a confirmation service, is a much-loved hymn of dedication to discipleship.

65 **O JESUS, THOU ART STANDING** – is our response to the words of Christ, "Behold, I stand at the door and knock." (Rev. 3:20)

266 **O LITTLE TOWN OF BETHLEHEM** – was written by the eminent Episcopalian minister Phillips Brooks, as he remembered his visit to Jesus' natal city in 1866.

1 **O Lord my God, when I in awesome wonder** (see HOW GREAT THOU ART)

139 **O LOVE THAT WILT NOT LET ME GO** – by the blind Scot George Matheson, says that the Christian's cross brings him fullness of love, light and joy.

211 **O MASTER, LET ME WALK WITH THEE** – is a modern disciple's prayer that we may be more like Christ in His character and His service to men.

229 **O MASTER OF THE WAKING WORLD** – voices the cry of all restless, hungry and oppressed people in our day, whose needs are only completely met in Christ.

34 **O SACRED HEAD, NOW WOUNDED** – is a translation of part of a medieval poem of devotion, directed to the crucified Christ; the tune has a secular origin.

252 **O THAT WILL BE GLORY** – was inspired by the radiant life of a rescue mission director, Ed Card of St. Louis. He often used the word "glory," was called "Old Glory Face," and always ended his prayers with "and that will be glory for me."

85 **O THE DEEP, DEEP LOVE OF JESUS** – repeats, in glowing phrases, that the love of Christ is boundless, resistless, changeless and endless.

71 **O THOU THAT HEAR'ST WHEN SINNERS CRY** – is based on David's prayer of contrition after his great sin, as found in Psalm 51.

48 **O WORSHIP THE KING** – based on Psalm 104, maintains that the God of cosmic infinity is concerned with us "frail . . . . feeble children of dust."

237 **O ZION, HASTE** – is a call to the church to "hurry up" with its challenge to bring the message of Christ to all the world.

90 **OH, HOW I LOVE JESUS** – a hymn written in an Anglican rectory, is here wedded to a tune and a refrain that originated in an early American camp meeting.

98 **OH, IT IS WONDERFUL!** – uses words like "amazed," "confused," "tremble" and "marvel" to express our wonder at the sacrifice of Christ.

146 **OH, TO BE LIKE THEE** – is a prayer that we may more resemble Christ, in our service to men and our personal holiness.

77 **On a hill far away** (see THE OLD RUGGED CROSS)
222 **ON OUR WAY REJOICING** – is a brilliant, vigorous hymn of pilgrimage, written by John Monsell, a preacher who argued that church singing should be "more fervent and joyous."
126 **Once far from God and dead in sin** (see CHRIST LIVETH IN ME)
119 **ONCE FOR ALL** – outlines the doctrine of grace as contrasted to law, and is based on Heb. 10:10.
116 **ONE DAY!** – recounts the story of Jesus Christ – His birth, life among men, passion, resurrection and ascension, and His anticipated second coming.
58 **ONLY TRUST HIM** – was written by a Methodist pastor John H. Stockton; the present version of the refrain is by the famous evangelistic singer Ira D. Sankey.
217 **ONWARD, CHRISTIAN SOLDIERS** – was written for a Sunday School "procession with cross and banners," conducted in Yorkshire, England in 1864.
153 **OPEN MY EYES, THAT I MAY SEE** – is a prayer that we may see God's truth, hear His voice, and then tell others what His Word has revealed to us.
241 **OUR GOD IS SOVEREIGN STILL** – expresses faith that God over-rules in the affairs of men and nations, and that the cause of Christ will eventually triumph.
4 **OUR GREAT SAVIOUR** – a modern hymn about Jesus Christ, quotes many phrases from Wesley's "Jesus, Lover of My Soul."
68 **Out of my bondage, sorrow, and night** (see JESUS, I COME)
236 **Out in the highways and byways of life** (see MAKE ME A BLESSING)

P

192 **PEACE, PERFECT PEACE** – develops the truth in the scripture "Thou wilt keep him in perfect peace, whose mind is stayed on thee." (Isa. 26:3)
29 **PRAISE HIM! PRAISE HIM!** – expresses worship of Christ because He is Redeemer, Shepherd, Rock, Saviour, Prophet, Priest and coming King.
10 **PRAISE, MY SOUL, THE KING OF HEAVEN** – a free paraphrase of Psalm 103, is a favorite of Queen Elizabeth II of England, and was sung at her coronation.
23 **PRAISE THE SAVIOUR, YE WHO KNOW HIM!** – a hymn of devotion and commitment, was written by Thomas Kelly (1769-1854), a prominent Irish evangelical.
46 **Praise ye the Father!** (see PRAISE YE THE TRIUNE GOD!)
19 **PRAISE YE THE LORD, THE ALMIGHTY** – quoting phrases from Psalms, was written by a 30-year-old German pastor, Joachim Neander, shortly before he died of tuberculosis.
46 **PRAISE YE THE TRIUNE GOD!** – lauds each member of the Trinity for providence extended to men, using words like "lovingkindness," "compassion" and "comforter."

R

99 **REDEEMED** – expresses the unbounded joy of the sinner who is "not redeemed with corruptible things, as silver and gold . . . but with the precious blood of Christ . . ." (I Pet. 1:18, 19)
20 **REJOICE, MY SOUL!** – is a new song of ecstatic praise, written by Avis Christiansen, a Chicago housewife who has given us many hymn poems.
6 **REJOICE, THE LORD IS KING** – speaks of the present and future reign of Christ; the refrain is based on Philippians 4:4.
26 **REJOICE, YE PURE IN HEART** – was written by a professor of theology, Edward H. Plumptre, for a festival in Peterborough Cathedral (England) in 1865.
227 **RESCUE THE PERISHING** – is a challenge to bring the gospel to every needy person, written by Fanny J. Crosby after she had spoken in a New York rescue mission.
156 **REVIVE US AGAIN** – is a prayer for spiritual renewal which also contains many expressions of praise; the original title was taken from Hab. 3:2.
210 **RISE UP, O MEN OF GOD!** – calls on strong men to give their all – heart, soul, mind and strength – to Christ and His church.

S

110 **SAVED!** – A familiar, but often misunderstood expression of Christian testimony is explained in this gospel song.
158 **SAVIOUR, MY HEART IS THINE** – explains that complete consecration is committing our thoughts and our actions to Christ, every moment we live.
161 **SAVIOUR, THY DYING LOVE** – lists the responses which a dedicated heart makes to the love shown by Christ on the cross.
148 **SEARCH ME, O GOD** – was written by J. Edwin Orr after a preaching visit to New Zealand, and is set to a favorite tune of the aborigines of that country.
268 **SILENT NIGHT! HOLY NIGHT!** – was written "on the spur of the moment" on Christmas eve, 1818, by the pastor and organist of an Austrian church.

183 **Simply trusting every day** (see TRUSTING JESUS)

120 **SINCE JESUS CAME INTO MY HEART** – first introduced in the 1915 Billy Sunday campaign at Philadelphia, became one of evangelism's favorite songs.

9 **SING PRAISE TO GOD WHO REIGNS ABOVE** – speaks both of the transcendent "God of all creation" and the immanent Lord who "is never far away."

242 **Sing the wondrous love of Jesus** (see WHEN WE ALL GET TO HEAVEN)

101 **Sing them over again to me** (see WONDERFUL WORDS OF LIFE)

55 **Sinners Jesus will receive** (see CHRIST RECEIVETH SINFUL MEN)

216 **SOLDIERS OF CHRIST, ARISE** – says that the Christian life is a warfare; Charles Wesley drew images and many phrases from Ephesians 6:11-18.

168 **SPEAK, LORD, IN THE STILLNESS** – is a good hymn to sing before a message from God's Word, or in beginning a time of prayer.

175 **SPIRIT OF GOD, DESCEND UPON MY HEART** – teaches us that maturing in faith requires self-crucifixion that is as painful as it is rewarding.

225 **STAND UP, STAND UP FOR JESUS** – was inspired by the last sermon of Rev. Dudley A. Tyng, a YMCA leader, and is based on Ephesians 6:14.

202 **STANDING ON THE PROMISES** – was written by R. Kelso Carter, in early life an athlete and professor of science, later a minister and a physician.

T

162 **TAKE MY LIFE, AND LET IT BE** – was a personal expression of consecration by Frances Havergal, written after she had won several to faith in Christ.

144 **TAKE THOU OUR MINDS, DEAR LORD** – is a favorite consecration hymn among Presbyterian students; it was written by Wm. H. Foulkes in 1918.

136 **TAKE TIME TO BE HOLY** – bears the unique challenge that spiritual maturity requires poise, patience, and perseverance.

215 **"Take up thy cross and follow Me"** (see WHEREVER HE LEADS I'LL GO)

137 **TEACH ME THY WILL, O LORD** – During his earthly ministry, Jesus was called "rabbi" (teacher); He still teaches those who follow Him.

96 **TELL ME THE OLD, OLD STORY** – is but a small part of Katherine Hankey's life of Christ in verse; the song, like the story, remains ever new.

91 **TELL ME THE STORY OF JESUS** – is a diminutive "Life of Christ," telling of His birth, temptation, earthly ministry, death and resurrection.

257 **THANKS TO GOD FOR MY REDEEMER** – translated from Swedish, gives thanks for the common blessings of life and for the eternal grace of God.

224 **THE BATTLE IS THE LORD'S!** – should keep us from worrying about failure in doing God's work, or from taking credit for its success!

231 **THE CALL FOR REAPERS** – is a response to the challenge, "Pray ye therefore the Lord of the harvest, that He will send forth labourers . . . ." (Matt. 9:38)

209 **THE CHURCH'S ONE FOUNDATION** – was written by an Anglican curate Samuel J. Stone, to explain the phrase in the creed: "I believe . . . in the holy catholic church."

38 **THE GOD OF ABRAHAM PRAISE** – tells the eternity of God in Bible phrases: "Ancient of everlasting days," "great I AM," and "He by Himself hath sworn."

249 **THE KING IN HIS BEAUTY** – is a favorite "second coming" hymn at Gordon College (Mass.), named for A. J. Gordon, the hymn's author.

240 **THE KING SHALL COME WHEN MORNING DAWNS** – is an ancient hymn which compares Christ's second coming with the glory of His birth and of His resurrection.

40 **THE LORD'S MY SHEPHERD, I'LL NOT WANT** – first appeared in the **Scottish Psalter** of 1650, and is here set to "Crimond," a favorite tune of the Scots.

226 **THE MORNING LIGHT IS BREAKING** – sees world evangelism as the coming of the new day; we should sing it in faith, even if it seems to be over-optimistic.

77 **THE OLD RUGGED CROSS** – is an all-time favorite gospel song, which the author George Bennard says was given him by God over a period of several weeks.

244 **THE SANDS OF TIME ARE SINKING** – said to be a favorite hymn of the evangelist D. L. Moody, presents Christ as the center of heaven's glory.

92 **THE SOLID ROCK** – describes our sure hope of salvation as "Jesus' blood and righteousness," "His unchanging grace," and "His oath and covenant."

223 **THE SON OF GOD GOES FORTH TO WAR** – a martyrs' hymn, pictures Stephen, the twelve disciples and "a noble army" following in the train of Christ.

275 **THE STRIFE IS O'ER** – an anonymous Latin hymn of the 17th century, presents many of the doctrinal truths of Christ's resurrection.

81 **THERE IS A FOUNTAIN** – is a much-criticized and often-rewritten hymn which still expresses the faith of many Christians; it is based on Zechariah 13:1.

90 **There is a name I love to hear** (see OH, HOW I LOVE JESUS)

193 **There is a place of quiet rest** (see NEAR TO THE HEART OF GOD)

21 **THERE IS NO NAME SO SWEET ON EARTH** – reminds us that the person of Christ adds lustre to a common, everyday name – Jesus.

264 **THERE'S A SONG IN THE AIR** – is one of the most fanciful of modern Christmas hymns; it is said that Karl Harrington improvised this melody at sight.

272 **THINE IS THE GLORY** – is a hymn of the risen, ever-living Christ; under the title "A toi la gloire," it is a favorite of French believers.

44 **THIS IS MY FATHER'S WORLD** – reminds us that a God who cares for lilies and for sparrows will not neglect man, the crowning glory of His creation.

259 **THOU DIDST LEAVE THY THRONE** – warns us to not make the mistake of the Bethlehem inn keeper – let us make room in our hearts and our homes for Christ.

174 **THY WILL, NOT MINE, BE DONE** – was Jesus' prayer in Gethsemane, and should voice our submission to God every time we pray.

203 **THY WORD HAVE I HID IN MY HEART** – is a gospel song adaptation of verses from Psalm 119, by E. O. Sellers, late teacher at New Orleans Baptist Theological Seminary.

203 **Thy Word is a lamp to my feet** (see THY WORD HAVE I HID IN MY HEART)

204 **THY WORD IS LIKE A GARDEN, LORD** – written by Edwin Hodder, a British civil servant, compares the Bible to a garden, a mine, a starry galaxy and a military armory!

109 **'TIS SO SWEET TO TRUST IN JESUS** – was written by Louisa M. R. Stead, missionary to South Africa from 1880 to 1917.

234 **TO ALL THE WORLD** – is a new missionary hymn, whose music was written by W. P. Loveless, long-time radio preacher in Chicago, Illinois and Honolulu, Hawaii.

3 **TO GOD BE THE GLORY** – is a gospel song that emphasizes worship; though written about 1875, it only recently became widely known in America.

181 **TRUST AND OBEY** – emphasizes the proper balance between "law and grace," between "faith and works" in Christian living.

183 **TRUSTING JESUS** – appeared first as a poem in a newspaper and was handed by evangelist D. L. Moody to his songleader Ira Sankey, who set it to music.

U

195 **UNDER HIS WINGS** – recalls a promise of God's protection and care: "He shall cover thee with his feathers, and under his wings shalt thou trust." (Ps. 91:4).

187 **UNTO THE HILLS** – is a fairly strict paraphrase of Psalm 121; this is a favorite hymn among college and university students.

W

254 **WE GATHER TOGETHER** – significant in the history of the Netherlands, is appropriate as a national hymn of petition and thanksgiving.

87 **We have heard the joyful sound** (see JESUS SAVES)

14 **WE LIFT OUR VOICE REJOICING** – won first prize in a "new hymn" contest sponsored by the National Church Music Fellowship in 1961.

156 **We praise Thee, O God** (see REVIVE US AGAIN)

22 **We sigh for human love** (see FOREVER)

230 **WE'VE A STORY TO TELL TO THE NATIONS** – reminds us of the promise that Christ's kingdom will come when every "tribe and tongue" has heard the gospel.

190 **What a fellowship, what a joy divine** (see LEANING ON THE EVERLASTING ARMS)

185 **WHAT A FRIEND WE HAVE IN JESUS** – a hymn of assurance, was written in 1855 by Joseph Scriven, whose life was filled with sorrows and disappointments.

120 **What a wonderful change in my life** (see SINCE JESUS CAME INTO MY HEART)

42 **WHAT A WONDERFUL SAVIOUR!** – is a long succession of phrases which explain why we love and worship Jesus Christ.

261 **WHAT CHILD IS THIS, WHO, LAID TO REST** – is an adaptation of an old English carol; this tune has a secular origin and is often called "Greensleeves."

239 **WHAT IF IT WERE TODAY?** – says that, because we believe Christ may return to earth today, we should live in such a way as to please Him.

60 **"What must I do?" the trembling jailor cried** (see BELIEVE ON THE LORD JESUS CHRIST)

252 **When all my labors and trials are o'er** (see O THAT WILL BE GLORY)

269 **WHEN, HIS SALVATION BRINGING** – is actually a children's hymn for Palm Sunday; notice the reference to Jesus' words in Luke 19:40.

247 **WHEN I CAN READ MY TITLE CLEAR** – likens our assurance of heaven to a title deed for property; the folk-like tune is of uncertain authorship.

70 **WHEN I SURVEY THE WONDROUS CROSS** – often called the finest English hymn, is set here to "Rockingham;" the more traditional tune is just below.

41 **WHEN MORNING GILDS THE SKIES** – whose author is unknown, first appeared in a German Catholic hymnal in 1828; it is a morning hymn of praise.
248 **When my lifework is ended** (see MY SAVIOUR FIRST OF ALL)
200 **When peace, like a river, attendeth my way** (see IT IS WELL WITH MY SOUL)
242 **WHEN WE ALL GET TO HEAVEN** – was written by two women, both of whom were regular participants in the Methodist summer conference at Ocean Grove, New Jersey.
181 **When we walk with the Lord** (see TRUST AND OBEY)
220 **WHERE CROSS THE CROWDED WAYS OF LIFE** – an "urban" missionary hymn, was written in 1903 while its author (Frank Mason North) was ministering in New York City.
215 **WHEREVER HE LEADS I'LL GO** – a favorite of Southern Baptists and written by their pioneer musician B. B. McKinney, recalls phrases found in several other consecration hymns.
267 **WHILE SHEPHERDS WATCHED THEIR FLOCKS** – is a poetic version of Luke 2:8-14; it first appeared in the **Tate and Brady Psalter** of 1700.
15 **WHO IS HE IN YONDER STALL?** – is a children's hymn of questions and answers (catechism style) about the life and ministry of Jesus Christ.
221 **WHO IS ON THE LORD'S SIDE?** – allows us to give the same response as did Joshua, "As for me and my house, we will serve the Lord." (Joshua 24:15)
118 **WHY DO I SING ABOUT JESUS?** – tells of the beauty of Christ; it can be sung equally well as a solo, or by the entire congregation.
106 **WONDERFUL GRACE OF JESUS** – in music worthy of a mighty choir, describes the loving favor of our Lord in phrases that stretch our imagination.
101 **WONDERFUL WORDS OF LIFE** – reminds us that one of Jesus' disciples once said, "Thou hast the words of eternal life." (John 6:68)
124 **WOUNDED FOR ME** – makes Isaiah 53:5 ("He was wounded for our transgressions") completely personal, and also tells Christ's complete ministry for us.

Y

54 **YE MUST BE BORN AGAIN** – was written by a Congregational minister, Wm. T. Sleeper, at the suggestion of song leader George C. Stebbins.
117 **Years I spent in vanity and pride** (see AT CALVARY)
159 **You have longed for sweet peace** (see IS YOUR ALL ON THE ALTAR?)